Coordinate Systems and Map Projections

GENERAL EDITORS

P. F. DALE, M.A., A.R.I.C.S., Senior Research Fellow in Cadastral Surveying, North East London Polytechnic

H. FULLARD, M.Sc., Cartographic Editor and Director, George Philip and Son Limited, London

EDITORS' NOTE

It has for some time been felt that the number of textbooks on cartography written in English fail to reflect the importance of the subject. The Editors very much hope that this text will be the first in a series dealing with cartographic topics.

Elementary textbooks on cartography in general are available but a book on map projections of somewhat higher standard has long been needed for the student of cartography and the professional cartographer. This volume is concerned with principles and practical methods and is firmly based on the principles of coordinate geometry. With a comprehensive statement of reference systems used in surveying and mapping both on the sphere and the spheroid and on the plane, with a thorough analysis of distortion for making proper choices of projection for specific purposes, with its study of projections as a series of coordinate transformations from geographical coordinates to computation finally of master grid coordinates for plotting, the Editors believe that this new book fills the gap in the literature. They also believe that it will be a valuable reference source for all those interested in the fundamental problems of mapping the Earth.

The Editors would like to acknowledge the role played by the British Cartographic Society in endeavouring to promote and foster this series.

P. F. D.   H. F.

Coordinate Systems

and Map Projections

D. H. MALING

LONDON: GEORGE PHILIP AND SON LIMITED

© 1973 D. H. MALING

PRINTED IN GREAT BRITAIN   SBN 540 00974 1

PREFACE

This book is one of a series of textbooks on Cartography which was suggested by
the British Cartographic Society. It is intended to cover the requirements of students
studying for the recently established Ordinary National Certificate and Higher
National Certificate in Surveying, Cartography and Planning – certificates which,
after more than twenty years of discussion, have at last created nationally-recognized
qualifications in Cartography. It is also intended to meet the needs of students in
Geography and Surveying in schools, colleges and universities throughout the
World.

It can be argued that the subject of Map Projections is better documented than
some other fields in Cartography: why then produce another book on this subject
rather than concentrate on these other fields? There are two reasons why this is
desirable. The first is that a textbook for the professional cartographer might
reasonably be expected to be up to date in its treatment of the practical tasks of
choosing projections for specific purposes, computing and plotting them as the
preliminary to compilation. Few of the textbooks which are available satisfy these
needs. The second reason is that a book of somewhat higher standard is needed
for the professional cartographer of tomorrow than has hitherto been regarded as
adequate for geography students. Very little has been published in Britain since
the beginning of the twentieth century which treats with the mathematics of map
projections at an intellectual level higher than the requirements for plane geometry
and trigonometry associated with the Ordinary Level Syllabus of the General
Certificate of Education. Consequently the subject of map projections often appears
to the intelligent outsider as a rag-bag of separate and apparently unrelated
geometrical exercises which has very little to do with the kind of map projections
which are used for published maps. The weaknesses in the systems of classification
evinced by many English textbooks suggest that the relationship between various
projections is also not very clear to the authors. Analysis of the distortions and
deformations which are inherent to all map projections are usually dealt with
qualitatively rather than quantitatively. The methods of construction which are
described are those of the schoolroom rather than the drawing office.

The present book is concerned with principles and practical methods rather
than the description of the fifty or so individual map projections which are
commonly used. Thus it is not until Chapter 8 that the derivation of any specific
map projection is described in any detail. Here only three are described and
primarily to demonstrate the methods of analysis which may be applied to define
map projections to satisfy specific requirements. However, the coordinate expressions
defining most of the commonly used projections are given in Appendix I and,
using the practical procedures described in Chapters 6 and 7, the reader can construct
any of them.

The approach to the subject adopted here may seem quite new to English
readers although it is well established in equivalent textbooks in French, German
and Russian. This is to regard the study of map projections as the study of a series
of coordinate transformations; from geographical coordinates into bearing and
distance coordinates on the curved surface of the sphere, into plane rectangular or
polar coordinates which define a projection algebraically, and finally into master
grid coordinates which can be plotted. The analysis of distortion, which is vital to
the proper understanding of the special properties of a map projection and which
is invaluable in choosing the most suitable projection for a particular map, is based
upon the classic work of Tissot. This was published nearly a century ago and has
been used by the majority of continental writers ever since, but is still remarkably

little known in Britain. This, too, is firmly based upon the principles of coordinate geometry.

The level of mathematical attainment expected for readers of this book is based upon the Guide Syllabus in Mathematics for the ONC and HNC courses. It must be assumed at the outset that the student already has some knowledge of algebra, plane geometry and plane trigonometry, up to the level of the three well-known books by P. Abbott: *Teach Yourself Geometry, Teach Yourself Algebra* and *Teach Yourself Trigonometry*, all published by the English Universities Press, originally during the 1940s. It is interesting to note that these three books have also been selected as providing the essential mathematical background for students entering the new courses in Cartography offered by the International Training Centre for Aerial Survey and Earth Sciences at Enschede in the Netherlands. In many places, especially in the introductory chapters, we refer to Abbott's books (e.g. Abbott/Trigonometry §79) when an important proof has been omitted. Later, too, we refer to Abbott's fourth book *Teach Yourself Calculus* to emphasise that the arguments followed or the conclusions reached have general mathematical application.

During the two years of study for the Ordinary National Certificate in Cartography or for similar certificates the student should become familiar with the elements of plane coordinate geometry, and spherical trigonometry, and will have some acquaintance with the calculus. This is not to say that the student will have become an accomplished practitioner in these branches of mathematics, but at least the notation used and the kinds of argument employed should have some meaning. The real problem seems to be to equate the standard reached in the 'Mathematics with Statistics' part of the course with the study of map projections in 'Principles of Cartography I'. Here it seems that map projections have to be studied before much of the formal mathematical training has been accomplished. One could therefore argue that some of the theory of map projections presented in this book might well be taught within the 'Mathematics with Statistics' part of the course. Examination of the details of the guide syllabus for mathematics indicates that at least one-half of the pure mathematics element covered in ONC I and ONC II appears somewhere in this book.

In Chapter 5 reference is made to the labours of the United Kingdom Working Group on Terminology and to the preparation of the *Glossary of Technical Terms in Cartography*, published by the Royal Society in 1966. The preferred terms relating to map projections which appear in that Glossary are used throughout the book. Definitions which are those appearing in the Glossary are prefaced with the symbol *.

The present author would like to acknowledge the considerable assistance which he has received from Clive Tomlinson, who has critically examined the manuscript, and from Guy Lewis and Tim Fearnside, who have prepared the fair drawings of all the text illustrations.

D. H. MALING

CONTENTS

Contents

THE SYMBOLS AND NOTATION
USED IN THIS BOOK

THE SYMBOLS AND NOTATION USED IN THIS BOOK

The number in brackets denotes the page where defined or first introduced.

a Major semiaxis of ellipsoid (2); maximum particular scale (63).

A Coefficient (47); scale factor for Stereographic Projection (176).

b Minor semiaxis of ellipsoid (2); minimum particular scale (63).

B Coefficient (47).

c Constant (105).

C Coefficient (47); integration constant (143); convergence (227).

e Eccentricity of ellipsoid (44); scale error (71).

E Easting coordinate (20); fundamental quantity of first order (61).

f Flattening of ellipsoid (2); indication of a function (49).

F Fundamental quantity of first order (61).

G Fundamental quantity of first order (61).

h Particular scale along the meridian at a point (62).

i Complex variable: $\sqrt{-1}$ (222).

J Harmonic of a satellite orbit (12); longitude function (212).

k Particular scale along the parallel at a point (62).

k_o Particular scale along the standard parallel (147); scale factor for Transverse Mercator Projection (219).

K Kavraisky's constant for locating standard parallels (174).

m Scale factor (26); meridional arc length on the spheroid (47); constant (236).

n Constant of the cone (146); constant (236).

N Northing coordinate (20).

p Area scale at any point on a map projection (67).

p   Longitude function in UTM tables (228).

P Rotation and scale coefficient used in general transformation of Cartesian coordinates (27).

q Isometric latitude (157).

Q Rotation and scale coefficient used in general transformation of Cartesian coordinates (27).

r Radius vector in polar coordinates (23); radius of a small circle (40); radius of a generating globe (50).

R Radius of the Earth regarded as spherical (4); radius of a great circle (31).

s Arc length on sphere (41); linear distance (202).

s_e Arc length on Equator (41).

s_m Arc length along meridian (40).

s_p Arc length along parallel (41).

s' Distance corresponding to s on plane (60); linear distance (202).

S Denominator of principal scale $1/S$ (50).

t Bearing of visual observation (213).

T Bearing of rhumb-line corresponding to t (213).

u Angle on sphere measured from principal direction (65).

u' Angle on plane corresponding to u and measured from principal direction (65).

x Abscissa of Cartesian coordinates (20). Numerous combinations of symbols such as x', x'', x_o etc. are defined in the text.

The Symbols and Notation used in this Book

y Ordinate of Cartesian coordinates (20). Numerous combinations of symbols such as y', y'', y_o etc. are defined in the text.

z Angular distance between two points on the spherical surface (4).

z' $180° - z$ (135).

Z Azimuth (37).

$\sin 1''$ Conversion factor, seconds of arc into radians (211).

*   Precedes definitions appearing in the *Glossary of Technical Terms in Cartography* (Royal Society 1966).

α (alpha)   Angle referred to Cartesian axes (26); bearing (37). Numerous combinations of symbols such as α_o, α', α'' etc. are defined in the text.

β (beta)   Spherical angle made between the meridian and principal direction (65); maximum extent of zone to be mapped (71); plane bearing (202); plane bearing on Cassini's projection (214).

β' Plane angle made between the meridian and principal direction on the projection, corresponding to the first definition of β (66).

γ (gamma)   Convergence (42).

δ (delta)   Finite difference (29); distance between two small circles (165); arc-to-chord conversion (214).

ϵ (epsilon)   The difference between the angle of intersection of a parallel and meridian on a map projection and a right angle (234).

η (eta)   The ordinate of curvature (211).

θ (theta)   Vectorial angle of polar coordinates (23).

θ' The angle formed between the meridian and parallel at any point on a map projection (60).

λ (lambda)   Longitude (34).

μ (mu)   Any unspecified particular scale (63).

μ_o The principal scale of a map projection (51).

ν (nu)   The transverse radius of curvature of a point on an ellipsoid (45).

π (pi) $3 \cdot 14159\ 26535\ \ldots$

ρ (rho)   The meridional radius of curvature of a point on an ellipsoid (45).

φ (phi)   Latitude (33); geodetic latitude (44).

χ (chi)   Colatitude (34).

ψ (psi)   Geocentric latitude (44); auxiliary angle related to latitude (240).

ω (omega)   Maximum angular deformation (67); difference in longitude from the central meridian of the Transverse Mercator Projection of the spheroid (222).

The use of the lower case Greek letter δ (delta) in conjunction with another symbol, e.g. δx, $\delta \varphi$ or $\delta \lambda$ denotes a finite difference in x, φ or λ etc.

The use of the lower case Roman letter d in conjunction with another symbol, e.g. $\mathrm{d}x$, $\mathrm{d}\varphi$ or $\mathrm{d}\lambda$ denotes an infinitely small difference, or increment, in x, φ, λ etc. The use of the symbol ∂ in conjunction with another symbol, e.g. ∂x, $\partial \varphi$ or $\partial \lambda$ also denotes an infinitely small difference but is used exclusively to denote the partial differential coefficient when more than two variables are present in one equation.

The coordinates of points such as A or B are denoted by x_a, x_b, φ_a, φ_b, λ_a, λ_b etc. Generally points A and B are on the spherical surface whereas the corresponding points on the plane are denoted A', B' etc. However, this distinction is usually only made when it is necessary to compare corresponding points. It is not made when the text obviously refers to the sphere or to the plane.

CHAPTER 1

THE FIGURE OF THE EARTH AND THE REFERENCE SURFACES USED IN SURVEYING AND MAPPING

'The question of the actual figure of the Earth has always proved a stumbling block to humanity. I recall the case of a very high Lama of Tibet who assured Sir Francis Younghusband, with a faith no argument was capable of shaking, that the figure of the Earth was that of a shoulder of mutton. Even today I have received two letters expressing great interest in the discussion to take place this afternoon, one of them suggesting that the meeting should look on the figure of the Earth as being an out-stretched circular plane, and the other asserting with complete conviction that the Earth is flat. I do not know if I am unduly optimistic in hoping that as a result of the discussion this afternoon persons, of whom the High Lama to whom I have referred and the correspondents whose letters I have quoted are typical, will know something more than they do at present . . .'

The Earl of Ronaldshay: *Geographical Journal*, 1924

Introduction

Geodesy is the science concerned with the study of the shape and size of the Earth in the geometrical sense and with the study of certain physical phenomena, such as gravity, in seeking explanation of fine irregularities in the Earth's shape. The subject is intimately linked with surveying and cartography. A major part of the evidence about the shape and size of the Earth is based upon surveys. Indeed in some European languages the word 'geodesy' is practically equivalent to English usage of the term 'surveying'. Knowledge about the Earth's size and shape is indispensable if we are to make maps of its surface. Put in the simplest form, it is necessary to know the size of the Earth in order to make maps of it at known scale.

We know that the Earth is a nearly spherical planet upon which are super-imposed the surface irregularities created by land and sea, highland and lowland, mountains and valleys. However, these topographical irregularities represent little more than a roughening of the surface. Since the radius of the Earth is about 6371 km. and since the major relief features do not rise more than 9 km. above or fall more than 11 km. below sea level, they are relatively less important than, say, the seam on a cricket ball or the indentations on the surface of a golf ball. For example, if the Earth is drawn to scale as a circle of radius 6 cm., which is almost as large as the width of this page can accommodate, the variation in line thickness of the circumference which would show the entire height range from Mount Everest to the Mariana Trench at the same scale is less than 0·2 mm.

The idea that the Earth is a sphere dates from the Greek geometers of the sixth century B.C. The first serious attempt to measure the size of this sphere was the classic experiment carried out by Eratosthenes in the third century B.C. This has been described so many times that there is no need to repeat it here. For example, Refs. 1, 2, 3 and 7 quoted at the end of this chapter contain descriptions of how he attempted the measurement.

Towards the end of the seventeenth century, Newton demonstrated that the concept of a truly spherical Earth was inadequate to explain the equilibrium of ocean surfaces. He argued that since the Earth is a rotating planet, the forces created by its own rotation would tend to force any liquids on the surface towards the Equator. Newton showed, by means of a simple theoretical model, that hydrostatic equilibrium would be maintained if the Equatorial axis of the Earth were longer than the Polar axis. This is equivalent to the statement that the body is flattened towards the poles. The three dimensional body which corresponds is called an *ellipsoid of rotation* which may be represented in section by means of an ellipse, as shown in Fig. 1 and elsewhere. The amount of polar flattening may be expressed by

$$f=\frac{a-b}{a} \qquad (1.01)$$

where a and b are the lengths of the major and minor semi-axes of the ellipse.

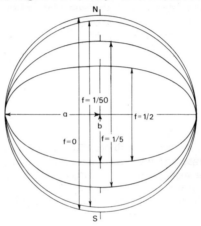

Figure 1 The relationship between ellipses of different ellipticity. This diagram shows three ellipses with ellipticity $f=1/2$, $f=1/5$ and $f=1/50$ which have the same major axis. The semiaxes of the ellipse for which $f=1/50$ are a and b respectively. These ellipses are compared with a circle of radius a, which is also an ellipse with ellipticity $f=0$. Since most Figures of the Earth have flattening of approximately $1/298$ it is clear from this figure that the terrestrial ellipsoid cannot be depicted in section at this scale in a form distinguishable from the circle. Consequently the terrestrial ellipsoid is usually represented by an ellipse with ellipticity of $1/5$ or thereabouts.

The value of f, which is also known as the *ellipticity* or *compression* of the body, is always expressed as a fraction. For the Earth this value is close to $1/300$. We now know that the difference in length between the two semi-axes is approximately $11\cdot5$ km., or the Polar axis is about 23 km. shorter than the Equatorial axis. It is interesting to reflect that this difference is about the same order of magnitude as the total relief variation on the Earth. Thus, at the approximate scale of $1/100,000,000$ which represents the Earth by a circle of radius 6 cm., the amount of polar flattening is also about $0\cdot2$ mm. Since $0\cdot2$ mm. is also the width or gauge of line used for the fine linear detail on maps, it follows that at very small scales the ellipticity of the Earth is about the width of the lines used to draw the map and is therefore negligible. This is an important conclusion from the cartographic viewpoint because it permits the assumption that the Earth can be regarded as truly spherical for certain purposes. We will examine the validity of this assumption elsewhere (pp. 15–16). However, we must also note that any attempt to represent the terrestrial ellipsoid diagrammatically by means of a recognisable ellipse must involve considerable exaggeration. This, in turn, leads to possible misinterpretation of some of the illustrations depicting the geometry of the ellipsoid.

Since the ellipsoid of rotation approximates so closely to the sphere it may also be called a *spheroid*. Since the flattening occurs at the poles rather than the Equator, the figure may be further defined as an *oblate spheroid*. In the literature of surveying and cartography no real distinction can be made between the use of the two words 'ellipsoid' and 'spheroid'. Both are used indiscriminately.

Measurement of the Earth's Figure

Five kinds of evidence have been used to determine the shape and size of the Earth. These are:

(1) Measurement of *astro-geodetic Arcs* on the Earths's surface,
(2) Measurement of variations of gravity at the Earth's surface,
(3) Measurement of small perturbations of the Moon's orbit,
(4) Measurement of the motion of the Earth's axis of rotation relative to the stars,
(5) Measurement of the Earth's gravity field from the orbits of artificial satellites.

Certain of the methods are only of value in determining the parameter f. The purely astronomical methods (3) and (4) are now only of historical interest.

Astro-geodetic arc measurement

This is the classic method which has been used to measure both the size and shape of the Earth. It is based upon comparison of the *angular distance* between two places on the Earth's surface and the linear *arc distance* between them. The first may be determined by making astronomical observations at the two places; the second by using the precise methods of surveying referred to as *geodetic* or *first order survey*. The *radii of curvature* of the Earth may be determined from these data and finally the lengths of the semi-axes of the ellipsoid can be calculated.

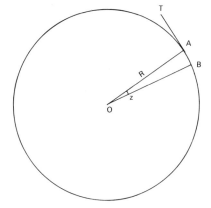

Figure 2 A sphere in section illustrating the constant relationship between angular distance and arc distance for all parts of the surface. *AT* represents a tangent to the circumference at *A*.

If the Earth were a true sphere, its radius would be easily calculated for it is a fundamental proptery of a sphere that all points on the surface are equidistant from its centre, i.e. it has constant radius. This is why it is possible to illustrate any section passing through the centre of a sphere by means of a circle as in Fig. 2. If there are two points, A and B, on the surface of a sphere with centre O, the angular distance between the points is the angle AOB measured at the centre and the arc distance between them is the shorter part of the circumference passing through the points. The relationship between these two measurements can be determined (e.g. Abbott/Trigonometry, §120) from

$$\text{Arc length } AB = R.z \qquad (1.02)$$

where R is the radius of the sphere and z is the angle AOB expressed in radians. For example, if $z = 10° = 0.174\ 53$ radians and $R = 6371$ km., the arc distance $AB = 1111.9$ km. This is constant for all values of $z = 10°$ on this sphere irrespective of where the arc is situated. The converse argument is used to derive the radius from the arc and angular measurements. Thus, if astronomical observations made at both A and B showed that they lie $10°$ apart and survey has established that the distance between them on the surface is 1111.9 km., from equation (1.02)

$$R = \frac{1111.9}{0.174\ 53}$$

$$= 6371 \text{ km.}$$

Note that the radius of the sphere has been defined as the line OA. A further property of the sphere, which may be proved from the elementary plane geometry of a circle (Theorem 48 in Abbott/Geometry), is that when a tangent meets a circle at the point A, the *normal*, or perpendicular to that tangent passes through the centre. Thus on the sphere, OA is perpendicular to any tangent at A and if a series of tangents are drawn through A in directions other than the section illustrated, these lie in the same *tangent plane*.

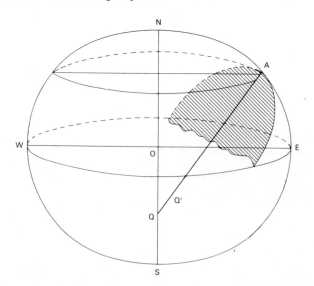

Figure 3 An ellipsoid in section illustrating the meridional radius of curvature AQ' and the transverse radius of curvature AQ of the point A. The shaded plane is perpendicular to the meridian *NAE* through A.

This is important in defining the radii of curvature of an ellipsoid which are *lines perpendicular to the tangent plane at any point on the curved surface.* They are *not* represented by straight lines joining points to the geometrical centre of the body. Thus, at some point *A* on the surface of an ellipsoid, we may imagine the tangent plane. In Fig. 3, the normal to this tangent plane is $AQ'Q$. A further difficulty in defining the geometry of the ellipsoid is that two separate radii may be distinguished. One of these is the radius of the arc *NAE*; the other is the radius of the arc which is perpendicular to *NAE*. The radii are represented in Fig. 3 by the line AQ' and AQ respectively. Thus both radii occupy the same position in space but have different lengths. Moreoever, the line $AQ'Q$ does not pass through the geometrical centre of the ellipse, *O*, except where the normal to the surface forms either *NO* or *EO*, which are the semi-axes of the figure. It follows that the radii of an ellipsoid are variable quantities. Two separate radii may be defined for each point on the surface and both of these vary with position of the point on the surface. It follows, therefore, that the linear distance corresponding to a given

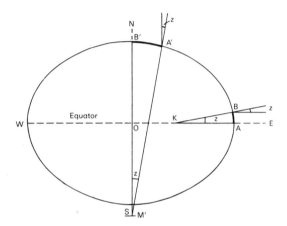

Figure 4 An ellipsoid in section illustrating how a given angular distance, *z*, is represented by a longer arc distance, *A'B'*, near the poles than is the arc distance, *AB*, near the Equator. Note that the radii of curvature *KA* and *M'A'* also increase towards the poles but are exaggerated here owing to the exaggerated ellipticity of the ellipse.

angular distance varies with latitude. For example, the angle $z = 10°$ between the points *A* and *B* near the Equator represents an arc distance of approximately 1105·6 km. on the surface of the terrestrial ellipsoid, whereas the same angle between the points *A'* and *B'* near the poles corresponds to about 1169·9 km. In other words *the arc distance corresponding to a given angle increases polewards.* This relationship is shown in Fig. 4 but care must be taken in the interpretation of the diagram. The ellipse is shown with exaggerated compression and the directions of the radii of curvature are shown as the normals to the tangents at the four points. These must be produced to give the points of intersection at *K* and *M'* to show that $AKB = 10° = A'M'B'$. The reader should avoid making the implied comparison with Fig. 2 which suggests that the radii of the ellipse are the lines *AK*, *BK* etc. and hence the fallacious interpretation of them as being much greater or less than *OA* or *OB* in Fig. 2.

This preliminary excursion into the geometrical properties of the sphere and ellipsoid, which are examined in greater detail in Chapter 3, has been made to

B

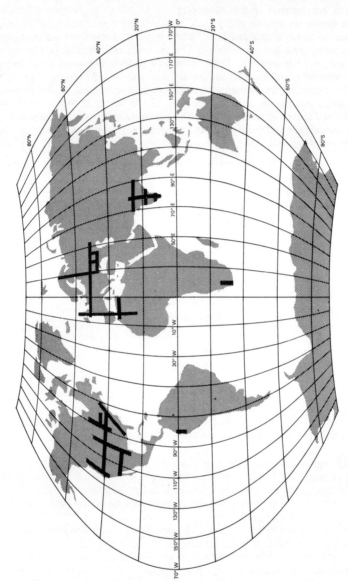

Figure 5 World map showing the location of the main astro-geodetic arcs used for determination of the Figure of the Earth during the classical period of arc measurement before 1914. The map is based upon the Aitoff-Wagner Projection (No. 39a in Appendix I) which is a member of the Polyconic Group of projections with equidistant spacing of the parallels along each meridian. Note, also, that the geographical poles are represented by curves.

indicate the kind of evidence to be obtained from astro-geodetic arc measurement. The variation in arc length with latitude was one of the first important pieces of evidence to be obtained which supported Newton's theoretical model. It was obtained from the measurement of two arcs, in Peru and Lapland, by the French during the early part of the eighteenth century.

The period of greatest activity in this field of geodesy occurred during the nineteenth and early twentieth centuries, when most of the data were collected, Fig. 5, which were used for determination of the different Figures of the Earth listed in Table 1. At that time the only satisfactory method for control surveys of the requisite order of precision was by means of triangulation. The techniques of electromagnetic distance measurement, which have revolutionised survey practices since the nineteen-fifties, arrived on the scene too late to be used for the determination of any of the Figures in common use. The preferred type of measurement was the *arc of the meridian*, i.e. a survey between terminal points which differed greatly

Table 1

Some of the principal determinations of the Figure of the Earth which are of practical use in modern cartography and surveying.
Primary source: Ref. 10

Name	Date	Major semi-axis, a (m.)	Minor semi-axis, b (m.)	Ellipticity f	Use
Delambre	1810	6 376 428	6 355 598	1/311.5	Belgium†
Plessis	1817	6 376 523	6 355 863	1/308.6	France†
Everest	1830	6 377 276	6 356 075	1/300.80	India, Burma, Ceylon, Malaysia (part)
Bessel	1841	6 377 397	6 356 079	1/299.15	Most parts of Central Europe, Chile, Indonesia
Airy	1849	6 377 563	6 356 257	1/299.32	Great Britain
Clarke	1858	6 378 293	6 356 619	1/294.3	Australia†
Struve	1860	6 378 298	6 356 657	1/294.7	Spain
Clarke	1866	6 378 206	6 356 584	1/294.98	North American continent, Philippines
Clarke	1880	6 378 249	6 356 515	1/293.47	France, most of African continent
Helmert	1907	6 378 200	6 356 818	1/298.30	Egypt†
Hayford or International	1909 } 1924 }	6 378 388	6 356 912	1/297.00	Whole world excluding N. America, Africa and a few other small areas
Krasovsky	1940	6 378 245	6 356 863	1/298.30	USSR and all other communist countries
'165'	—	6 378 165	6 356 783	1/298.3	Australia†
International Astronomical Union	1965	6 378 160	6 356 775	1/298.25	Australia
Danish	—	6 377 104	6 355 762	1/300	Denmark, Iceland

† Obsolescent use for some old map series which have not been superseded.
There are numerous inconsistencies in use for different map series by certain national survey organisations. In military mapping other doctrines prevail. For example NATO policy for use with the UTM system (see pp. 224–33) favours use of the International Spheroid almost everywhere except North America and Africa. Soviet policy has been to adopt the Krasovsky figure for all Warsaw Pact mapping.

in latitude but little in longitude so that the network of connecting triangles was aligned along the same meridian.

Note how early in the history of science some of these determinations were made. For example, the Great Trigonometrical Survey of India had measured the arc following the meridian 78° East, which crosses the centre of the subcontinent from Cape Comorin to Kalianpur by 1825 and reached the Himalayas by 1841.‡ Everest, who was at that time Superintendent of the Great Trigonometrical Survey, determined the Figure of the Earth which bears his name during a prolonged spell of sick leave. Completion of such an enterprise so long ago was a remarkable achievement.

The small differences in the size and ellipticity which are shown in Table 1 result from subtle and small variations in the Earth's figure causing it to depart from a perfect spheroid. Consequently the parameters for each Figure of the Earth depend upon which astro-geodetic arc measurements were used in the determination and therefore the different figures tend to fit certain parts of the World better than others.

Gravity measurements

Newton arrived at the conclusion that the Earth was an ellipsoid from the theoretical consideration of the forces created by the Earth's mass and rotation. Consequently the second important line of evidence concerning the shape of the Earth has been from the study of variation in gravity.

In the absolute sense, gravity varies with latitude and it was early recognised that pendulum clocks which kept good time in Europe tended to lose time near the Equator. About the middle of the eighteenth century, Clairaut demonstrated the relationship between latitude and gravity, leading to the possibility of determining ellipticity from this evidence.

Gravity also affects the observations made during astro-geodetic arc measurement. It is this relative aspect of gravity which is particularly important in geodesy. In order to make observations in survey and astronomy it is necessary to align the instruments to a common datum. This datum is provided by the tangent plane to the Earth's curved surface at the point of observation. We have already seen that this plane is geometrically important. It also has a physical significance because this plane can be defined by means of the spirit bubble mounted on a theodolite and the adjustment of the instrument by means of its footscrews until the spirit bubble is stationary in the centre of its run. We assume that the instrument is perfectly adjusted and ignore any corrections which have to be made for other reasons. The normal to this tangent plane is defined by the plumb line which is used to set the instrument precisely over the point from which the observations are to be made. In short, we use gravity to determine both the horizontal plane of reference and the direction of the vertical. These adjustments are normal survey practice and are especially important in geodetic measurement. 'Horizontal' angles observed by a theodolite which is not level contain errors which consequently deform the shapes of the triangles which have been observed. This, in turn, leads to errors in the computed distances between points and therefore to error in the computed positions of the stations. Precise determination of the horizontal plane of reference is an even more vital requirement for astronomical observations for these comprise measurements of vertical angles (known as altitudes) to stars. The datum for these measurements is the horizontal plane indicated by a spirit bubble, or an artificial horizon formed by a liquid such as a dish of mercury which takes a

---

‡ See the remarkable *Gemini* 9 photograph of the subcontinent on the front cover.

horizontal position through gravitational attraction. The consequence of a slight inclination of either plane of reference leads to incorrect measurement of the vertical angle and therefore to the determination of an incorrect astronomical position for the instrument.

If the height of each observation station is reduced to sea-level, then by virtue of the fact that the instruments have always been carefully levelled, this is equivalent to stating that the observations have all been reduced to the same *equipotential surface* where the spirit bubble is always at rest. This surface is known as the geoid.† The geoid can be likened to the surface of an imaginary ocean without waves, swell, tides or currents, and with the continuation of this surface beneath the land masses.

If the Earth were a homogeneous body, then from classical gravitational theory the surface of the geoid would coincide everywhere with the surface of an ellipsoid. However, this is not so. The geological history of the Earth has led to irregular distribution of crustal rocks having different densities. The denser rocks exert their own attraction upon a spirit bubble, although this is small compared with the main gravitational component. Thus an instrument may *seem* to be level but the plumb line is not normal to the spheroid and is deflected slightly towards the areas of greater rock density. Since the amount of deflection varies from place to place it follows that the geoid has an undulating surface. Figure 6 illustrates how these undulations occur. Since all observations have been made with reference to the geoid, additional measurements of the *gravity anomalies* which are present can be used to correct for and increase knowledge about the location of undulations of its surface. Stokes first demonstrated these principles in 1849 and methods of correcting for anomalies have been used since 1855, when Pratt attempted to account for discre-

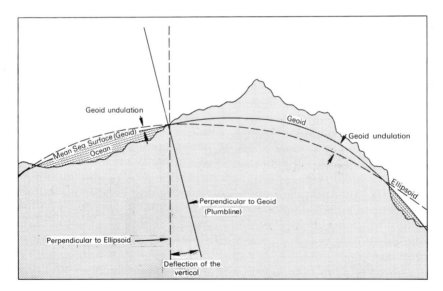

Figure 6 The relationship between the geoid and reference spheroid indicating the deflection of the perpendicular to the geoid and resulting undulations in the surface of the geoid.

---

† It is possible to distinguish between several different geoids, but this complication refers to the methods used to make the reductions. It will serve our purposes to recognise only one.

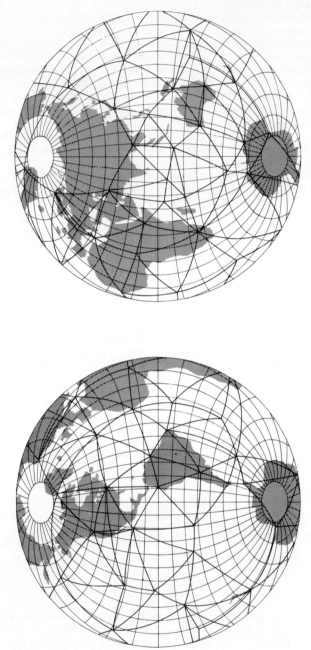

Figure 7 Maps showing the world-wide triangulation network being observed with the aid of the PAGEOS artificial satellite as part of the U.S. National Geodetic Satellite Program. The maps are equatorial aspect Stereographic Projections (No. 6 in Appendix l). This is a member of the Azimuthal Class of projections. The two maps have been extended to represent more than hemispheres ($z=110°$) so that the edges overlap. The Stereographic Projection is conformal. Therefore the angles within the triangulation network are correctly depicted at each observation station. Moreover all great circle arcs are shown as circular arcs on the Stereographic Projection. Therefore all the sides of the triangulation network are represented by circular arcs.

pancies in the position of Kalianpur observed in the astro-geodetic arc measured by the Great Trigonometrical Survey of India. The attempts to explain this and similar inconsistencies in other arc measurements led to the formulation of the different theories of *isostasy*, which have been a major preoccupation of geodesists and which also revolutionised structural geology.

It follows that the increasing refinement of determinations of the Figure of the Earth, characterised by the small variation of f obtained after 1900, is largely owing to the increasing availability of gravity data and the methods of employing these to adjust the astro-geodetic observations. By the late 1940's sufficient information about gravity anomalies had been collected to attempt the compilation of maps showing the undulations of the geoid by means of contours. However these maps were confined to showing parts of the Northern Hemisphere (notably the USA and Western Europe) where there was sufficient density of information. Ultimately it might have been possible to proceed with such work on a World basis but it would have been a long job. At that time there was still very little information about gravity anomalies in the Southern Hemisphere and, moreover, there were still practical difficulties about obtaining satisfactory gravity measurements at sea. This meant that there were no data from more than 70% of the Earth's surface. The first successful measurements of gravity from a surface ship were only made in November 1957.

The first artificial satellite had been launched a month earlier. This heralded a major step forward in advancement of knowledge about the Earth's true shape and size. Moreover it made it unnecessary to piece together the map of the geoid using millions of individual gravity stations which would otherwise have been required. The primary reason for the advance was that artificial satellites overcame a fundamental difficulty in deciphering the Earth's gravity field, namely that all measurements had been confined to the Earth's surface and that observations to our natural satellite, the Moon, were somewhat insensitive because of the great distance between Earth and Moon.

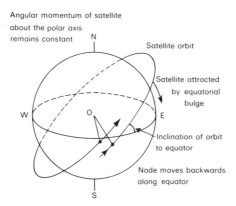

Figure 8 Diagrammatic representation of the Precession of the Nodes. The Equatorwards force, resulting from the Earth's equatorial bulge, causes an artificial satellite to cross the Equator on a different meridian at each successive orbit.

The earliest and some of the most significant information was obtained within a year or two simply from observation of the changing orbits of the early Sputnik and Vanguard satellites. Satellite tracking has yielded much information about the gravity potential of the Earth and led eventually to remarkably detailed mapping of the geoid throughout the World (Fig. 10). The second use of satellites has been as survey beacons which are visible from widely separated places on the Earth and which can therefore be used to create a unified and worldwide network of geodetic stations (Fig. 7). Hitherto the principal astro-geodetic arcs have been separated by the oceans and it was impossible to judge how one system might fit another.

If the Earth were spherical and of homogeneous density, the orbit of a satellite would be an ellipse fixed in shape and size, and with its plane in a fixed direction in space (Refs. 1, 2). Any departure of the Earth from a spherical form causes changes in the gravitational force acting on the satellite, and consequently its orbit departs from the simple form. The main effect of the Earth's ellipticity upon a satellite orbit is to make the plane of the orbit rotate about the Earth's axis in the direction opposite to the satellite's motion, while leaving the inclination of the orbit to the Equator virtually constant. This phenomenon is known as the *Precession of the Nodes*, Fig. 8. The rate of precession can be measured with extraordinarily high precision using quite simple equipment because the movement is regular and therefore it can be allowed to accumulate over long periods of observation. The value of ellipticity, obtained only a year or so after the first artificial satellites had been launched, was $f = 1/298 \cdot 24$, or practically the same as that determined by Helmert in 1907 and Krasovsky in 1940.

Following these initial discoveries a great deal of additional work has been carried out on the analysis of the Earth's gravity field. Study of variation of gravity potential with latitude has led to the evaluation of a series of numerical coefficients, called *J-harmonics* which describe a sequence of increasingly elaborate geometrical figures. The J_1 coefficient, which defines the ellipticity of the ellipsoid is by far the most important of these but some of the other coefficients are not wholly insignificant. These indicate that the Earth is somewhat asymmetrical in section, for the North Pole is about 10 metres further from the Equator than can be accounted for by ellipticity of $1/298 \cdot 24$, but the South Pole lies about 30 metres nearer the

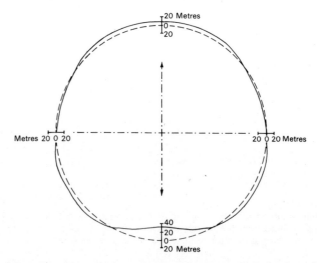

Figure 9 Inferred meridional section of the Earth based upon the calculation of variations in gravity potential with latitude but excluding any variation with longitude. The diagram indicates the departures (in metres) of this section (full line) from an ellipse with ellipticity $1/298 \cdot 24$ (broken line).

Equator than this amount of compression suggests. The resulting meridional section has been likened to the shape of a pear. Figure 9 indicates the difference of the figure thus determined compared with the ellipsoid having $f=1/298\cdot24$.

Further analysis of satellite motion with respect to longitude has shown the location of the major peaks and hollows in the geoid. Figure 10 indicates that the two most important features measure 67 metres above and 79 metres below the surface of the ellipsoid.

The choice of a suitable reference surface for mapping

The problem which is introduced by our increased knowledge of the Earth's shape and size is how this should be described mathematically for the practical purposes of mapping. Since there is no merit to be gained from increasing the mathematical complexity of the solution beyond defining those irregularities which have practical significance, it is desirable to consider the possibility of using different *reference surfaces* which describe the shape and size of the Earth adequately for the purposes intended. The Earth is now known to be more complicated than an ellipsoid of rotation, but the known variations in the surface of the geoid as shown in Fig. 10 amount to only a few metres. These variations are of practical importance in geodesy and some branches of geophysics. For work in these fields of study there are cogent reasons for defining as reference surface a *triaxial ellipsoid* in which the plane of the Equator is also represented by an ellipse. However these variations in the geoid are practically negligible for most other kinds of survey and in carto-graphy. Just as it has been shown that discrepancies of 20 km cannot be depicted graphically at very small scales, so the much smaller departures of the geoid from the ellipsoid of rotation are unimportant in cartography. The reason why we have devoted so much space to their consideration is to explain why different reference ellipsoids are still used to describe one planet.

Thus we may simplify the problem and consider three different ways in which we may define the shape and size of the Earth for different purposes in surveying and mapping.

These are:
(1) A plane which is tangential to the Earth at some point,
(2) A perfect sphere of suitable radius,
(3) An ellipsoid of rotation of suitable dimensions and ellipticity.

They are listed in ascending order of refinement. Thus a suitable ellipsoid fits the shape of the geoid better than a perfect sphere of equivalent size. The sphere, in turn, is a better approximation of the curved surface than is a plane. On the other hand, the list is in order of increasing mathematical difficulty. The formulae needed to define position, to determine the relationships between distances and angles on a plane are simpler than are those for the curved surface of a sphere. These, in turn, are simpler than the corresponding formulae for an ellipsoid. Bearing in mind the desirability to use the simplest reference figure which is compatible with accuracy of representation, it follows that we should inspect the properties of each kind of reference surface to discover when it should be used.

The plane reference surface

At first sight it may seem to be a retrograde step to assume that the Earth is a plane. However it is a very useful assumption because it is so simple to use. If it can be assumed that for the purposes of a survey or a map that to all intents and purposes the Earth is flat, then we avoid the whole problem of map projection

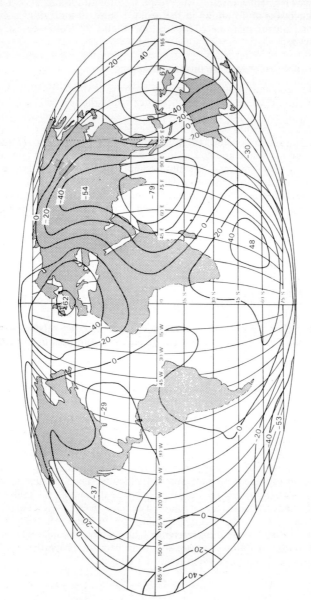

Figure 10 Inferred contours of the geoid (in metres) for the whole World, based upon Kuala's analysis of variations in gravity potential with both latitude and longitude. The map is based on Mollweide's Projection (No. 21 in Appendix I) which is an equal-area pseudocylindrical projection with elliptical meridians.

transformations which are the main preoccupation of this book. Inspection of Fig. 2 indicates that in the vicinity of any point such as A on the curved surface of the Earth, the tangent to the curved surface lies close to it. It may therefore be argued that if a survey or map is only intended to measure or depict features situated in the immediate vicinity of the point A it is reasonable to assume that the Earth is a plane. When this assumption can be justified, the survey can be computed by the methods of plane trigonometry (it is then called *plane surveying*). Plotting of the map can be done simply by converting ground dimensions to the required map scale. The crux of the argument is the definition of what is represented by 'the immediate vicinity of the point A'. It implies that the plane assumption should be confined to the preparation of maps of small areas, but it still remains necessary to define what we mean by a small area. We defer quantitative consideration of this problem until Chapter 11 (pp. 202–4) because it is desirable to consider this assumption together with the kinds of map projections which are used by surveyors and which are also important in large scale cartography of small areas.

The spherical assumption

We have already commented upon the fact that at a scale of about 1/100,000,000 the two axes of the ellipsoid differ in length by about the width of lines needed to draw them. This implies that the main use of the spherical assumption will occur in the preparation of comparatively small format maps showing large parts of the Earth's surface, i.e. maps of the World, a hemisphere, a continent or even a large country, such as appear in atlases. The question to be answered is: 'What is the approximate maximum scale at which the spherical assumption can be justified?'

There is useful quantitative information on this subject, computed by Tobler (Ref. 9) which indicates the sort of error which may arise in using the spherical assumption to map a large country. Tobler investigated the differences in distance and bearing between 200 randomly selected places in the United States based upon computations of arc distance and bearing for both a sphere and the Clarke 1866 spheroid used for North America. In performing these computations Tobler assumed a sphere of radius $R = 6378 \cdot 206$ km., which is the equatorial radius of the Clarke 1866 Figure. This value is greater than the recommended radius given on p. 42. These results are summarised in Table 2.

Table 2

Comparison of the differences in distances and bearing between 200 points in the United States of America computed on both a sphere and a spheroid.

	Distance Difference (km.)	Angular Difference (degrees)
Average	0·074	0·006
Standard Deviation	3·053	0·083
Minimum	−6·100	−0·150
Maximum	+7·844	+0·159

If we assume $0 \cdot 2$ mm. to be the smallest linear distance which can be measured on a map and if we take Tobler's average difference in distance as being equal to this, then the largest scale at which the United States of America might be represented by a projection of the sphere is 1/370,000. However the spread of the results, characterised by the values for the standard deviation and the two extreme values indicates that it would be optimistic to use the spherical assumption at such a large scale and imagine that no errors in mapping would arise from this cause. The figures suggest that, strictly speaking, the spherical assumption ought to be confined to use in maps of scale 1/15,000,000 or smaller, which is about the scale at which 7·8 km. is represented by 0·2 mm., but in practical cartography the limit of using the spherical assumption is usually taken to be a scale of 1/5,000,000 or thereabouts. Using Tobler's data, it can be argued that at a scale of 1/5,000,000 about two-thirds of all points lie within 1 mm. of the spheroidal position if mapped on a sphere. We will see later that this discrepancy is small compared with the displacements which are inherent in the process of representing a large country at a small scale on a plane map.

The spheroidal assumption

Obviously the spheroid fits the shape of the geoid more closely than does a sphere. Consequently this is the reference surface which ought to be employed in surveying. This is because the survey of a country is first computed to determine the positions of the control points as it were at the scale of 1/1. Consequently the small discrepancies of position (or *closing errors*) can be expressed to the nearest millimetre on the ground and not absorbed by scale reduction as would happen if the results of a survey were plotted graphically on a sheet of paper. In order to appreciate the quality and precision of the work it is desirable to make these computations with respect to a particular reference spheroid rather than risking the introduction of errors arising from assuming a flat or spherical Earth. At the later stage of producing topographical and other map series, extending throughout an entire country, continuity of information across the boundaries of adjacent map sheets is important. Hence it is desirable to use the reference ellipsoid as the basis of such maps. It is also used for the compilation of large-scale navigation charts and small-scale charts to the approximate limit of 1/4,000,000–1/5,000,000.

Table 1 on page 7 indicated that about 15 different reference ellipsoids may be encountered in World mapping and about six of these are in common use. From the point of view of practical cartographic work the correct spheroid for use should always be clearly stated in the mapping specification. From the point of view of evaluating existing topographical or other maps as source documents for compilation, a reference such as Ref. 10 or national survey reports provide the information which is needed.

Originally a particular spheroid was selected by the national survey because the parameters of the figure fitted the observed data better than any other. A typical example of this was the use of the Airy spheroid for Great Britain, for this had been derived from astro-geodetic distances obtained during the original Primary Triangulation of the country. Once a national survey has been computed using a particular reference figure it is extremely inconvenient and costly to convert the positions of many hundreds or even thousands of control points to another spheroid. It follows that a national survey will usually continue to use a particular figure long after the original reasons for its adoption cease to be valid. This argument carries less weight today than before high speed digital computers became commonplace. It is interesting to note in this context that probably the first major use of digital computers in surveying and geodesy was the work undertaken by the U.S. Army Map Service shortly after World War II, when they accomplished the formidable task of reducing the national surveys of Europe, which had hitherto been based upon a multiplicity of different points of origin, reference spheroids and projections, to a common datum on the International Spheroid. Nevertheless the use of different figures still remains. It arises partly from historical accident, partly from inertia and partly for reasons of national prestige. Sometimes, also, it happens that the chosen spheroid fits the shape of the geoid in that country better than any of the others.

References

A great deal has been written about the shape and size of the Earth and the methods used to determine these. These range from simple, entertaining historical introductions to severely mathematical studies. Jules Verne even wrote a novel about an imaginary astro-geodetic expedition to southern Africa in the mid-nineteenth century. In the English translation it is entitled *Measuring a Meridian*, Arco Publications, London, 1964.

The following are recommended. Refs. 1–6 are elementary introductions to the subject. Refs. 7 and 8 are much more advanced.

1 King-Hele, D. G.: 'The shape of the Earth', *Scientific American*, 217, 1967, pp. 67–76.
2 King-Hele, D. G.: 'The shape of the Earth', *Journal of the Institute of Navigation*, 17, 1964, pp. 1–16.
3 King-Hele, D. G.: *Satellites and Scientific Research*, London, 1960, Routledge and Kegan Paul, 180 pp.
4 Garland, G. D.: *The Earth's Shape and Gravity*, Oxford, 1965, Pergamon Press, 183 pp.
5 Burkard, R. K.: *Geodesy for the Layman*, St. Louis, 1964, Aeronautical Chart and Information Center, USAF, 93 pp.
6 — *The Admiralty Manual of Hydrographic Surveying*, Vol. I, London, 1965, Hydrographic Dept., 671 pp.
7 Heiskanen, W. A. and Vening Meinesz, F. A.: *The Earth and Its Gravity Field*, New York, 1958, McGraw-Hill, 470 pp.
8 Bomford, G.: *Geodesy*, Oxford, 3rd edition, 1971, The Clarendon Press, 731 pp.
9 Tobler, W. R.: *Geographical Coordinate Computations, Part I General Considerations*, 1964, The University of Michigan, Department of Geography, Technical Report No. 2. ONR Task No. 389–137.
10 — 'The status of world topographic mapping', *World Cartography*, 10, 1970. pp. 1–96.

CHAPTER 2

COORDINATE REFERENCE SYSTEMS ON THE PLANE

It is impossible not to feel stirred at the thought of the emotions of men at certain historic moments of adventure and discovery—Columbus when he first saw the Western shore, Pizarro when he stared at the Pacific Ocean, Franklin when the electric spark came from the string of his kite, Galileo when he first turned his telescope to the heavens. Such moments are also granted to students in the abstract regions of thought, and high among them must be placed the morning when Descartes lay in bed and invented the method of co-ordinate geometry.

A. N. Whitehead

Introduction

In this chapter we review some of the fundamental ideas about the plane coordinate systems which are used in surveying and mapping, both from the viewpoint of studying the mathematics of map projections and the practical tasks which arise in cartography.

Coordinates are a convenient method of recording position in space. They may be used to locate position in two dimensions, such as a point on a graph. An extension of this method to map use allows the location of a place by its *grid reference*. Definition of coordinate position on the surface of a three dimensional body such as a sphere or spheroid is rather more difficult. However the reader should already be aware of the method of describing location by means of latitude and longitude, which are *geographical coordinates*. These are defined in Chapter 3, where the differences between defining latitude on a sphere and on a spheroid are introduced. In addition to providing a means of reference, coordinates can also be used as a convenient way of solving certain geometrical problems. The branch of mathematics known as *coordinate geometry* analyses problems through the relationship between points as defined by their coordinates. By these means, for example, it is possible to derive algebraic expressions defining different kinds of curve which cannot be done by Euclidean geometry. Coordinate geometry is an exceptionally powerful tool in the study of the theory of map projections and without its help it is practically impossible to pass beyond the elementary descriptive stage. Plane coordinate geometry is usually studied first through the medium of the *conic sections* or the definition of the different kinds of curve formed by the surface of a cone where this is intersected by a plane. Two of the resulting sections, the ellipse and the circle, are of fundamental importance to the theory of distortions in map projections.

Plane coordinate systems

There are an infinite number of ways in which one point on a plane surface may be referred to another point on the same plane. Every map projection creates a unique reference system which satisfies this requirement and an infinity of different map projections could theoretically be described. However it is desirable to use some kind of coordinate system to describe, analyse and construct each of these

18

projections. Any system to be used for such purposes ought to be easy to understand and simple to express algebraically. For plane representation the choice lies between *Plane Cartesian Coordinates* and *Polar Coordinates*.

Plane Cartesian Coordinates

The reader will already be familiar with graphs as a method of plotting two variables on specially ruled paper and with the National Grid on Ordnance Survey maps. The simple graph and the National Grid are simple, but special, examples of plane Cartesian coordinates. In the general case, *any* plane coordinate system which makes use of linear measurements in two directions from a pair of fixed axes can be regarded as a Cartesian system. The coordinate system comprises sets or *families* of lines which intersect one another to form a *network* when plotted. The only necessary conditions which must be fulfilled are:

(1) That the two families of lines are distinct from one another;
(2) That every line of one family should intersect every line of the other family at one point only;
(3) That no two lines of the same family should intersect one another.

Thus a Cartesian coordinate system can comprise families of straight lines or curves which may intersect at any angle. However it is a distinct advantage if the special case is chosen in which both families of lines are straight and that they are *orthogonal,* or intersect at right angles. This special case, characterised by ordinary graph paper and by the National Grid printed on Ordnance Survey maps may be called a *Plane Rectangular Cartesian Coordinate System* or, in short, *Rectangular Coordinates.*

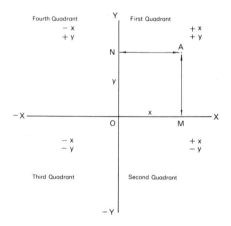

Figure 11 Plane Rectangular Cartesian Coordinates.

In Fig. 11, the *origin* of the rectangular coordinate system is the point O, through which two orthogonal *axes,* OX and OY, have been plotted. These axes define the directions of the two families of lines. Since the axes are straight lines and perpendicular to one another, it follows that all the lines composing one family will be parallel to one another and that all points of intersection within the network are made from lines which are perpendicular to one another. The position of a point A is defined by the two linear measurements OM and ON made from the origin to the points M and N on the two axes, which are drawn from A as perpendiculars to the axes. Clearly *AM* is parallel to *OY* and *AN* is parallel to *OX*. The mathematical convention is to refer to the horizontal axis *OX* as the *X-axis* or *abscissa*. The vertical line *OY* is called the *Y-axis* or *ordinate*. However this convention is not always observed in the study of geodesy, surveying and map projections. In some books, for example Ref. 1, the notation is reversed and *OX* is the vertical axis. There are cogent reasons for this change in notation but it is extremely confusing, not only to the beginner. We will use the standard mathematical convention throughout this book and refer to the coordinates of a point such as *A* as being (x, y), according to the axes illustrated in Fig. 11.

The units into which the axes are subdivided for the purposes of linear measurement are quite arbitrary. For example, graph paper is available with both millimetre and inch ruling, with various combinations of multiples and fractions of these. The National Grid is measured in metres. There is also considerable practical value in using coordinate tables to describe map projections in which the units of measurement are multiples and fractions of the Earth's radius.

There is a sign convention to be observed in the use of rectangular coordinates. This states that the *X*-axis is positive towards the right and the *Y*-axis is positive towards the top of the page. In other words, a point in the top right-hand quarter of a graph is defined by positive values of x and y, whereas a point in the bottom left-hand quarter has negative values for x and y. The quarters are termed *quadrants* and these are numbered 1–4 in a clockwise direction commencing with the top right quadrant. Hence the sign convention is:

1st quadrant	$+x$,	$+y$
2nd quadrant	$+x$,	$-y$
3rd quadrant	$-x$,	$-y$
4th quadrant	$-x$,	$+y$

The map grid as an example of plane rectangular coordinates

A *grid* has been defined in the *Glossary of Technical Terms in Cartography* as *a Cartesian reference system using distances measured on a chosen projection*. The last seven words of this definition are probably necessary but tend to confuse the the issue. For the moment it will suffice to regard a grid as a system of rectangular coordinates superimposed upon a plane corresponding to the ground. One family of lines is orientated approximately North–South and the other family, by definition, is perpendicular to them. Measurements along the axes are made in some units used for ground measurement. Nowadays the metric system is used almost everywhere, but formerly some grids used feet or yards as the unit. By virtue of the approximate orientation of a grid, the abscissa of a point usually called its *Easting* and the ordinate is called its *Northing*. Thus *E* is equivalent to x and *N* is equivalent to y in the mathematical graph convention. We will introduce this substitution without further comment where it is appropriate to refer to a point by its (E, N) coordinates rather than by (x, y). The order in which the grid coordinates are recorded is often confusing to the beginner, who has probably only just learnt to describe geographical position in the order 'latitude-followed-by-longitude'. If it is remembered that a grid is like a graph, then the logic of using 'Easting-followed-by-Northing' is apparent.

We do not attempt to describe in this book how a grid reference may be obtained from a map for the reader ought to be able to do this already. Military manuals, such as Refs. 2 and 3, are always painstaking in describing how to give grid references for these are vital in military map reading and communication. The practices adopted by the Ordnance Survey for use with the National Grid are described in a special pamphlet (Ref. 4) which distinguishes the procedures to be adopted at different Ordnance Survey map scales. Moreover many Ordnance Survey and other national survey maps have the appropriate instructions, with a worked example, printed in the margin.

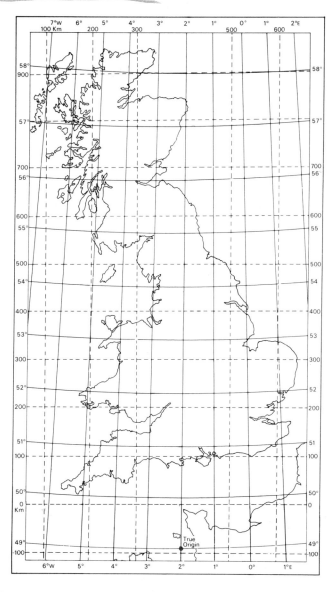

Figure 12 The National Grid of Great Britain, showing the relationship between the grid lines (broken) at every 100 km, and the graticule of meridians and parallels (full lines) at 1° intervals of latitude and longitude. The True Origin of the Grid in latitude 49° N, longitude 2° W is indicated, but the False Origin, from which the grid lines are numbered lies beyond the western edge of the map.

c

Because a grid is a form of graph it must have an origin. Moreover if the grid is to satisfy its purpose to serve as a national or international standard of reference, the point of origin must be explicitly stated, together with the orientation of the axes at this point. It is this aspect of a grid which introduces the confusing ideas contained in the second part of the definition given on page 20. For example, the National Grid (Fig. 12) has its origin at the point with latitude 49° North, longitude 2° West. This is situated in the Golfe de St. Malo, about 20 km. south east of St. Helier in Jersey. The same point is also taken as the origin of the map projection used by the Ordnance Survey for all topographical maps of England, Scotland and Wales. We defer the projection part of the problem to a later chapter. Here it is desirable to consider two properties of the grid, its orientation and the system of numbering along the axes.

The ordinate of the system is orientated so that it coincides with the meridian 2° West. It follows that since all meridians point towards True North, the ordinate of the National Grid also points towards True North. Since the grid is composed of families of straight lines, it follows that all other vertical grid lines point in the constant direction defined by the ordinate. This constant direction may be called *Grid North*. On the other hand all meridians converge towards the geographical poles, therefore a meridian through a point lying east or west of longitude 2° West does not coincide everywhere with a grid line through the same point. This gives rise to the angular discrepancy between meridians and grid lines which is illustrated in exaggerated form in Fig. 13. The angle is known as *Grid Convergence*. Within the range of longitude occupied by Southern England, the amount of convergence is small, for example it is 2° 54′ near Land's End and nearly 3° on the Norfolk coast.

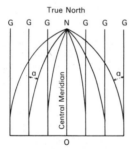

Figure 13 The relationship between true north, represented by the meridians converging to the geographical pole, *N*, and grid north which is a constant direction for any particular grid. Grid convergence is indicated by the angles, *a*.

The choice of the meridian 2° West as the longitude of origin is simply because this lies near the middle of the part of the British Isles covered by the National Grid. It is a line which passes through the Isle of Purbeck in Dorset, through Birmingham, Berwick and Fraserburgh. From the sign convention used with graphs this means that all places situated to the West of the ordinate have negative Easting coordinates. In Britain this would mean that everywhere in Wales, in most of Scotland and the whole of England lying to the west of the Birmingham–Berwick axis would have to be referred to in this inconvenient fashion. The method of overcoming likely confusion is to imagine that the origin of the National Grid has been shifted westwards until the whole country lies in the first quadrant of the grid. In the example of the National Grid the shift in origin is 400 km. to the West and 100 km to the North of the point near the Channel Islands, so that numbering of the National Grid begins at a point situated about 80 km. West of the Scilly Isles. This is equivalent to assigning the arbitrary coordinate values $E = 400\,000$ metres, $N = 100\,000$ metres to the true origin and renumbering the grid lines. The point $E=0$ metres, $N=0$ metres is referred to as the *False Origin* of the grid to distinguish this from the *True Origin* which is still the point in latitude 49° North, 2° West. The way in which the shift may be imagined mathematically is that each axis has been moved parallel to itself through the defined distances. This is called *translation of the axes*.

Plane Polar Coordinates

Polar coordinates define position by means of one linear measurement and one angular measurement. The pair of orthogonal axes passing through the origin is replaced by a single line, OQ, in Fig. 14, passing through the origin, O, or *pole* of the system. The position of any point A may be defined with reference to this pole and the *polar axis* or *initial line*, OQ, by means of the distance $OA=r$ and the angle $QOA=\theta$. The line OA is known as the *radius vector* and the angle θ is the *vectorial angle* which the radius vector makes with the initial line. Hence the position of A may be defined by the coordinates (r, θ). The order of referring to the radius vector followed by the vectorial angle is standard in all branches of mathematics.

Figure 14 Plane Polar Coordinates

The vectorial angle may be expressed in sexagesimal (degree) or centisimal (grad) units to plot or locate a point instrumentally.† However, in the theoretical derivation of map projections, where θ enters directly into an equation and is not introduced as some trigonometric function of the angle, it is necessary to express this angle in *absolute angular units*, or radians. This is because both elements of the coordinate system must have the character of length.

The direction in which the vectorial angle is measured depends upon the purpose for which polar coordinates are used. Usually the mathematician regards $+\theta$ as *the anticlockwise angle measured from the initial line*. This is the sign convention which is used, for example, in vector algebra. On the other hand, the navigator, surveyor and cartographer have become accustomed to *measure a positive angle in the clockwise direction*. This is because direction on the Earth's surface is conventionally measured clockwise from North or clockwise from a reference object and therefore we tend to measure all directions according to this rule. In most practical problems, formal recognition of the sign of an angle is unimportant because the user can understand the convention used in the 360° circle measured clockwise. However difficulties arise in automatic data processing because computer subroutines are usually programmed according to the mathematical convention. For example, the Hewlett-Packard series of desk-top computers have vector subroutines which permit transformation from rectangular to polar coordinates and vice versa at the touch of one or two keys. This kind of calculation, which is described in the next section, is extremely common in surveying and cartography. Consequently the user of such an instrument must be aware of the difference in convention and write suitable programme steps which overcome this difficulty. Similarly in writing programmes for digital computers it is frequently

---

† One right angle is represented by 90° in sexagesimal notation, 100^g in centisimal units or $\pi/2$ radians.

necessary to introduce a series of tests and conditional statements to allow un-interrupted processing of data which have been collected according to the clockwise convention.

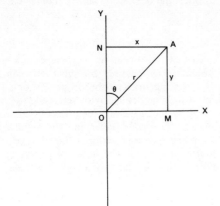

Figure 15 The relationship between plane rectangular and plane polar co-ordinates with common origin and one common axis.

Transformation from polar to rectangular coordinates and vice versa

Figure 15 illustrates the relationship between the rectangular and polar coordinates of a point A. The rectangular coordinates of the point are (x, y) referred to the origin O and the axes OX and OY. Superimposed upon this is the system of polar coordinates in which the pole also lies at O and the initial line coincides with OY. Then the polar coordinates of A are (r, θ), where $r = OA$, $\theta =$ angle YOA, $AN = x$ and $AM = NO = y$. It is evident from the right-angled triangle AON that

$$x = r . \sin \theta \qquad (2.01)$$

$$y = r . \cos \theta \qquad (2.02)$$

The inverse transformation from rectangular to polar coordinates can be carried out using a variety of different formulae. For example

$$\tan \theta = x/y \qquad (2.03)$$

$$r = y . \sec \theta \qquad (2.04)$$

$$r = x . \operatorname{cosec} \theta \qquad (2.05)$$

$$r^2 = x^2 + y^2 \qquad (2.06)$$

$$\sin \theta = x/r \qquad (2.07)$$

$$\cos \theta = y/r \qquad (2.08)$$

Note that these expressions are based upon the assumption that the angle θ is measured 'clockwise from grid north'. The coordinate expressions corresponding to these in most mathematical textbooks are derived for the complement of the vectorial angle, i.e. $AOX = 90° - \theta$.

From the expressions which may be used to transform from rectangular to polar coordinates, the formulae (2.03) and either (2.04) or (2.05) are the most useful in numerical work. The reader should be warned to avoid using Pythagoras' Theorem (2.06) to find the length of the radius vector. This is slow and inconvenient to calculate by logarithms or using one of the simpler kinds of desk-top calculator.

Only the more sophisticated models of calculator can be used to obtain square roots directly. Without access to one of these it is necessary to resort to the use of tables, approximate slide-rule calculations or solutions by Newton's iterative method of finding square roots.

Transformations of Cartesian Coordinates

In addition to the transformation from polar to rectangular coordinates, there are three basic kinds of transformation which may be applied to plane rectangular coordinates. These allow for conversion from one system of (x, y) coordinates into a second system of (x', y') coordinates. The three transformations are:

(1) *Translation of the axes* or *change of origin*,
(2) *Change of scale* from one system to another,
(3) *Rotation of the axes* about a common origin.

These three transformations are especially important in topographical cartography because they are the problems which arise in changing from one grid to another. Generally the practical problem of changing grids involves at least two and probably all three operations. Consequently we must also consider the general case of transformation which combines rotation, scale change and translation of the axes.

Translation of the axes or change of origin

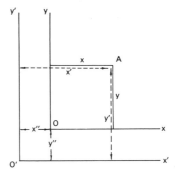

Figure 16 Translation of the axes of a plane rectangular coordinate system.

We have already described this transformation for it is used to introduce a false origin to a grid. This is only possible if the axes of the original system and those of the final system are parallel to one another as illustrated in Fig. 16. Expressed algebraically, if a point $A = (x, y)$ in the original system and the origin of this system is translated to O' through displacements x'' and y'', the new coordinates of A may be written

$$x' = x \pm x'' \qquad\qquad (2.09)$$

$$y' = y \pm y'' \qquad\qquad (2.10)$$

The signs of x'' and y'' depend upon the direction in which the shift has been made.

Change in scale from one coordinate system to another

Consider two points, A and B, which are common to two coordinate systems. In the first system the straight line AB joins the pair of points and in the second system the corresponding line is *ab*. If *AB≠ab*, a scale factor must be used to convert coordinates in the first system into coordinates within the second system. This scale factor is

$$m = ab/AB \qquad (2.11)$$

from which it follows that

$$x' = m \cdot x \qquad (2.12)$$

$$y' = m \cdot y \qquad (2.13)$$

The most important practical application of scale transformation which we will encounter in the study of map projections is described in Chapter 6, pp. 109–25. This describes the scale transformation applied to the (*x*, *y*) system of *projection coordinates*, which are given in units of Earth radius, in order to convert to the (*x'*, *y'*) system of *master grid coordinates* which are needed to plot points in millimetres and construct a map projection to the desired scale.

Rotation of the axes about the origin

We assume that the origin of each system is the same point, *O*, but the axes have been rotated through the angle α. Thus *OX* becomes *OX'* and *OY* becomes *OY'* as illustrated in Figs. 17 and 18. These two figures show the difference between the clockwise and anticlockwise rotations of the axes. We will study the effect of a clockwise rotation of the axes in detail.

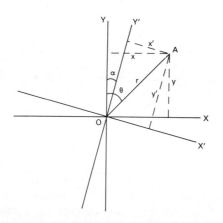

Figure 17 Clockwise rotation of plane rectangular coordinate axes about the origin.

    If the point *A* has rectangular coordinates (*x*, *y*) in the first system it is required to determine its (*x'*, *y'*) coordinates after rotation of the axes to form the second system. From equations (2.01) and (2.02) we know that $x = r \cdot \sin \theta$ and $y = r \cdot \cos \theta$, where θ is the angle *AOY*. Moreover the angle $AOY' = \theta - \alpha$.

    Therefore

$$x' = r \cdot \sin (\theta - \alpha) \qquad (2.14)$$

$$y' = r \cdot \cos (\theta - \alpha) \qquad (2.15)$$

The sine and the cosine of the difference of two angles is a well known formula from plane trigonometry (Abbott/Trigonometry §79). In this case,

$$\sin (\theta - \alpha) = \sin \theta \cdot \cos \alpha - \cos \theta \cdot \sin \alpha \qquad (2.16)$$

$$\cos (\theta - \alpha) = \cos \theta \cdot \cos \alpha + \sin \theta \cdot \sin \alpha \qquad (2.17)$$

Substituting these expressions in equations (2.14) and (2.15)

$$x' = r.\sin\theta.\cos a - r.\cos\theta.\sin a \qquad (2.18)$$

$$y' = r.\cos\theta.\cos a + r.\sin\theta.\sin a \qquad (2.19)$$

From equations (2.01) and (2.02) we may now substitute x and y for $r.\sin\theta$ and $r.\cos\theta$ respectively. Thus

$$x' = x.\cos a - y.\sin a \qquad (2.20)$$

$$y' = y.\cos a + x.\sin a \qquad (2.21)$$

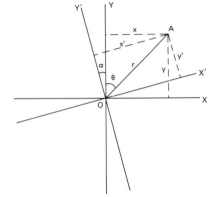

Figure 18 Anticlockwise rotation of plane rectangular coordinate axes about the origin.

For the anticlockwise rotation of the axes illustrated by Fig. 18 the angle $Y'OA$ becomes $\theta + a$. Using the same arguments with the trigonometric expressions defining the sine and cosine of the sum of two angles, the final equations are

$$x' = x.\cos a + y.\sin a \qquad (2.22)$$

$$y' = y.\cos a - x.\sin a \qquad (2.23)$$

Coordinate transformations involving all three displacements

The general case of transformation involves rotation, change in scale and translation of the origin. It is convenient to regard the transformations as being carried out in the same order.

Assuming that the rotation is anticlockwise, so that equations (2.22) and (2.23) apply, the coordinates transformed by rotation and scale change are

$$x' = m.x.\cos a + m.y.\sin a \qquad (2.24)$$

$$y' = m.y.\cos a - m.x.\sin a \qquad (2.25)$$

A common convention in the surveying literature is to write $P = m.\sin a$ and $Q = m.\cos a$. Substituting these values

$$x' = Q.x + P.y \qquad (2.26)$$

$$y' = Q.y - P.x \qquad (2.27)$$

Since the scale change has brought the coordinates into the units of the second system, the final translation is simply the application of the displacements x'' and y'' as illustrated in Fig. 16. The finally transformed coordinates (x_0, y_0) will be

$$x_0 = x'' \pm (Q \cdot x + P \cdot y) \qquad (2.28)$$

$$y_0 = y'' \pm (P \cdot y - Q \cdot x) \qquad (2.29)$$

Grid on Grid Calculations

The general transformation from one Cartesian system to another, expressed algebraically in equations (2.28) and (2.29), is the kind of computation which is encountered often in topographical cartography. Four examples of its use include

(1) Determination of the positions of intersections of a grid to be plotted on a map manuscript compiled from and showing a different grid. This happens often in the zones of common overlap of two grid systems where it is necessary to show both on the map.

(2) Determination of the positions of intersections of a new grid to be plotted on a map manuscript originally compiled on a different grid which has been superseded.

(3) Conversion of the coordinate output of some other mapping process so that the results can be used with a particular grid. A typical example of this work is when aerial triangulation has been carried out in a photogrammetric plotter. The output from this includes a stream of X, Y coordinates for minor control points which have been observed in the plotter on the (X, Y) system of model coordinates. These have to be related to the map grid through a series of ground control points whose model coordinates are known.

(4) Another example of this kind of transformation arises in the use of digitised map information in modern techniques of automated cartography. The majority of cartographic digitisers comprise a special table which contains the electronic hardware to convert the positions of a measuring mark into rectangular coordinates defined by the manufacturer of the table. Information about position is obtained by pointing to or tracing map detail with the measuring mark. This information is recorded and stored in digital form on paper or magnetic tape according to the (x, y) coordinate system built into the instrument. Hence the (E, N) grid of a topographical map is converted into the (x, y) coordinates of the digitiser and the relationship between the two depends upon the way in which the map was placed on the table. In order to reproduce any of the map detail in a desired form it is necessary to convert back from the (x, y) system of digitised coordinates into the (E, N) system of the map grid. This is often done by digitising the four corners of the map and using these control points to determine the translation, rotation and scale change components of the transformation.

From the nature of the first problem, all these transformations may be called *Grid on Grid Calculations*.

Although equations (2.28) and (2.29), with appropriate changes in notation from x to E and y to N, specify the final equations needed to convert from the known (E', N') coordinates into the required (E, N) values, it is still necessary to determine suitable numerical values for P, Q, E'' and N''.

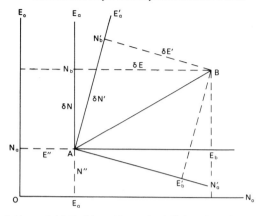

Figure 19 The Grid-on-Grid Problem. Stage 1, defining the relationship of two points, A and B, whose coordinates on both grids are already known. E' and N' denote the initial grid; E and N denote the second grid to which other points are to be transformed.

Provided that there are at least two points which are common to both systems, these terms can be calculated and used to convert as many additional points as are required. The method of solving the unknowns may be carried out as below:

In Fig. 19 the two points A and B are common to both grids. We use the following notation to describe each point:

Point	1st grid	2nd grid
A	E'_a, N'_a	E_a, N_a
B	E'_b, N'_b	E_b, N_b

The coordinate differences between the two points may be expressed as follows, using the convention that the Greek letter δ signifies the difference.

1st grid

$$E'_a - E'_b = \delta E'$$
$$N'_a - N'_b = \delta N'$$

2nd grid

$$E_a - E_b = \delta E$$
$$N_a - N_b = \delta N$$

These terms have the geometrical significance which is illustrated in Fig. 19.

Using arguments similar to those already used to determine the effects of rotation and scale change upon coordinates, it can be shown that

$$Q = \frac{\delta E. \delta N' - \delta N. \delta E'}{\delta E'^2 + \delta N'^2} \qquad (2.30)$$

$$P = \frac{\delta N. \delta N' + \delta E. \delta E'}{\delta E'^2 + \delta N'^2} \qquad (2.31)$$

Moreover it can be shown that the translation terms E'' and N'' (corresponding to x'' and y'') in (2.28) and (2.29) may be found from

$$E'' = E_a - P.E'_a - Q.N'_a \qquad (2.32)$$

$$= E_b - P.E'_b - Q.N'_b \qquad (2.33)$$

$$N'' = N_a + Q.E'_a - P.N'_a \qquad (2.34)$$

$$= N_b + Q.E'_b - P.N'_b \qquad (2.35)$$

Hence the required equations to transform (E', N') to (E, N) of any other point, P (Fig. 20), are

$$E = Q \cdot E' + P \cdot N' \pm E'' \qquad (2.36)$$

$$N = P \cdot N' - Q \cdot E' \pm N'' \qquad (2.37)$$

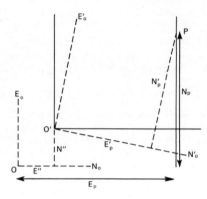

Figure 20 The Grid-on-Grid Problem. Stage 2, indicating the relationship of any point, P, whose coordinates on the initial grid (E'_p, N'_p) are known, to the second grid upon which it must be plotted.

The equations (2.30)–(2.35) have been given here without proof. This can be found in several references such as Ref. 5. In Ref. 1 there is also described the method of solving the coefficients for Grid on Grid calculations where there are three points common to both systems. If there are more than three common points, such as occurs in cartographic digitising and in the adjustment of aerial triangulation to many ground control points, the determination of the coefficients from only two or three of the points is unsatisfactory. The coordinates of any of these points may contain small errors and the use of them will introduce error into the transformation of all other points. Under these circumstances, all the data which is available for determination of P and Q ought to be taken into consideration. This involves a solution of the coefficients by the methods of *least squares*, which is a more sophisticated numerical solution based upon statistical theory of errors. Advanced textbooks on survey adjustments and computations describe suitable procedures.

References

1 *Admiralty Manual of Hydrographic Surveying*, Vol. I, London, 1965, Hydrographic Department, 671 pp.
2 *Manual of Map Reading, Air Photo Reading and Field Sketching*, Part I, *Map Reading*, London, 1957, HMSO, 132pp.
3 *Military Engineering, Vol. XIII—Survey, Part XII, Cartography*, London, 1962, The War Office, 323 pp.
4 *The Projection for Ordnance Survey Maps and Plans and the National Reference System*, London, 1951 (reprinted 1962), HMSO, 4 pp.
5 *Military Engineering, Vol. XIII—Survey, Part VI, Survey Computations*, London, 1966, Ministry of Defence, 243 pp.

CHAPTER 3

COORDINATE REFERENCE SYSTEMS ON THE SPHERE AND SPHEROID

'What's the good of Mercator's North Poles and Equators,
Tropics, Zones and Meridian Lines?'
So the Bellman would cry: and the crew would reply
'They are merely conventional signs.'

Lewis Carroll: *The Hunting of the Snark*

Introduction

It has been assumed in Chapters 1 and 2 that the reader already knows something about the terms which are used to describe planes, arcs and angles on the Earth. For example, the ideas of latitude and longitude; parallels and meridians and the convergence of the meridians towards the poles have been introduced without formal definition. However it is desirable to comment further about the geometry of the Earth when this can be assumed to be a perfect sphere. There are two reasons for this. First, we wish to introduce a standardised system of algebraic notation for the different quantities which will be used throughout this book. Secondly it is necessary to demonstrate certain important geometrical differences between the sphere and the spheroid. In order to appreciate the distinctions to be made between these bodies it is essential to know precisely what is represented by planes, arcs and angles on each of them.

Some of the properties of a sphere have already been described in Chapter 1. These may be summarised as a preliminary to further definitions:

(1) A sphere is a solid body whose curved surface is everywhere equidistant from its centre.
(2) It follows that any sphere has constant radius.
(3) If a tangent plane meets any point on the curved surface, a line normal to this plane at the point of tangency is a radius to the centre of the sphere.
(4) The distance between two points on the sphere can be defined and measured either as the angular distance or the arc distance. There is a simple relationship between the two measures of distance, which has been given in equation (1.02).

Additional definitions of planes, arcs and angles on the sphere

If a plane intersects a sphere, the resulting section of the curved surface which is traced on the plane is a circle. Two kinds of circle may be distinguished; a *great circle* and a *small circle*. If the intersecting plane passes through the centre of the sphere, the resulting section is the circle whose radius is the largest which can occur and is equal to the radius of the sphere itself. This is a great circle, illustrated by the outline of the sphere in Figs. 2, 21, and many other diagrams. Only one great circle can be drawn through any two points on the spherical surface which are not diametrically opposite to one another. The shorter arc of the great circle through two points is *the shortest distance between the points on the spherical surface*.

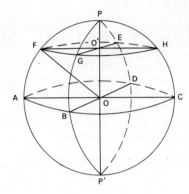

Figure 21 Great circles and small circles on the sphere.

If the plane does not pass through the centre of the sphere, the radius of the resulting circle is less than that of the sphere. This is a small circle, shown in Fig. 21 by the line *EFGH*. These points all lie on the circumference of the circle with centre *O'*.

The *axis* of any circle is the straight line passing through the centre of the sphere at right angles to the plane of the circle. Thus, in Fig. 21, the line *POP'* is the axis of the great circle *DABC*. From the definition that only one great circle can be drawn through a pair of points which are not diametrically opposite, it follows that the axes of two or more great circles cannot coincide. However, one great circle and any number of small circles can have a common axis. From the definition of an axis, it follows that, in this special case, the planes of the great circle and all the small circles will be parallel to one another. Moreover if the planes are parallel, the circumferences of the circles are also parallel.

The *poles* of any circle are the points where the axis to a circle intersects the surface of the sphere. These are shown in Fig. 21 by the points *P* and *P'*, which are the poles to the great circle *DABC*. From the definitions that a sphere has constant radius and that the section of a great circle passes through the centre of the sphere, it follows that the poles to a great circle are equidistant from its plane. From the corresponding definition of a small circle, clearly one pole is nearer than the other.

If the great circle *DABC* is further described as a *primary* or *primitive great circle*, then any great circle which passes through its poles may be called a *secondary great circle*. Since the poles are diametrically opposite to one another any number of secondaries may be specified. In Fig. 21, the great circle arcs *PFAP'CH* and *PGBP'DE* are both secondaries to the great circle *DABC*. Since the axis to the primary great circle coincides with the plane of each secondary, it follows that the plane and therefore the circumference of each secondary is perpendicular to the plane and circumference of the primary great circle. Moreover any small circles with an axis common to a primary great circle will also have planes and circumferences which are perpendicular to the secondaries to that great circle.

Geographical coordinates

Since the Earth is a rotating body, the obvious datum from which we may define its geometry is its axis of rotation. This axis intersects the surface at two points which are poles to the primary great circle whose plane is perpendicular to the axis. This primary great circle is the *Equator* and its poles are the *North* and *South Geographical Poles*. The secondaries to the Equator are not given a single name but the word *meridian* describes each semicircle of a pair which together form a single secondary. The word meridian should be used in the restricted sense of being the arc of any great circle passing through and limited by the geographical poles. The complete secondary comprises one meridian together with its *antimeridian*.

It follows from the use of angles at the centre of a sphere to measure distances between points on the curved surface, that a system of three-dimensional polar coordinates may be used as a method of locating position with respect to the centre of the sphere as origin. By extension of the concept of plane polar coordinates described in Chapter 2, a point may be located in space if we know *two* vectorial angles and the radius vector. These are known as *spherical polar coordinates* in mathematics. However, all points on the surface of a sphere are equidistant from the centre. Therefore the radius vector is always equal to the radius of the sphere and serves no useful purpose in this special case of coordinate location. Thus coordinate position on the spherical surface is uniquely defined by means of two vectorial angles. For these, two orthogonal planes are chosen which intersect at the origin (i.e. the centre of the sphere). One plane has already been defined and is the plane of the Equator. This is used as the datum for measurement of the vectorial angle which we know as *latitude*. The other plane is that of the meridian chosen as zero *longitude*.

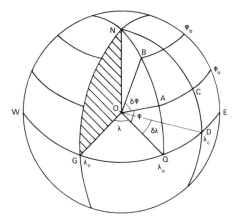

Figure 22 Latitude and longitude on the sphere. The plane of the Greenwich Meridian is shaded.

The latitude of a point may be formally defined as *the angle measured at the centre of the Earth between the plane of the Equator and the radius drawn to the point*. It is, for example, the angle AOQ in Fig. 22. This definition applies only to latitude measured on a true sphere. It will be seen later that *it is necessary to use a different definition of latitude on the spheroid*. For most practical purposes, latitude may be expressed in sexagesimal units North or South of the Equator. Centisimal units are used for this purpose in certain countries or for certain purposes, but it is important to realise that because a nation uses the metric system and decimal notation for most other kinds of measurement this does not automatically mean that angles are measured in grads. Geographical coordinates expressed in centisimal units are the exception rather than the rule. Algebraically the angle is usually denoted by φ and this symbol will be used to mean latitude throughout the present book. In order to use a logical sign convention for algebraic purposes it is customary to regard North latitude as $+\varphi$ whereas South latitude is $-\varphi$.

The *difference in latitude* between any two points is the quantity

$$\delta\varphi = \varphi_a - \varphi_b \tag{3.01}$$

where the symbol δ indicates a finite angular difference between the latitude of some point $A = \varphi_a$ and another point $B = \varphi_b$, both angles measured from the plane of the Equator according to the definition given above. If we need to refer to a very (infinitely) small change in latitude, we introduce the notation of the calculus and state that as $\delta\varphi \rightarrow 0$ (which is the mathematical shorthand for the statement 'as the difference in latitude approaches Zero') it may be represented by $d\varphi$.

For any given value of φ there are an infinity of points on the surface of the Earth each of which makes this angle with the plane of the Equator. The locus of these points is the circumference of a circle, the plane of which is parallel to that of the Equator. Consequently, it may be called a *parallel of latitude*, or simply a *parallel*. It follows that as the plane of this circle is parallel to the Equatorial plane they share a common axis. Because the Equator is a great circle, it follows that any parallel of latitude must be a small circle.

Since the plane of the Equator is perpendicular to the Earth's axis of rotation, the angle measured at the centre of the sphere between this axis and the radius to a point in latitude φ, such as NOA in Fig. 22, is the complement of the latitude ($90° - \varphi°$ or $\pi/2 - \varphi$ radians). This angle is therefore called the *colatitude* of the point and will be denoted algebraically by χ.

The *longitude* of any point on the Earth's surface represents the second vectorial angle required to define position. This may be defined as *the angle measured in the plane of the Equator between the plane of the meridian through the point and the plane of some other meridian selected as datum.*

The choice of a datum meridian for measurement of longitude is arbitrary. Although we are generally accustomed to the use of the meridian passing through the former site of the Royal Observatory at Greenwich as the *Prime Meridian* for measurement of longitude, any other meridian would be equally satisfactory.

From the viewpoint of a national survey and the production of topographical map series it can be argued that no particular national advantage is served by relating longitude to the Greenwich Meridian. Thus many countries have employed as the datum for longitude the meridian passing through the national capital or through the origin of the survey. For example, the longitude of Paris is used as the datum for French topographical maps. The meridians of Oslo, Rome and Leningrad (Pulkova Observatory) have been respectively employed for the origin of longitude on maps of Norway, Italy and the U.S.S.R. Sometimes a more or less arbitrary origin has been used. The classic example of this was the use of the approximate meridian of Ferro in the Canary Islands as the datum for longitude, first in France, later in the Austro-Hungarian and German Empires and therefore to quite modern maps of Austria, Czechoslovakia and Hungary. To confuse the issue further, precise definition of the Ferro meridian varies according to how a particular survey organisation originally interpreted this. For other purposes, particularly in navigation and astronomy, where the apparent movements of heavenly bodies with time must be referred to longitude, it is extremely inconvenient to have more than one origin for measurement of longitude. The use of the Greenwich Meridian as the Prime Meridian was agreed internationally in 1884 and this remains the preferred datum.

Longitude is measured from this plane, normally in sexagesimal units East and West of Greenwich. The algebraic symbol used for the angle is λ. The sign convention is that $+\lambda$ indicates East longitude whereas $-\lambda$ means West longitude.

The term

$$\delta\lambda = \lambda_a - \lambda_c \qquad (3.02)$$

signifies the *difference in longitude* between two places, $A = \lambda_a$ and $C = \lambda_c$. This is the angle DOQ in Fig. 22. The symbol δ again indicates a finite difference in longitude and for an infinitely small increment in longitude we use dλ. Frequently in the derivation of general expressions for map projections it is convenient to refer longitude to some arbitrary meridian other than Greenwich. Then we will denote this meridian as λ_0.

The resulting network of parallels and meridians which comprise the system of geographical coordinates is known as a *graticule*, both with reference to the Earth's surface and to the representation of it on a plane surface by means of a map projection. A *graticule intersection* is the point where the parallel φ intersects the meridian λ and is referred to by its geographical coordinates (φ, λ). The convention of describing these coordinates in the order latitude-followed-by-longitude is universally accepted.

Geographical coordinates are by far the best known method of providing unique reference of location in geography, navigation and all the other sciences and technologies which are concerned with position on the Earth's surface. The network of parallels and meridians on the map or chart constitute a form of geometrical control to map use, which is understood universally and at many different levels of education. It is a reference system which is taught to school-children early in their geographical education. It follows that the network of parallels and meridians as remembered from maps in a school atlas and from a globe ought to remain an important spatial frame of reference for map use in later life. Moreover the graticule has historical importance for it is much older than the general concept of spherical polar coordinates or other systems. Some kind of representation of the parallels and meridians has been used since the time of Marinus and Ptolemy (first century A.D.) and few worthwhile maps have been produced since the early seventeenth century without showing some kind of graticule.

Nevertheless it would be wrong to suppose that geographical coordinates are the only method of defining position upon the Earth's surface. Reference has already been made to the generalised system of polar coordinates in three dimensions of which the (φ, λ) system is a special case. Another system of spherical polar coordinates which are, again, suitably simplified for representation of the curved surface of a sphere are the *Bearing and Distance Coordinates* which have particular value in the construction of map projections. These are studied in Chapter 7. A third, and quite different system of location is by *Three-dimensional Cartesian Coordinates* which differ from plane rectangular coordinates by the addition of a third, *Z*, axis which is perpendicular to the other two. The three-dimensional Cartesian system of reference is particularly useful for the study of the Earth as an ellipsoid (Ref. 4), though at the elementary level of this book, we do not define it further or make use of its methods.

Angles and distances on the Earth

Having established the properties of geographical coordinates as the primary method of location, it is now desirable to introduce some additional concepts about the geometry of the sphere.

A *spherical angle* is the inclination, at their point of intersection, of two arcs of great circles measured on the curved surface of the sphere. It is also equal to the plane angle formed between the two tangents, drawn at the point of intersection, one to each great circle. Thus, in Fig. 23 the spherical angle between the two great circles *PA* and *PD* is the angle *DPA* which is equal to the plane angle *KPJ*. For the purpose of the present study spherical angles are encountered in two forms. The first is to permit an alternative definition of longitude. That given on page 34, describing longitude as an angle measured at the centre of the sphere in the plane of the Equator is so worded to emphasise that geographical coordinates are a form of polar coordinates and the vectorial angles should therefore be measured at the origin of the system. However, we can see from Figs. 21, 22 and 23 that the angle λ can be measured anywhere on the Earth's axis of rotation, provided that this angle is measured in a plane parallel to the Equator. Thus the angle $FO'G = AOB$ in Fig. 21 and the longitude can be measured in the plane of any parallel of latitude. Extending this argument to the geographical poles, such as P in Figs. 21 and 23 it follows that the plane through P which is parallel to the Equator is also the tangent plane at P. Hence longitude can be measured as the plane angle KPJ in Fig. 23 or as the spherical angle APD.

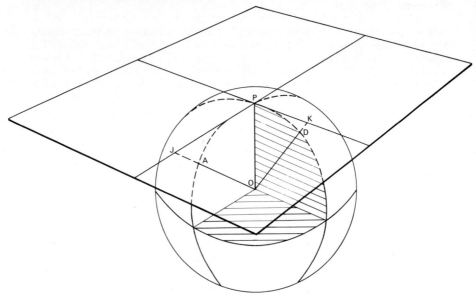

Figure 23 Definition of a spherical angle

The second important kind of angle encountered on the Earth's surface is the *azimuth* or *bearing* of one point measured from another. This introduces the concept of *direction* on the Earth and also some rather fine distinctions of definition. Consider the three points N, A and B illustrated in Fig. 24. The point N is the North Pole, so that the great circle arc NA represents part of the meridian through A. Similarly the arc NB is part of the meridian through B. The line AB represents the shortest distance between A and B and is therefore the arc of a great circle. Hence a *spherical triangle* has been formed by the intersection of three great circle arcs.

Azimuth may be defined as **the spherical angle between any great circle and a meridian*. Thus the angle NAB represents the azimuth of B measured at A; the angle NBA represents the azimuth of A from B. In the southern hemisphere the equivalent azimuths are SAB and SBA.

We have seen in Chapter 2 that in navigation, surveying and cartography the usual convention is to measure angles according to the 360° or 400^g circle in a clockwise direction. This convention is contained in the formal definition of *bearing* which is **the horizontal angle at a given point measured clockwise from a specific reference point to a third point*. If the specific reference point is the North

Pole, then we have the definition of a *true bearing* which is **the direction of an object from a point, expressed as a horizontal angle measured clockwise from True North.*

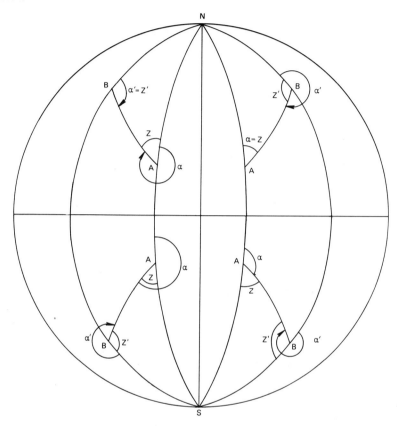

Figure 24 The definition of bearing (a), reverse bearing (a'), azimuth (Z) and reverse azimuth (Z') for four different versions of the arc *AB* on the spherical surface. The description in the text specifically refers to the arc *AB* in the north-east part of the diagram

In the north east quadrant of Fig. 24, the azimuth at *A* is the acute angle *Z*, measured clockwise from the meridian *AN*. Here $a = Z$ and the angle also represents the true bearing of *B* from *A*.

From the definition of azimuth, the angle *NBA* represents the azimuth of *A* from *B*. However, according to the clockwise convention of bearing, the true bearing of *A* from *B* is the clockwise angle at this point indicated as a'. In the southern hemisphere of Fig. 24, the azimuths would have been referred to the South Pole, whereas the true bearings are still measured as clockwise from true North. These distinctions have not always been made in the literature.

Spherical triangles

A spherical triangle is the figure formed by the intersection of any three arcs of great circles. Like a plane triangle it comprises six parts; three angles and three

D

sides. The notation which is used to describe these parts for simple algebraic expression is the same as plane geometry. Thus in Fig. 25 we may write for the angles, $ABC=B$, $ACB=C$ and $BAC=A$. Similarly the three sides are described as $CB=a$, $AC=b$ and $AB=c$. Since the arc of a great circle has length proportional to the radius of the sphere and since all the sides belong to the same sphere, it is sufficient to define the lengths of sides only by angular distances. This, as we saw in Chapter 1, is measured at the centre of the sphere by the angles between the radii drawn to the three points.

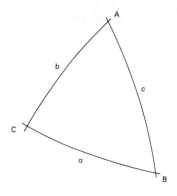

Figure 25 The Spherical Triangle

　　　Many of the fundamental properties of a spherical triangle are equivalent to those of a plane triangle. To quote just one example, the greatest side of a spherical triangle is always opposite the largest angle. However, the properties of a spherical triangle differ from those of a plane triangle in one extremely important respect. *The sum of the three angles of a spherical triangle does not equal 180° but is always greater.* The difference between the sum of the angles and 180° is known as the *spherical excess* and is proportional to the area of the triangle. For example, the spherical triangle representing $\frac{1}{8}$ of the total surface area of the sphere, in which all the sides and angles are equal to 90° will have spherical excess equal to 90°. The existence of spherical excess profoundly influences the methods of spherical geometry and trigonometry. *It is not possible, as in plane geometry, to determine the value of an unknown angle of a spherical triangle by subtracting the sum of two known angles from 180°.*

Determination of the unknown parts of a spherical triangle

Just as plane trigonometry can be used to determine the length of an unknown side or the size of an unknown angle in a plane triangle, so equivalent calculations can be used to solve unknown parts of spherical triangles. The methods of solution may be grouped under the heading of *spherical trigonometry*. It is a branch of mathematics which is particularly important in certain practical applications such as navigation, surveying and astronomy. For example, position finding by astronomical methods is almost wholly dependent upon the solution of triangles on the celestial sphere and the Earth. The subject is also important to the study of map projections. Space does not permit full derivation of the formulae which are useful to the cartographer. We therefore refer to certain other books (Refs. 1, 2 and 3) which are devoted to spherical trigonometry or navigation books which review the basic essentials of the subject.

The two most important formulae of spherical trigonometry, from which all others may be derived are:

(1) The Cosine or Fundamental Formula,
(2) The Sine Formula.

(1) *The Cosine Formula*

This gives the relationship between one unknown side of a spherical triangle when the other two sides and their included angle are known. For the triangle *ABC* illustrated in Fig. 25 this may be written for three variants:

(1) Unknown side *a*; known sides *b* and *c*; known angle *A*
$$\cos a = \cos b \cdot \cos c + \sin b \cdot \sin c \cdot \cos A \tag{3.03}$$

(2) Unknown side *b*; known sides *a* and *c*; known angle *B*
$$\cos b = \cos a \cdot \cos c + \sin a \cdot \sin c \cdot \cos B \tag{3.04}$$

(3) Unknown side *c*; known sides *a* and *b*; known angle *C*
$$\cos c = \cos a \cdot \cos b + \sin a \cdot \sin b \cdot \cos C \tag{3.05}$$

On the other hand, if the three sides of the triangle are known, the formulae may be modified to solve one unknown angle, e.g.

$$\cos A = \frac{\cos a - \cos b \cdot \cos c}{\sin b \cdot \sin c} \tag{3.06}$$

These formulae give a single, unambiguous, result for the unknown side or angle. By convention, the sides and angles of a spherical triangle cannot exceed 180°. Therefore the result must be the cosine of an angle in the first or second quadrant. If the answer is positive, this indicates that the angle lies in the first quadrant $(0° < a < 90°)$ but if it is negative this means that the angle lies in the second quadrant $(90° < a < 180°)$. These sign differences are important in computing and we will return to the subject later.

(2) *The Sine Formula*

This has the form

$$\frac{\sin a}{\sin A} = \frac{\sin b}{\sin B} = \frac{\sin c}{\sin C} \tag{3.07}$$

Thus, knowing three of the parts (sides and angles) for any pair of ratios, it is possible to find the unknown part. For example, if *a*, *b* and *B* are known,

$$\sin A = \frac{\sin a \cdot \sin B}{\sin b} \tag{3.08}$$

or

$$\sin A = \sin a \cdot \sin B \cdot \operatorname{cosec} b \tag{3.09}$$

The Sine Formula suffers from the important disadvantage that there is ambiguity about the part found, for $\sin A = \sin (180° - A)$. Various rules are given in the textbooks of spherical trigonometry which attempt to overcome this difficulty.

The lengths of arcs on the Earth's surface

There are three kinds of arc measurement which are important to the study of map projections. These are:

(1) The length of the arc of a meridian,
(2) The length of the arc of a parallel,
(3) The length of the arc of any great circle.

The first two are essential to the derivation of the scale errors and distortions in the directions of the meridian and parallel at a point. Knowledge about these is an essential prerequisite to the derivation of any map projection which is intended to satisfy one of the mathematical properties described in Chapter 4. The third kind of measurement is more commonly thought of as a procedure in navigation and in other kinds of quantitative map or chart use. This is the way to determine the great circle distance between two places when a high order of accuracy is not required and the spherical assumption suffices. However, this general expression for determining the arc of any great circle arises in the transformation from Geographical to Bearing and Distance Coordinates as used in Chapter 7 (pp. 127–36).

(1) *The length of the arc of a meridian*

The problem was examined superficially in Chapter 1 to indicate the methods of astro-geodetic arc measurement as a means of determining the Figure of the Earth. From equation (1.02) and using the algebraic notation already introduced, various meridional arc relationships may be written down as follows:

The length of the arc measured from the plane of the Equator to a point A, in latitude φ_a:

$$s_m = R \cdot \varphi_a \tag{3.10}$$

The length of the arc measured from the nearer pole to the same point:

$$s'_m = R \cdot \chi_a \tag{3.11}$$

The arc distance between two points $A = (\varphi_a, \lambda_a)$ and $F = (\varphi_f, \lambda_a)$ both of which lie on the same meridian:

$$s''_m = R \cdot \delta\varphi \tag{3.12}$$

where $\delta\varphi = \varphi_a - \varphi_f$.

Following the derivation of (1.02) all the angles in (3.10)–(3.12) are expressed in radians.

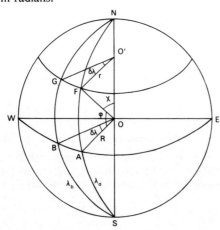

Figure 26 The relationship of the radius of a parallel, r, and the radius of the sphere, R.

(2) *The length of the arc of a parallel*

It has been shown that a parallel of latitude is a small circle. This has radius r and, by definition $r < R$. Thus, for any given angular distance, the arc distance along a parallel is less than the corresponding arc distance along the Equator.

In Fig. 26, for example, NFA represents the meridian λ_a and NGB is the meridian λ_b. Therefore the angle $AOB = FO'G = \delta\lambda$. From equation (1.02):

$$AB = R.\,\delta\lambda \tag{3.13}$$

and

$$FG = r.\,\delta\lambda \tag{3.14}$$

In the right-angled triangle OFO', $OF = R$ and $O'F = r$. Moreover the angle $O'OF$ corresponds to colatitude χ of F.
Therefore

$$r = R.\sin\chi \tag{3.15}$$

or

$$r = R.\cos\varphi \tag{3.16}$$

Consequently the arc distance along the parallel of latitude φ is

$$s_p = R.\cos\varphi.\,\delta\lambda \tag{3.17}$$

For an arc on the Equator, we put $\varphi = 0°$ so that $\cos\varphi = 1\cdot0$. Then (3.17) becomes

$$s_e = R.\,\delta\lambda \tag{3.18}$$

which is the result which we would expect from the definition of the Equator as a great circle.

(3) *The length of the arc of any great circle*

In equation (1.02) we used z to indicate the angular distance between two points. We now return to the use of this letter to indicate the unknown angular distance between any two points for the general case where both of them lie on different parallels and meridians. Thus, if $A = (\varphi_a, \lambda_a)$ and $B = (\varphi_b, \lambda_b)$, as illustrated in Fig. 24, we have to solve the spherical triangle NAB to find the unknown side $AB = z$.

The two known sides of the triangle are the meridional arcs NA and NB which are of length χ_a and χ_b respectively. The spherical angle $ANB = \lambda_a - \lambda_b = \delta\lambda$ is also known.

From the Cosine Formula (3.03)–(3.05),

$$\cos z = \cos\chi_a.\cos\chi_b + \sin\chi_a.\sin\chi_b.\cos\delta\lambda \tag{3.19}$$

This is more conveniently expressed in terms of latitude rather than colatitude. Thus

$$\cos z = \sin\varphi_a.\sin\varphi_b + \cos\varphi_a.\cos\varphi_b.\cos\delta\lambda \tag{3.20}$$

and, finally, the arc AB

$$s = R.z \tag{3.21}$$

Conversion of arc length into linear distance

In order to convert any of the values of s, s_e, s_p or s_m into linear units, a value for R must be chosen. This value may be determined from the Figure of the Earth, either as the radius of the sphere which has the same volume as the spheroid or the radius of the sphere which has the same surface area as the selected Figure. Both calculations yield similar values. For example, the alternative calculations for R determined from the Krasovsky (1940) Figure of the Earth are 6 371 100 metres and 6 371 116 metres respectively. The two determinations differ by only one part in one million which is negligible. It must be remembered that the initial assumption has been made that the Earth is a perfect sphere. This assumption will naturally influence all subsequent calculations so that use of R correct to the nearest metre would introduce a spurious appearance of accuracy to the calculations. *For all practical purposes it is sufficient to regard $R = 6371 \cdot 1$ km.*

In much practical work with map projections it is not necessary to convert angular distances into their linear equivalents at this stage. Conversion is more conveniently done after the scale of mapping has been chosen so that distances are available in millimetres for plotting. It is therefore sufficient to derive all projections in terms of a sphere of unit radius ($R = 1$) and then convert the numerical values obtained by a factor which corresponds to the radius of the Earth in millimetres reduced to the required map scale. This procedure will be described in detail in Chapter 6.

Determination of Azimuth

From the definition of azimuth given on page 36, this is the angle $NAB = Z$ in the simplest case. This may be determined from a modification of the Cosine Formula (3.06). Using the same notation employed in (3.19)

$$\cos Z = \frac{\cos \chi_b - \cos \chi_a \cdot \cos z}{\sin \chi_a \cdot \sin z} \tag{3.22}$$

$$= \frac{\sin \varphi_b - \sin \varphi_a \cdot \cos z}{\cos \varphi_a \cdot \sin z} \tag{3.23}$$

Alternatively, from the Sine Formula (3.09)

$$\sin Z = \cos \varphi_b \cdot \sin \delta\lambda \cdot \operatorname{cosec} z \tag{3.24}$$

Both of these equations contain terms in z. If z is not required, then the preliminary calculation of it can be avoided. It is possible to combine equations (3.19) and (3.22) which, after some algebraic manipulation, results in the equation

$$\cot Z = \cos \varphi_a \cdot \tan \varphi_b \cdot \operatorname{cosec} \delta\lambda - \sin \varphi_a \cdot \cot \delta\lambda \tag{3.25}$$

which is independent of z.

Convergence of meridians

It should be noted that the bearing from B to A, denoted by clockwise angle NBA, is not the reciprocal of α. In other words $180° - NBA \neq NAB$, but differs by the angle, γ, shown in Fig. 27. This leads to the interesting and important conclusion that the azimuth of any great circle arc which crosses the meridians obliquely can only be defined uniquely at the point where it is measured. In other words, *a great circle arc changes bearing continuously.*

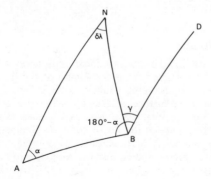

Figure 27 The relationship between bearing (α), reverse bearing ($180° - \alpha$) and convergence of the meridians (γ) on the sphere.

The reason for this is the *convergence of the meridians*. On the Equator, the arc distance between two meridians is (3.18)

$$s_e = R . \delta\lambda$$

At the geographical poles the corresponding arc distance is zero. On the Equator, two meridians λ_a and λ_b are perpendicular to it. At the poles the same meridians intersect to make the spherical angle $\delta\lambda$.

The angle of convergence (or *convergency*) between the meridians in any intermediate latitude may be expressed by the angle γ. Since the value of γ varies from $\gamma = 0 . \delta\lambda$ on the Equator to $\gamma = 1 . \delta\lambda$ at the poles, it may be presumed that the convergence of the meridians varies with the sine of the latitude, i.e.

$$\gamma = \delta\lambda . \sin \varphi \qquad (3.26)$$

For any line *AB* lying between the parallels φ_a and φ_b it is usual to express the convergency of their meridians in terms of the mean or *middle latitude* as

$$\gamma = \delta\lambda . \sin \frac{(\varphi_a + \varphi_b)}{2} \qquad (3.27)$$

This formula is adequate for most uses in navigation but it is too crude for use in surveying.

The geometry of the spheroid

We now turn to the definition and expression of the corresponding planes, arcs and angles on the spheroid. In Chapter 1 it was noted that the ellipsoid of rotation can be defined by the two basic measurements of the major semi-axis, *a*, and the minor semi-axis, *b*. It follows from Fig. 1 that the meridional section of the figure is an ellipse but that the Equator is represented by a circle of radius *a*. With the exception of the Equator and the parallels of latitude there are no circles defined by plane sections through an ellipsoid. The curve which corresponds to any great circle on the sphere may be called a *geodesic* but there are mathematical difficulties in defining this word. We will avoid these difficulties in this elementary exposition by referring only to an *arc*.

One way of describing the compression of the body is through the parameter, *f*, defined in (1.01). An alternative parameter which has greater practical value in evaluation of the radii of curvature and other quantities is the *eccentricity* of the body.

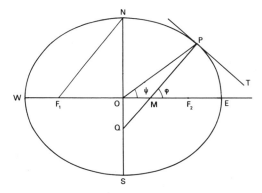

Figure 28 The definition of latitude on the spheroid

An ellipse may be defined as the locus of points, the sum of whose distances from two fixed points is constant and equal to $2a$. These two points are known as the *foci* of the ellipse. They lie on the major axis and are indicated by the points F_1 and F_2 in Fig. 28. The eccentricity is equal to the ratio OF_1/OW. From the right-angled triangle F_1NO

$$OF_1 = a^2 - b^2$$

or

$$OF_1 = (a^2 - b^2)^{\frac{1}{2}} \tag{3.28}$$

(In equation (3.28) we introduce the convention that $(x)^{\frac{1}{2}} = \sqrt{x}$ because the use of fractional indices is going to appear soon and it may be helpful for the reader to receive prior warning of this in an equation which is easy to understand.)

Since $e = OF_1/OW$, it follows that

$$e^2 = \frac{a^2 - b^2}{a^2} \tag{3.29}$$

The numerical value of e^2 for the Earth is about $0 \cdot 0067 \ldots$ but this depends upon the particular reference spheroid and its values of a and b.

Geocentric and geodetic latitude

We have already noted in Chapter 1 that the radii of curvature at any point on an ellipsoid must be normal to the tangent plane to the point. Thus, for a point P in Fig. 28, the normal to the tangent plane is the line PQ. This line intersects the major axis of the ellipse at the point M and therefore makes the angle PME with the plane of the Equator. By contrast the line PO drawn to the point of intersection of the two axes makes the angle POE with the major axis in the plane of the Equator. Clearly these angles differ but both of them correspond in part to the definition of latitude on the sphere. Thus the angle POE corresponds to the idea that it is the angle measured at the centre of the Earth, but the angle PME corresponds to the idea that the angle is measured between the plane of the Equator and the radius drawn to the point. We distinguish the two concepts of latitude as follows:

Geocentric Latitude is *the angle, measured at the point of intersection of the semi-axes of the spheroid, between the plane containing the major semi-axis and the straight line to some point on the spheroid.* This is the angle POE which is usually denoted by ψ.

Geodetic Latitude is *the angle between the major axis of the spheroid and the normal to the tangent plane at any point on this surface, measured at the point of intersection of the normal with the equatorial plane.* This is the angle PME which is denoted by φ.

There is a relationship between these two angles which may be expressed in terms of the eccentricity, but this is not of direct importance to us in the present context.

Geodetic latitude is the more important quantity and this is the variable which enters into all subsequent calculations. For all practical purposes, geographical coordinates on the spheroid are the (φ, λ) system, where φ is geodetic latitude and λ is longitude, defined as for the sphere.

The radii of curvature of an ellipsoid

It has already been noted in Chapter 1 that the concept of radius applied to the ellipsoid is more complicated than that for the sphere. The first difficulty is that two radii of curvature may be defined at any point; the second is that both of these radii vary with latitude.

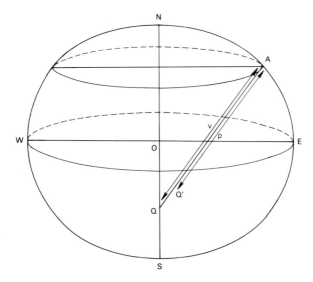

Figure 29 The definition of the meridional radius of curvature (ρ) and the transverse radius of curvature (ν) of any point, A, on the surface of an ellipsoid.

The two radii at a point such as *A* may be resolved into

(1) The *meridional radius of curvature*. This is the radius of curvature of the ellipse *NAE* at the point *A*. This quantity is usually referred to as ρ.

(2) The *transverse radius of curvature* at *A*. This is the radius of the curve formed by the plane intersecting the ellipsoid at *A* which is normal to the surface and also perpendicular to the meridian at the point. This is a difficult concept to illustrate in a plane figure but is represented by the shaded plane in Fig. 3. Note that it is *not* the radius of the parallel at *A*. This is a mistake which is often made by beginners. The transverse radius is usually referred to as ν.

From these definitions it follows that both radii lie on the same straight line. The transverse radius is represented by the line *AQ*, to terminate on the minor semi-axis. The meridional radius is somewhat shorter as depicted by *AQ'*. Derivation of the formulae for the two radii of curvature is not attempted here because it is too difficult at the elementary level. The two formulae may be written:

$$\rho = \frac{a(1-e^2)}{(1-e^2 \cdot \sin^2\varphi)^{3/2}} \qquad (3.30)$$

$$\nu = \frac{a}{(1-e^2 \cdot \sin^2\varphi)^{\frac{1}{2}}} \qquad (3.31)$$

These equations indicate that both radii may be completely described in terms of *a*, *e* and *φ*. Since *a* and *e* are constant for any particular Figure, the only variable is latitude. Most national surveys have produced tables for ρ and ν together with several other quantities based upon them for the particular Figure of the Earth in use and within the range of latitude where their work is concentrated. A few of the older textbooks and manuals also contain shortened versions of the tables.

Using these it is possible to obtain, by interpolation, the radii for any desired latitude. Nowadays, however, calculations on the spheroid of the sort to be described are frequently done by digital computer or even on the more sophisticated models of desk-top calculator. When using these it is comparatively simple to write a suitable subroutine which calculates ρ and ν from equations (3.30) and (3.31) without any need to refer to tables.

It is worth remembering the following properties of the two radii:

(1) At the Pole, $\rho = \nu$ and both have their maximum values.
(2) In latitude 55° or thereabouts, $\rho = a$.
(3) In latitude 35° or thereabouts, $\rho = b$.
(4) On the Equator, $\nu = a$ and both ρ and ν have their minimum values.
(5) Whatever the latitude, $\nu \geqslant \rho$.

Arc distances on the spheroid

We deal with the two simple cases first. These are the length of an arc of the Equator and the arc of any parallel. On the ellipsoid of rotation both are circles and therefore the simple geometry of the sphere applies. The only difference is that the appropriate radius of curvature for the spheroid is used.

On the Equator, $\varphi = 0°$. Moreover the curvature at right angles to the meridian is the curvature of the Equator itself. From property (4) above,

$$s_e = \delta\lambda . a \tag{3.32}$$

For the parallel of latitude, φ,

$$s_p = \delta\lambda . \nu . \cos\varphi \tag{3.33}$$

The arc of the meridian is more complicated to evaluate because the meridional radius of curvature varies continuously with latitude. Therefore it is necessary to determine, first, the length of a very short arc at a point and then add together the values of all these small elements at all the points which make up the arc. This is a much simplified statement of the methods of the calculus. Since the nature of the problem is easy to state, it is worth considering how the problem is tackled in further detail.

Let us assume that it is required to determine the arc s_m measured from the Equator to latitude φ_1. At any point along this arc we may consider an infinitely small part, corresponding to an infinitely small change in latitude, $d\varphi$. Within such a small arc distance it is reasonable to state that the arc itself can be regarded as part of the circumference of a circle. This is shown by Fig. 30.

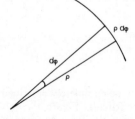

Figure 30 An infinitely short meridional arc on the spheroid.

Thus for the infinitely short arc we may write (3.12) in the form

$$ds_m = \rho . d\varphi \tag{3.34}$$

In order to define the whole curve from $\varphi=0$ to $\varphi=\varphi_1$ it is now desirable to *integrate* the multitude of short arcs which form the whole arc. Since the limits of the arc have already been specified, the arc distance on the ellipsoid, m, may be written as the *definite integral*

$$m = \int_{\varphi=0}^{\varphi=\varphi_1} \mathrm{d}s_m \tag{3.35}$$

or, from (3.34)

$$m = \int_{\varphi=0}^{\varphi=\varphi_1} \rho \cdot \mathrm{d}\varphi \tag{3.36}$$

and substituting the value for ρ given in (3.30)

$$m = \int_{\varphi=0}^{\varphi=\varphi_1} \frac{a(1-e^2)}{(1-e^2 \cdot \sin^2 \varphi)^{3/2}} \cdot \mathrm{d}\varphi \tag{3.37}$$

after integration of this expression, the equation which can be evaluated numerically has the form

$$m = a(1-e^2) \cdot \left\{ A \cdot \varphi_1 - \tfrac{1}{2}(B \cdot \sin 2\varphi_1) + \frac{C \cdot \sin 4\varphi_1}{4} + \ldots \right\} \tag{3.38}$$

where φ_1 is expressed in radians.

In this equation the coefficients A, B and C are expressed in terms of e as

$$A = 1 + \frac{3}{4}e^2 + \frac{45}{64}e^4 + \frac{175}{256}e^6 + \ldots \approx 1 \cdot 005\ 1092$$

$$B = \frac{3}{4}e^2 + \frac{15}{16}e^4 + \frac{525}{512}e^6 + \ldots \qquad \approx 0 \cdot 005\ 1202$$

$$C = \frac{15}{64}e^4 + \frac{105}{256}e^6 + \ldots \qquad \approx 0 \cdot 000\ 0108$$

(The numerical values for A, B and C are for the Clarke (1866) spheroid.)

We do not expect the reader to have understood the algebraic steps which are involved between equations (3.37) and (3.38). A fuller derivation can be found, for example, in Ref. 5. However, it has been worth indicating the initial steps in the argument together with the final equation because it demonstrates how much greater difficulty is encountered in solving a problem on the ellipsoid which was almost trivial on the sphere. Moreover an exact solution is not possible. Equation (3.38) is terminated after the term $C \cdot \sin 4\varphi_1/4$, but can be extended to include additional coefficients such as D. Each of the expressions for A through C are terminated at the term in e^6 but could be extended to include terms in e^8 and e^{10}. However, we can see that the numerical value for C is already quite small and the additional coefficients and terms in the series would have negligible influence upon the calculated amount.

The calculation of the length of any arc and its azimuth on the spheroid

Since the simple meridional arc introduces such difficulties it is not surprising that the determination of the length and azimuth of any arc is even more complicated. Yet this kind of problem arises in control surveys, either in the sort of work which extends through a big country or for extremely precise work in a smaller area. In other words, it arises in those cases where the spheroidal assumption is mandatory. One problem is to find the geographical coordinates of a new survey station from those of a point already fixed, using the measured or calculated bearing and distance to the new station. The converse problem, which is less common, is to determine the bearing and distance between two stations from their known geographical coordinates. In mathematical geodesy a variety of different formulae have been described. These are usually referred to by the name of their originator, such as *Clarke's Formula for Long Lines, Puissant's Formula, Rainsford's Extension of Clarke's Approximate Formula*. Bomford (Ref. 6) discusses the merits and accuracies of about ten such formulae.

In the days before digital computers were easily accessible these kinds of geodetic computations tended to strain the services available in most survey offices and were a headache to the field surveyor who was ever required to do the work himself. For this reason, various methods were employed to simplify the problem of calculation. The most useful modification was that originally adopted by Gauss for his *Mid-Latitude Formulae* and later by Clarke in his well-known approximate formula for short and medium length lines. Both make use of the idea that if a sphere be fitted tangentially to the surface of the ellipsoid near the middle of the arc, these two surfaces do not depart appreciably from one another over distances of a few tens of kilometres. Hence the computations make use of the radii of curvature of the spheroid but the methods of spherical trigonometry to solve the triangles.

References

1   Clough-Smith, J. H.: *An Introduction to Spherical Trigonometry*, Glasgow, 1966, Brown, Son and Ferguson, 111 pp.
2   — *Admiralty Navigation Manual, Vol.* II. London, 1938, HMSO, 268 pp. Appendix 2.
3   Cotter, C. H.: *The Complete Nautical Astronomer*, London, 1969, Hollis and Carter, 336 pp. Appendix.
4   — *Admiralty Manual of Hydrographic Surveying*, Vol. 1, London, 1965, Hydrographic Dept., 671 pp. Chapter 2.
5   Clark, D.: *Plane and Geodetic Surveying for Engineers, Vol.* 2, *Higher Surveying*. 3rd Edition revised and enlarged by J. Clendinning. London, 1944, Constable, 511 pp.
6   Bomford, G.: *Geodesy*, Oxford, 1971, 3rd Edition, The Clarendon Press, 731 pp.

CHAPTER 4

SOME BASIC IDEAS ABOUT THE MATHEMATICS OF MAP PROJECTIONS

Mathematicians are like Frenchmen: whatever you say to them they translate into their own language, and forthwith it is something entirely different.

Goethe

Introduction

A map projection may be defined as *any systematic arrangement of meridians and parallels portraying the curved surface of the sphere or spheroid upon a plane*. For most purposes in the present book, *it will suffice to regard the Earth as a perfect sphere*. This has the advantage of being mathematically simpler to understand without losing sight of any of the salient problems which have to be tackled. The main exception occurs in Chapter 11, where the specialised use of projections in surveying and topographical cartography is considered. Because of the need to regard the Earth as a spheroid for many kinds of surveys it is also necessary to consider plane representation of this kind of reference figure in that context. It was stated in Chapter 2 (p. 18) that every map projection is a form of coordinate representation upon the plane and that its graticule intersection may be located by means of either Cartesian or polar coordinates. In other words, each point on the Earth's surface, with geographical coordinates (φ, λ) may be reproduced on the plane by a point located in either the (x, y) or (r, θ) systems of plane coordinates.

Functional relationships

We may express this idea in the generalised form of *functional relationships* (or *functions*) and write:

$$x = f_1(\varphi, \lambda) \tag{4.01}$$

$$y = f_2(\varphi, \lambda) \tag{4.02}$$

or

$$r = f_3(\varphi, \lambda) \tag{4.03}$$

$$\theta = f_4(\varphi, \lambda) \tag{4.04}$$

These expressions are the mathematical shorthand for statements such as 'x is a function of latitude and longitude' etc. The suffices f_1–f_4 indicate that these are different functions. Thus we can distinguish between (4.01) and (4.02) by the statement 'whereas x is one function of both latitude and longitude, y is a different function of these variables'. We can further state that in (4.01), x is the *dependent variable* which is a function of two *independent variables*, φ and λ.

At this stage we do not precisely specify the nature of these functions. Each map projection has unique equations for x and y or r and θ which will be used to define and construct it. Appendix I, on pages 234–45, indicates some of the formulae which these functions represent. For the present, however, the generalised expressions (4.01)–(4.04) are useful in the preliminary study of the subject for they indicate certain important relationships between the sphere and plane. Moreover they serve as a convenient basis for the systematic classification of all map projections.

From the statements that x and y (or r and θ) are functions of latitude and longitude it follows that one point (φ, λ) on the Earth is represented by one point (x, y) or (r, θ) on the map. In other words, there is a *one-to-one correspondence* between the Earth and the map. We will have to qualify this statement later because some map projections show the same meridian twice, because the geographical poles are represented by lines instead of points or because certain parts of the Earth's surface cannot be shown on certain map projections. These peculiarities arise from the simple fact that a sphere has a continuous surface whereas a plane map must have a boundary. The kinds of peculiarities which have been mentioned generally occur at the edge of the map projection and they must be considered to be exceptional or *singular points*. Within the body of the majority of map projections each point on the Earth is only shown once and therefore the idea of corresponding points may be applied.

The correspondence between points on the surface of the Earth and the plane map cannot be exact. In the first place, some kind of scale change must occur because a map of the Earth at the scale of 1/1 is a physical impossibility. Secondly, the curved surface of the Earth cannot be fitted to a plane without introducing some *deformation* or *distortion* which is equivalent to stretching or tearing the curved surface.

Principal scale

Because a map is always a small-scale representation of the Earth it is necessary to consider this part of the transformation first.

In the everyday meaning of the word, *scale* may be defined as *the ratio of distance on a map, globe or vertical section to the actual distances they represent.* Expressed geometrically, if the map distance is $A'B'$, corresponding to the ground distance AB, the scale of the map over the section AB is the fraction $A'B'/AB$, expressed as a fraction whose numerator is 1. Thus, if 40 mm. on the map corresponds to 1 km. on the ground, $A'B'=40$ and $AB=1000\times1000=1,000,000$ (to bring AB into the same units as $A'B'$) and the scale 40/1,000,000 may be described as the *representative fraction* 1/25,000.

From the definition of scale given above, precisely the same reasoning may be used to describe the scale of a globe used to represent the Earth. In this case, comparison is made between the lengths of two corresponding arcs of great circles, AB on the Earth and $A'B'$ on the globe. From equation (1.02) and the arguments presented in Chapter 3,

$$AB = R.z$$

and

$$A'B' = r.z$$

Hence the scale of the globe may also be expressed as

$$\frac{A'B'}{AB} = \frac{r.z}{R.z} \tag{4.05}$$

or

$$\frac{1}{S} = \frac{r}{R} \tag{4.06}$$

where S is the denominator of the representative fraction, r is the radius of the globe and R is the radius of the Earth. For example, a globe of radius 212 mm. will have a scale denominator

$$S = 6371100/0 \cdot 212 = 30,052,358$$
$$\approx 30,000,000$$

and the globe has scale 1/30,000,000.

We assume that a *generating globe* is an exact replica of the Earth but at a scale indicated by (4.06). We call this the *Principal Scale* and therefore can define it as **the scale of a reduced or generating globe representing the sphere or spheroid defined by the fractional relation of their respective radii.*

The concept of a generating globe of known principal scale is extremely valuable in the discussion which follows. We know that, in human terms, the Earth is a large body. Therefore a map can only be the small-scale representation of the whole or part of the surface. Since we must consider in detail how the transformations from sphere to plane can be accomplished and, in particular, investigate how and where distortion in scale may occur, it is inconvenient to have to think in terms of the large-scale changes between the Earth and map defined by the representative fraction. We therefore sweep away this difficulty by thinking in terms of a generating globe which is a replica of the Earth at the scale of the map. Since we wish to eliminate the use of awkward fractions altogether, we define the principal scale as

$$\mu_0 = 1 \cdot 0 \qquad (4.07)$$

and evaluate distortion as some multiple of this.

It follows, moreover, that *the principal scale is equivalent to the representative fraction printed in the margin of the map.*

Hence we have the statement that

$$\frac{1}{S} = \mu_0 = 1 \cdot 0 \qquad (4.08)$$

Introduction to the concepts of distortion

At the manageable dimensions of a generating globe it is easy to demonstrate that the curved surface of a sphere cannot be fitted to a plane. This fundamental principle can be verified easily by any one who experiments with a globe, beach ball or similar smooth sphere. If we attempt to fit a small piece of plane paper—a postage stamp, for example—to the surface of a large beach ball, it is possible to make it adhere without creating any wrinkles or tears in the paper. This is because the piece of paper is small compared with the ball and the deformation of the plane which is needed to make the two surfaces fit is less than can be accommodated by the elasticity of the paper. On the other hand, the postage stamp cannot be fitted to the curved surface of a table tennis ball without the introduction of considerable folding, tearing or creasing.

An important conclusion to be derived from these simple experiments is that if the area of the plane surface is small compared with the total surface area of the sphere, the amount of distortion introduced is less than occurs when the area of the plane corresponds to a large part of the curved surface. This is a qualitative, empirical observation similar to that made in Chapter 1, page 15, with reference to the use of the assumption that the Earth is a plane surface. However, it is now important for us to learn more about these processes of distortion and, in particular, discover how they may be expressed algebraically and used quantitatively to illustrate how a map projection distorts the curved surface of the globe.

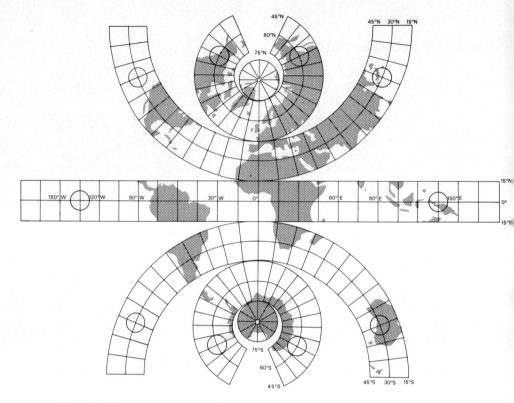

Figure 31 Plane representation of the curved surface of the Earth obtained by cutting the spherical surface along the parallels 15° North and South, 45° North and South, 75° North and South and along the antimeridian of Greenwich.

Of course, the experiments with a ball and postage stamp are the converse of the object of creating a map projection. This is to make parts of the curved surface fit a plane. A useful illustration, which may be simulated by cutting orange peel and laying this flat, is to imagine that the curved surface of a globe has been cut along certain parallels and meridians, as shown in Fig. 31. If the spherical surface is cut thus it is very nearly possible to lay it flat. However, this result is only obtained at the expense of showing certain parallels of latitude twice and interrupting the continuity of the map by leaving gaps between these parallels. If it is desirable to map the whole surface continuously, these gaps must be closed by stretching each zone in a meridional direction until the corresponding parallels meet as illustrated in Fig. 32. Stretching of the map involves distortion and comparison of Figs. 31 and 32 indicates that the amount of stretching increases progressively towards the edges of the map. The amount of distortion may be indicated by the deformation of the little circles shown in Fig. 31 into the ellipses shown in Fig. 32.

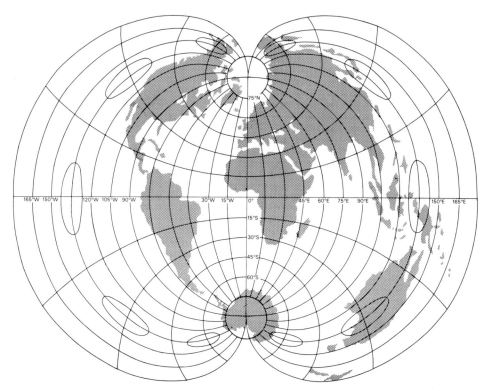

Figure 32 Continuous plane representation of the Earth derived from Fig. 31 by meridional stretching. Note how the circles shown in Fig. 31 have been deformed into ellipses on this diagram. The map is the World development of the Simple Polyconic Projection (No. 38 in Appendix I) in which the parallels have equidistant separation along each meridian.

In the creation of the continuous map illustrated by Fig. 32 the distortion described is *Linear Distortion* directed along the meridians. The graphical result is that the distance between any two parallels of latitude increases from the middle of the map towards the edges. On the other hand, the distances between successive meridians varies only with latitude. We have already seen that this is a property of the spherical surface. Equation (3.17) describes it. If, however, we consider the spacing between the meridians along any particular parallel of latitude, we see that it is almost constant and equivalent to the spacing illustrated in Fig. 31. This means that linear distortion in this projection occurs in one direction but not the other. This is clearly likely to influence the representation of both *angles* and *areas* on the map. The effect may be demonstrated by drawing two graphs as shown in Figs. 33 and 34. In Fig. 33, the point P has rectangular coordinates (10, 10). Then the angle $YOP = 45°$ and the area of the figure $YOXP = 100$ square units. In Fig. 34, the scale along the ordinate is doubled but that along the abscissa remains the same. Thus $P' = (10, 20)$. The angle $Y'OP' = 30°$ and the area of the rectangle $Y'OX'P' = 200$ square units. We will call the change in angle $Y'OP' - YOP$ the *angular deformation* and the change in area $Y'OX'P' - YOXP$ the *exaggeration area*. In a map projection they are not as easily defined as they are in a pair of plane

E

graphs, but the essential characteristic is clear. *Both angular deformation and exaggeration of area depend upon linear distortion and therefore they may be defined in terms of this.* Consequently it is the change which occurs in the length of any line which is fundamentally important to the study of map projections.

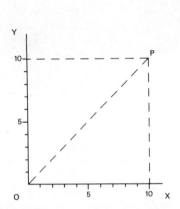

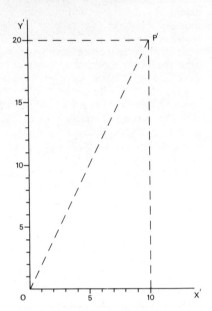

Figure 33 Demonstration of the influence of linear distortion upon angular and area representation. Stage 1, initial condition where $P = (10, 10)$.

Figure 34 Demonstration of the influence of linear distortion upon angular and area representation. Stage 2, showing the result of changing the ordinate so that $P = (10, 20)$.

Linear distortion

When the scale of a map is known from its representative fraction, one might suppose that this scale is constant in three respects:

(1) That *the ratio established by the representative fraction applies to the lengths of all lines measured on the map.* For example, if the scale of a map is 1/25,000, we expect that a line of length 40 mm. corresponds to a ground distance of 1 km. We might further assume that a line of length 80 mm. corresponds to 2 km. and that a line of length 400 mm. is equal to 10 km. on the ground. Hence we might assume that the relationship established by the representative fraction is constant for linear measurements of any distance which can be contained within the neat lines of the map. Moreover we might also assume that the same relationship will apply to all maps of the same scale irrespective of the part of the World which they depict.

(2) That *the relationship established by the representative fraction is constant for all parts of the map.* Thus we suppose that a line of length 40 mm. corresponds to a ground distance of 1 km. whether this be measured in the centre of the map or near one edge or a corner of the sheet.

(3) That *the relationship is also independent of direction.* Thus, at 1/25,000 scale, 40 mm. represents 1 km. irrespective of whether the line is measured North–South or East–West or in any intermediate direction.

The three assumptions seem to be axiomatic in most kinds of map use, to the extent that most map and chart users, apart from navigators, apply them without thought. However, *the supposition that scale is constant for all distances, at all places and in all directions is not true.* If it were possible to reproduce the principal scale in all directions and everywhere upon the plane surface of the map, then the map would be a perfect representation of the spherical surface and therefore it would be part of the spherical surface. Since a curved surface is not a plane it follows that the transformation to the plane *must* involve variation in scale in some or all of the three ways which have been specified.

The numerical example refers to a map of scale 1/25,000 which probably represents a ground area of 100–200 square kilometres. Within this small portion of the Earth's surface the scale changes are small; so small that negligible errors are introduced by making the assumption that scale is constant. The errors are much less than the uncertainty in position caused by representing ground detail by legible lines of exaggerated width; they are also less than the variations in paper size and shape which occur with changes in temperature and humidity. But it is important to realise that linear distortion is present, even if it is too small to be recognised.

Lines and Points of Zero Distortion

Although it is clearly impossible to create a perfect map in which the principal scale is preserved everywhere, it is quite easy to maintain the principal scale along certain lines or at certain points on the map. Along these lines, or at these points, scale is constant and equal to the principal scale so that no linear distortion is present. Thus we have the following terms and their definitions:

*Line(s) of Zero Distortion are great circle or small circle arcs on a map projection along which the principal scale is preserved.

Point(s) of Zero Distortion is the point(s) on a map projection where the principal scale is preserved.

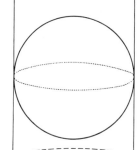

Figure 35 The Tangent Cylinder

The meaning of these definitions may be demonstrated by some well-known experiments with a globe or ball and a sheet of paper. These are illustrated by

Figs. 35, 36, 37, 38, 39 and 40. If the sheet of paper is wrapped round the sphere in the form of a cylinder, it makes contact with the spherical surface along the circumference of a great circle, as illustrated by Fig. 35. By marking the paper, we see that the length of the line of contact on the plane sheet, unrolled from its cylindrical form, is the same as the length of the circumference of the great circle.

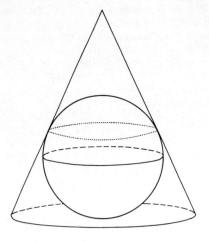

Figure 36 The Tangent Cone

The second possibility is to wrap the sheet of paper in the form of a cone (Fig. 36) so that this surface makes contact with the spherical surface along the circumference of a small circle. Again it is obvious that the length of the line of contact between the paper cone and the globe corresponds to the length of the circumference of the small circle. The third possibility is to hold the paper as a plane surface so that it forms a tangent plane to the globe (Fig. 37). Although it cannot now be demonstrated that lines of finite length are represented at true scale, it follows from the definition of a spherical angle (p. 35) that any angle drawn on the plane at the point of contact is equal to the corresponding spherical angle on the globe.

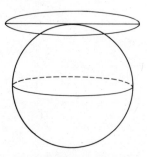

Figure 37 The Tangent Plane

We may also consider three cases where the surface of the paper intersects the surface of the globe. These are more difficult to simulate by experiment but are easy enough to illustrate. Figure 38 shows the secant cylinder which intersects the sphere along two arcs of small circles, *AB* and *CD*. It is easy to demonstrate from the geometry of a sphere that since a cylinder has constant radius, the small circles have the same radii and therefore they are equidistant from the plane of the great circle defined by the co-axial tangent cylinder. By reasoning analogous to that followed for the tangent cylinder, the principal scale is preserved along the circumferences of both small circles.

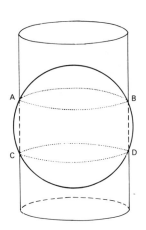
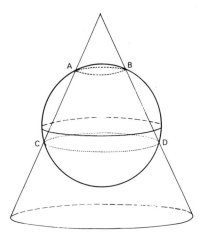

Figure 38 The Secant Cylinder   *Figure 39* The Secant Cone

The example of the secant cone is illustrated in Fig. 39, where it can be seen that two small circles of different radii are defined by *AB* and *CD* and each of them is represented on the cone at its correct length. In Fig. 40 the tangent plane has been displaced so that it intersects the spherical surface and the small circle *AB* is traced upon this plane. It follows from the definition of a small circle that the circumference traced on the plane is identical with the circumference of it on the sphere.

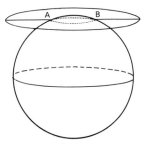

Figure 40 The Secant Plane

The experiments and illustrations which depict the various ways in which the location of lines or a point of zero distortion may be imagined indicate that the lengths of the lines should be the same as those on the generating globe. It is less easy to demonstrate that this principle applies also within the infinitely small circle centred on a point of zero distortion. The main difficulty is to imagine how we can define scale at a point. We have to reconcile the elementary concept of scale as a fraction relating finite distances whereas the Euclidean definition of a point is that it has position but no magnitude. To proceed further necessitates some reconsideration of the concept of scale in terms of the differential calculus. In other words we must determine the rate at which scale may change along a line which is infinitely short.

Particular scales

Let us consider a map projection of part of the surface of a globe which satisfies equations (4·01) and (4.02). In other words we define positions on the plane by the rectangular coordinates (x, y) and we know that the positions of points plotted within this system are some function of both latitude and longitude. In other words, if φ changes both x and y are altered. Similarly, if λ changes, both x and y are altered. Figure 41 represents part of the curved surface of the generating globe and shows the spherical quadrilateral formed by the intersections of a pair of meridians with a pair of parallels. We assume that the point A has geographical coordinates (φ, λ) and that the other three points, B, C and D lie to the North and East of A. Then, denoting the difference in latitude between the parallels as $\delta\varphi$ and the difference in longitude between the meridians as $\delta\lambda$ we may write down the geographical coordinates of the four points according to the following system:

Point	Latitude	Longitude
A	φ	λ
B	$\varphi + \delta\varphi$	λ
C	$\varphi + \delta\varphi$	$\lambda + \delta\lambda$
D	φ	$\lambda + \delta\lambda$

Figure 42 shows a map of the corresponding points $A'B'C'$ and D'. The point A' has rectangular coordinates (x, y) and the coordinate differences between A' and C' are δx and δy.

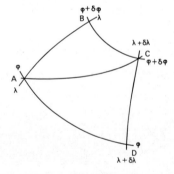

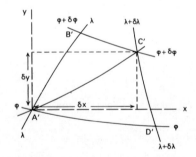

Figure 41 A spherical quadrilateral, $ABCD$, of finite size formed by the intersection of the parallels φ and $\varphi + \delta\varphi$ with the meridians λ and $\lambda + \delta\lambda$.

Figure 42 The plane representation, $A'B'C'D'$ of the spherical quadrilateral illustrated by Fig. 41.

Thus far we have regarded the spherical quadrilateral and its projection as having finite size. In other words, the quantities $\delta\varphi$, $\delta\lambda$, δx and δy can be measured on the globe or map. Because we have specified a generalised functional relationship, the sides and the diagonal of $A'B'C'D'$ may be composed of curves and the angles between these sides may be of any size. In order to proceed with the analysis it is now necessary to consider that the corresponding figures have been reduced in size until they are infinitely small. This has two important consequences:

(1) *The shapes of corresponding lines on both globe and map approximate more and more closely to straight lines.*
(2) *The angles formed by the intersection of pairs of lines remain unchanged.*

It follows that the spherical quadrilateral formed originally by pairs of meridians and parallels intersecting at right angles is transformed into a rectilinear figure in which all four angles are still right angles. Hence, in Fig. 43 *ABCD* is a

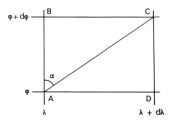

Figure 43 An infinitely small spherical quadrilateral, *ABCD*, formed by the intersection of the parallels φ and $\varphi + d\varphi$ with the meridians λ and $\lambda + d\lambda$.

rectangle. On the map, the sides and diagonals of the figure $A'B'C'D'$ are transformed into straight lines, but angles such as θ' are preserved. Figure 44 illustrates this transformation in enlarged form. We regard the points A and A' as having the coordinates already allocated to them, but denote the incremental changes in latitude, longitude, x and y as being $d\varphi$, $d\lambda$, dx and dy respectively. This is the usual notation used to indicate infinitesimally small increments. Consequently, the four points on the globe are:

Point	Latitude	Longitude
A	φ	λ
B	$\varphi + d\varphi$	λ
C	$\varphi + d\varphi$	$\lambda + d\lambda$
D	φ	$\lambda + d\lambda$

From equation (3.12) we may express the length of the element of the meridional arc through A as

$$ds_m = R \cdot d\varphi \qquad (4.09)$$

where R is the radius of the globe.

From equation (3.17) the length of the element of the arc of the parallel through A is

$$ds_p = R \cdot \cos \varphi \cdot d\lambda \qquad (4.10)$$

Moreover, since the angles at the four corners of *ABCD* are right angles, we may use Pythagoras' Theorem to find the length of the diagonal arc element *AC*. Thus

$$ds^2 = ds^2_m + ds^2_p \qquad (4.11)$$

or

$$ds = (R^2 \cdot d\varphi^2 + R^2 \cdot \cos^2 \varphi \cdot d\lambda^2)^{\frac{1}{2}} \qquad (4.12)$$

On the plane, the point $A' = (x, y)$ and $C' = (x + dx, y + dy)$. In order to aid further interpretation, we construct the lines $A'S'$, $B'P'$, $C'Q'$ and $D'R'$ parallel to the *x*-axis. We also construct the lines $A'P'$, $B'Q'$, $C'R'$ and $D'S'$ parallel to the *y*-axis.

At this stage it is desirable to introduce a word of warning about the understanding of the equations which follow. These are presented in the logical order in which they may be derived and they employ the symbolic notation to be expected in mathematical writings. However, the rigorous derivation of them calls for a higher standard of mathematical knowledge than is appropriate for the standard of this book. Consequently we do not attempt to prove equations algebraically, but merely present the important results. Each of these may be interpreted in geometrical terms, using Fig. 44 as the guide and it is more important for the beginner to

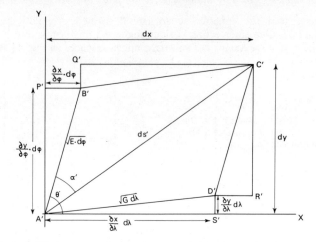

Figure 44 The plane representation $A'B'C'D'$ of the infinitely small spherical quadrilateral illustrated in Fig. 43.

understand this part of the argument than the algebraic gymnastics which are involved in the derivation of certain equations. In order to demonstrate how the equations which follow have practical application, we give an example of their use at the end of this chapter. Each of the lines represented in Fig. 44 has a geometrical significance which may also be represented symbolically using the notation of *partial differentiation*. Thus $A'B'$ represents the arc of the meridian through A' and $A'D'$ is the arc of the parallel through the same point. $A'C'$ represents any arc through A' which makes the bearing α' with the meridian through A'. The additional construction lines represent the following variables:

(1) $A'P'$ represents the increment in y which results from an increase $d\varphi$ in latitude. This may be expressed symbolically by the term

$$\frac{\partial y}{\partial \varphi}\, d\varphi$$

(2) $P'B'$ is the increment in x which results from the same increase $d\varphi$ in latitude. This may be expressed symbolically by the term

$$\frac{\partial x}{\partial \varphi}\, d\varphi$$

(3) $A'S'$ represents the increment in x resulting from an increase $d\lambda$ in longitude. This may be expressed symbolically by the term

$$\frac{\partial x}{\partial \lambda}\, d\lambda$$

(4) $D'S'$ is the increment in y resulting from the same increase $d\lambda$ in longitude. This may be expressed symbolically by the term

$$\frac{\partial y}{\partial \lambda} \, d\lambda$$

From Fig. 44 we can see that the increment dx between A' and C' is composed of the two linear elements $B'P'$ and $Q'C'$, or

$$dx = B'P' + Q'C'$$

Substituting the appropriate terms from (2) and (3) above,

$$dx = \frac{\partial x}{\partial \varphi} \, d\varphi + \frac{\partial x}{\partial \lambda} \, d\lambda \qquad (4.13)$$

In calculus this is known as the *total differential of x*. Similarly we can see that the increment dy between A' and C' is also composed of two linear elements $A'P'$ and $B'Q'$. Thus

$$dy = A'P' + B'Q'$$

Substituting the appropriate terms from (1) and (4) above,

$$dy = \frac{\partial y}{\partial \varphi} \, d\varphi + \frac{\partial y}{\partial \lambda} \, d\lambda \qquad (4.14)$$

which is the total differential of y.

Both of these expressions may be derived algebraically from the functions (4.01) and (4.02). For example, Abbott/Calculus §194 describes the steps in detail.

From Pythagoras' Theorem applied to the right-angled triangles in Fig. 44, the sides and diagonal of the figure $A'B'C'D'$ may be expressed as

$$A'B'^2 = B'P'^2 + A'P'^2 \qquad (4.15)$$

$$A'D'^2 = A'S'^2 + D'S'^2 \qquad (4.16)$$

$$A'C'^2 = B'P'^2 + Q'C'^2 + A'P'^2 + B'Q'^2 \qquad (4.17)$$

$$= dx^2 + dy^2 \qquad (4.18)$$

Substituting the right-hand sides of equations (4.13) and (4.14), we obtain for the diagonal arc $A'C' = ds'$, the expression

$$ds'^2 = \left\{ \frac{\partial x}{\partial \varphi} \, d\varphi + \frac{\partial x}{\partial \lambda} \, d\lambda \right\}^2 + \left\{ \frac{\partial y}{\partial \varphi} \, d\varphi + \frac{\partial y}{\partial \lambda} \, d\lambda \right\}^2 \qquad (4.19)$$

Some simplification of this equation can be obtained if the following expressions are substituted:

$$E = \left(\frac{\partial x}{\partial \varphi} \right)^2 + \left(\frac{\partial y}{\partial \varphi} \right)^2 \qquad (4.20)$$

$$F = \left(\frac{\partial y}{\partial \varphi} \cdot \frac{\partial y}{\partial \lambda} \right) - \left(\frac{\partial x}{\partial \varphi} \cdot \frac{\partial x}{\partial \lambda} \right) \qquad (4.21)$$

$$G = \left(\frac{\partial x}{\partial \lambda} \right)^2 + \left(\frac{\partial y}{\partial \lambda} \right)^2 \qquad (4.22)$$

leading to the more convenient expression

$$ds'^2 = E \cdot d\varphi^2 + 2F \cdot d\varphi \cdot d\lambda + G \cdot d\lambda^2 \qquad (4.23)$$

From the equations which have been derived it is now possible to determine three scales which refer to the point A' on the map.

(1) *The scale along the meridian*

This is the ratio $A'B'/AB=h$

Since $A'B'^2 = B'P'^2 + A'P'^2$

$$A'B'^2 = \left(\frac{\partial x}{\partial \varphi} \, \mathrm{d}\varphi\right)^2 + \left(\frac{\partial y}{\partial \varphi} . \, \mathrm{d}\varphi\right)^2$$

and, from (4.20)

$$A'B' = \sqrt{E} . \mathrm{d}\varphi \qquad (4.24)$$

The arc element $AB = \mathrm{d}s_m$ has already been determined in equation (4.09). Therefore

$$h = \frac{\sqrt{E} . \mathrm{d}\varphi}{R . \mathrm{d}\varphi}$$

$$= \frac{\sqrt{E}}{R} \qquad (4.25)$$

and since we have to relate this scale to the principal scale, we put $R=1$ so that

$$h = \sqrt{E} \qquad (4.26)$$

(2) *The scale along the parallel*

This is the ratio $A'D'/AD=k$

Since $A'D'^2 = A'S'^2 + D'S'^2$

$$A'D'^2 = \left(\frac{\partial x}{\partial \lambda} \, \mathrm{d}\lambda\right)^2 + \left(\frac{\partial y}{\partial \lambda} \, \mathrm{d}\lambda\right)^2$$

and, from (4.22)

$$A'D' = \sqrt{G} . \mathrm{d}\lambda \qquad (4.27)$$

The arc element $AD = \mathrm{d}s_p$ has already been found in equation (4.10). Therefore

$$k = \frac{\sqrt{G} . \mathrm{d}\lambda}{R . \cos \varphi . \mathrm{d}\lambda} \qquad (4.28)$$

This simplifies to

$$k = \frac{\sqrt{G}}{R . \cos \varphi} \qquad (4.29)$$

or, where $R=1$,

$$k = \frac{\sqrt{G}}{\cos \varphi} \qquad (4.30)$$

(3) *The scale along any arc through A which makes the bearing* α *with the meridian through A.*

This is the general expression illustrated by the ratio $A'C'/AC$ or ds'/ds which we will denote by μ. The value for $A'C'^2$ has been given in equation (4.23) and that for AC in (4.12). Hence we can write

$$\frac{ds'}{ds} = \frac{(E.d\varphi^2 + 2F.d\varphi.d\lambda + G.d\lambda^2)^{\frac{1}{2}}}{(R^2.d\varphi^2 + R^2.\cos^2\varphi.d\lambda^2)^{\frac{1}{2}}} \qquad (4.31)$$

or, putting $R=1$, as before

$$\mu = \frac{(E.d\varphi^2 + 2F.d\varphi.d\lambda + G.d\lambda^2)^{\frac{1}{2}}}{(d\varphi^2 + \cos^2\varphi.d\lambda^2)^{\frac{1}{2}}} \qquad (4.32)$$

The scales along the meridian, the parallel or in any direction are known as the *Particular Scales* at the point and these may now be defined as *the relation between an infinitesimal linear distance in any direction at any point on a map projection and the corresponding linear distance on the globe.*

The idea of direction is contained in the angles α′ and θ′ on the map. We can see in Fig. 44 that α′ is the bearing of the line $A'C'$ measured at A' and corresponds to the bearing of $AC=\alpha$ on the globe. The angle θ′ is the angle made at A' by the intersection of the meridian and parallel.

It can be shown that

$$\sin\theta' = \frac{F}{h.k.\cos\varphi} \qquad (4.33)$$

The angle α′ may also be shown to be a function of E, F and G so that it is also possible to express (4.32) in terms of α. This has the form

$$\mu^2{}_\alpha = \frac{E}{R^2}\cos^2\alpha + \frac{F}{R^2\cos\varphi}\sin 2\alpha + \frac{G}{R^2\cos^2\varphi}\sin^2\alpha\ldots \qquad (4.34)$$

where μ_α is the particular scale in the direction α′. Since E, F, G and H change continuously with both latitude and longitude, the particular scales vary with position on the map. Since μ can also be expressed in terms of bearing, it follows that, at any given point, the particular scales also vary with direction about that point.

It follows that any number of particular scales can be evaluated for a point, but, in practice, only four of these are needed in the subsequent analysis of the distortion characteristics of any map projection. These are:

(1) The particular scale along the meridian, h, from (4.26),
(2) The particular scale along the parallel, k, from (4.30),
(3) The maximum particular scale, a, at the point,
(4) The minimum particular scale, b, at the point.

The maximum and minimum particular scales still remain to be determined.

Tissot's Theorem and the principal directions

Most of the foregoing analysis had been undertaken by Gauss in the early years of the nineteenth century. The next major advance in the mathematical theory of map projections was made by Tissot in the 1850's. He proposed the theorem which bears his name and also developed the concept of the *ellipse of distortion* which is also known as *Tissot's Indicatrix*.

Tissot's Theorem was stated by him as follows:

'Whatever the system of projection there are, at every point on one of the surfaces two directions perpendicular to one another and, if angles are not preserved, there are only two of them, such that the directions which correspond to them on the other surface also intersect one another at right angles.'

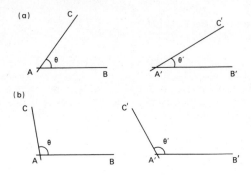

Figure 45 The concept of principal directions. The diagrams on the left relate to the spherical surface and those on the right to its plane representation. In (a), $\theta<90°$ and $\theta'<90°$. In (b) $\theta>90°$ and $\theta'>90°$. The principal directions are defined where $BAC=B'A'C'=90°$.

Tissot's original reasoning is quite easy to follow. If a point A on the globe represents the intersections of two arcs AB and AC making the angle θ (Fig. 45a), the corresponding points on the plane are A',B' and C' and the corresponding angle is θ'. We assume that $\theta\neq\theta'$ but that both of them are acute angles. If the line AC is rotated until it is an obtuse angle (Fig. 45b) it has, at some stage, passed through the angle $\theta=90°$ in this rotation. Similarly, if the line $A'C'$ is also rotated about A' until it is an obtuse angle, then at some stage $\theta'=90°$. Where $\theta=\theta'=90°$, the two orthogonal directions have been defined. These are called the *principal directions*.

The ellipse of distortion

The next stage in the argument is the most difficult to prove rigorously but simply. The idea is simple enough, namely that an infinitely small circle on the surface of the globe will be transformed on the plane into an infinitely small ellipse whose semi-axes lie along the two principal directions. Reference to Figs. 31 and 32 indicate that the idea is plausible, so we assume it to be proved. The reader who is insistent that proof be obtained will find this in any number of advanced textbooks, for example Ref. 1 or Ref. 2.

Figure 46 illustrates a point A on the globe which has geographical coordinates (φ_a, λ_a). AC represents an infinitely short arc, ds, which corresponds to the arc AC in Fig. 43 and the preceding section defining particular scales. Since scale is constant on the curved surface of the globe and everywhere equal to the principal scale, the locus of all points such as C traces the circumference of the circle with centre A and radius ds. Since we have set the principal scale $\mu_0=1$, it is convenient to make $ds=1$.

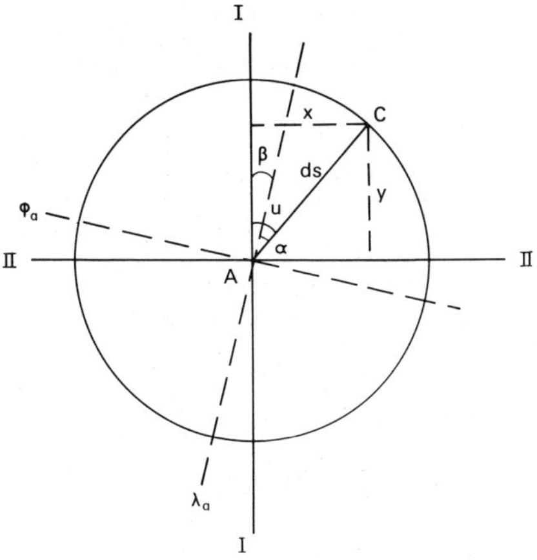

Figure 46 The representation of an infinitely small circle upon the spherical surface.

Figure 47 illustrates the corresponding figure on the plane. The lines $A'I'$ and $A'II'$ represent the principal directions through the point A' and we use these to define corresponding coordinate axes in both Fig. 46 and 47. In Fig. 47 the line $A'C'$ corresponds to the arc element ds' which, in Fig. 44 made the angle a' with the meridian through A'. However, it is now necessary to refer angles to one of the principal directions so we define the angle $IAC=u$ and $I'A'C'=u'$. Because the length of the arc element ds' varies continuously with direction, or, in other words, according to u, it follows that the locus of points such as C' trace the circumference of the ellipse. Let $C=(x, y)$ and $C'=(x', y')$ both systems having the principal directions as axes.

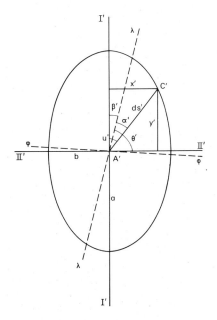

Figure 47 Tissot's Indicatrix or the Ellipse of Distortion. The deformation of the infinitely small circle illustrated in Fig. 46 into an ellipse by the transformation to the plane. Compare, also, Figs. 31 and 32.

The lengths of the two semi-axes of the ellipse may be expressed as

$$a = \frac{y'}{y} \tag{4.35}$$

$$b = \frac{x'}{x} \tag{4.36}$$

so that

$$x' = b \cdot x \tag{4.37}$$

$$y' = a \cdot y \tag{4.38}$$

Moreover

$$x' = ds' \cdot \sin u' \tag{4.39}$$

$$y' = ds' \cdot \cos u' \tag{4.40}$$

$$x = ds \cdot \sin u = \sin u \tag{4.41}$$

$$y = ds \cdot \cos u = \cos u \tag{4.42}$$

Substituting from equations (4.39)–(4.42) in (4.37) and (4.38)

$$ds' \cdot \sin u' = b \cdot \sin u \tag{4.43}$$

$$ds' \cdot \cos u' = a \cdot \cos u \tag{4.44}$$

Combination of these equations leads eventually to

$$ds'^2 = a^2 \cos^2 u + b^2 \sin^2 u \tag{4.45}$$

Two of the particular scales at A' refer to the scales along the meridian and parallel. If β is the angle on the globe between the principal direction I and the meridian λ_a through A, with the corresponding angle β' on the map then, from (4.45)

$$h^2 = a^2 \cos^2 \beta' + b^2 \sin^2 \beta' \tag{4.46}$$

and

$$k^2 = a^2 \sin^2 \beta' + b^2 \cos^2 \beta' \tag{4.47}$$

Adding equations (4.46) and (4.47), the terms in β' equal unity (because $\sin^2 \beta' + \cos^2 \beta' = 1$), therefore

$$h^2 + k^2 = a^2 + b^2 \tag{4.48}$$

This is the algebraic expression for the *First Theorem of Apollonius*, well known in plane coordinate geometry, which states that the sum of the squares of two conjugate diameters of an ellipse is constant.

The *Second Theorem of Apollonius* states that the area of the parallelogram formed by two conjugate semidiameters of an ellipse is equal to the area of the rectangle formed by the semi-axes of that ellipse. In the present notation, this may be expressed as

$$h \cdot k \cdot \sin \theta' = ab \tag{4.49}$$

Equations (4.48) and (4.49) are valuable to the analysis of the distortion characteristics of any map projection for they permit the evaluation of a and b from known values of h, k and θ'.
Thus

$$h^2 \pm 2h \cdot k \cdot \sin \theta' + k^2 = a^2 \pm 2ab + b^2 \tag{4.50}$$

whence

$$a \pm b = (h^2 + k^2 \pm 2h \cdot k \cdot \sin \theta')^{\frac{1}{2}} \tag{4.51}$$

Exaggeration of area

The area or a small quadrilateral, such as $A'B'C'D'$ in Fig. 44 may be defined as $A'B'.A'D'.\sin\theta'$. Thus

$$p = h.k.\sin\theta' \tag{4.52}$$

which is the left-hand side of (4.49). Consequently we may also write

$$p = a.b \tag{4.53}$$

The parameter p is defined in the same units as the particular scales and since these are multiples of the principal scale, p may also be called the *area scale*.

Angular deformation

From the difference between the angles u and u', both being referred to the same principal direction, it is possible to evaluate the alteration in direction of the line $A'C'$ as follows:

$$\tan u' = \frac{b}{a}\tan u \tag{4.54}$$

and

$$\tan u \pm \tan u' = \tan u \pm \frac{b}{a}\tan u \tag{4.55}$$

It can be shown that

$$\frac{\sin(u-u')}{\cos u.\cos u'} = \frac{a+b}{a}\tan u \tag{4.56}$$

and

$$\frac{\sin(u-u')}{\cos u.\cos u'} = \frac{a-b}{a}\tan u \tag{4.57}$$

Dividing (4.57) by (4.56)

$$\sin(u-u') = \frac{a-b}{a+b}\sin(u+u') \tag{4.58}$$

This equation will have the maximum value when $\sin(u+u')=1$, corresponding to $(u+u')=90°$. There will be four such directions located one in each of the four quadrants of the coordinate system defined by the principal directions. If an angle is composed of two such directions, so that each side of the angle has been deflected through the maximum amount, we have a quantity called the *maximum angular deformation*, ω, at the point. It follows from (4.58) that

$$\sin\frac{\omega}{2} = \frac{a-b}{a+b} \tag{4.59}$$

and this is the formula which is most commonly used to find this parameter for any point in a map projection.

Summary of the main conclusions derived in Chapter 4

This chapter has contained some fairly difficult mathematical ideas and unfamiliar concepts. To help the beginner to keep track of the argument it is worth summarising the main conclusions which have so far been obtained.

(1) It is necessary to distinguish two kinds of scale on any map projection.
(2) The principal scale, μ_0, is the nominal scale of the map which can only be preserved at all points in all directions on the curved surface of the globe. On the map the principal scale can only be preserved at certain points or along certain lines.
(3) These are known as points or lines of zero distortion.
(4) The principal scale is allocated a numerical value of $1\cdot0$.
(5) The *particular scales*, μ, at any point on a map projection are those defined for infinitely short arcs in different directions. These are expressed as a multiple of μ_0.
(6) Particular scales vary throughout the map according to position and direction.
(7) Two particular scales through any point can always be determined. These are the particular *scale along the meridian*, h, and that *along the parallel*, k.
(8) Tissot's Theorem demonstrates that at every point there are two orthogonal *principal directions* which are perpendicular on both the globe and the map.
(9) An infinitely small circle on the globe will be represented on the map by an infinitely small ellipse, known as *Tissot's Indicatrix* or the *ellipse of distortion*.
(10) The axes of the ellipse of distortion correspond to the two principal directions and the maximum and minimum particular scales, a and b, at any point occur in these directions.
(11) These particular scales may be evaluated if h and k are known, together with the angle θ' made by the intersection of the meridian and parallel on the map.
(12) From the Second Theorem of Apollonius it is possible to derive the *area scale*, or *exaggeration of area*, p, which relates the areas of infinitely small figures on the map to the corresponding figure on the globe.
(13) It is also possible to evaluate the *maximum angular deformation*, ω, from the maximum and minimum particular scales at a point.

The special properties of map projections

Despite the fact that the principal scale can only be preserved along certain lines or at certain points in a projection; despite the fact that the particular scales are variables in both position and direction on the map, it is possible to create certain special combinations of particular scale which can be maintained throughout an entire map projection with the exception of the singular points where Tissot's theory does not apply. These arrangements of the particular scales may be called the *special properties of a map projection* (some writers call them *the* properties) which may be defined as *the properties of a projection which arise from the mutual relationship between the maximum and minimum particular scales at any point and which are preserved at all except the singular points of a map*.

There are about eleven different arrangements of the particular scales which may be regarded as special properties (Ref. 3) but only four of these are really important. These are the properties of:

(1) Conformality
(2) Equivalence
(3) Equidistance
(4) Minimum-error representation

Conformality

A conformal map projection is one in which

$$a = b \qquad (4.60)$$

at all points on the map. It follows that if this condition can be satisfied, the infinitely small circle on the surface of the globe will always project as a circle on the plane. Moreover, since the maximum angular deformation is determined from the relationship $(a-b)/(a+b)$ in equation (4.59) it follows that where a and b are equal, $\omega = 0°$. Thus a conformal map projection has no angular deformation, or, to paraphrase part of Tissot's Theorem quoted on page 64, *angles are preserved*. This is the essential and important special property of a conformal projection. It is a desirable requirement for any map which is to be used for measurement of angles. Hence conformal projections are used as the bases for navigation charts, topographical maps and military maps.

The fact that an infinitesimally small circle on the globe remains a circle on the projection implies a further property of a conformal map, namely that the shapes of objects are also preserved. However, this statement must be accepted only with certain reservations. The condition expressed in equation (4.60) is not equivalent to the statement that $a = b = 1$. Conformality can only be obtained at the expense of increasing the particular scales by the same amount. This means that the area scale increases according to the square of the particular scale. Hence we discover the paradox that although a conformal map provides a good representation of shape for a small area round every point on the map, the rapid increase in particular scales away from the points or lines of zero distortion make the projections less satisfactory for representing the shapes of large terrestrial features like continents or oceans.

The alternative name for this property is *orthomorphism*, but use of this term has tended to divert attention from correct angular representation to the much less important consideration of shape. In mathematics a *conformal transformation* means a transformation where every angle is transformed into another angle of equal size. This is precisely what we mean by (4.60) and therefore we prefer to use the adjective conformal rather than the misleading word orthomorphic.

It follows that in any projection where $\omega = 0°$ that all graticule intersections will be orthogonal. This must be true irrespective of the nature of the mapped parallels and meridians. If a conformal projection is composed of curved parallels or meridians, it is necessary to imagine two tangents, one to each line, drawn at the graticule intersection. These two tangents are perpendicular to one another. The converse does not necessarily apply. Thus a map projection in which the parallels and meridians all intersect at right angles is not necessarily a conformal projection.

Equivalence

An equal-area map is one in which

$$a.b = 1 \qquad (4.61)$$

It therefore follows that

$$a = 1/b \qquad (4.62)$$

and

$$b = 1/a \qquad (4.63)$$

or the maximum and minimum particular scales are reciprocals of one another. It follows that although the ellipses of distortion may have considerable eccentricity,

F

they have uniform area. Moreover the principle of equivalence may also be maintained for areas of finite size and an important aspect in the derivation of equal-area map projections of different classes has been the ability to argue that the whole or part of the generating globe is mapped into a square, rectangle, circle, ellipse or other geometrical figure having the same area as the required part of the globe.

The equal-area map projections are most important in the field of distribution mapping of statistical variables. For example, if it is required to map population, agricultural or industrial statistics this may be done by using symbols of equal size, each to denote a particular quantity of the variate. An important aspect of interpretation of such a map is the visual impression of *density* of population, agricultural production or industrial output as this varies from place to place in a country or continent. If the variable is plotted on an equal-area map projection this pattern of density of distribution has some meaning but if it is plotted on a projection in which areas are much exaggerated the map can be extremely misleading. We may also wish to measure the area occupied by some distribution, such as a category of land use. Then a projection in which there is no exaggeration of areas is needed.

It should be noted that the properties of conformality and equivalence are mutually incompatible. *A map projection may be conformal; it may be equal-area, but it can never be both.* It follows from equations (4.62) and (4.63) that to create such a projection would necessitate putting $a=b=1$. This would mean that the principal scale is preserved at all points and in all directions and we have already seen that this can only be obtained on the curved surface of a globe.

Equidistance

The third important mathematical property which may be satisfied is that one particular scale is made equal to the principal scale throughout the map. For example, we may make the meridional scale

$$h = 1 \cdot 0 \tag{4.64}$$

thereby creating a map projection in which all the parallels intersect all the meridians at a separation corresponding to the arc distance between the parallels on the globe.

The alternative is to make $k=1$ throughout the map. This property arises incidentally in the derivation of certain map projections but it is less valuable than preserving the principal scale along great circle arcs.

Since we have specified that one particular scale is equal to unity it follows that equidistance is incompatible with both conformality and equivalence. Clearly if $a=1$ in an equidistant map projection, the conditions specified by either (4.60) or (4.61) would lead once more to the perfect but impossible projection.

Equidistance is a less valuable property than either conformality or equivalence because it is seldom desirable to have a map in which distances may be measured correctly in only one direction. However an equidistant map is a useful compromise between the conformal and equal-area maps. Thus the area scale of an equidistant map increases more slowly than that of a conformal map. The maximum angular deformation of an equidistant map increases more slowly than that of an equal-area map. Consequently equidistant map projections are often used in atlas maps, strategic planning maps and similar representations of large parts of the Earth's surface where it is not essential to preserve either of the other properties.

Minimum-error representation

The three special properties which have been described are mutually exclusive of one another. Minimum-error representation is a rather different kind of property because it may be used with some other special property. Thus we may have a *minimum-error conformal projection* of a particular class. However, minimum-error representation can also be considered as a special property in its own right, giving rise to what may be termed an 'absolute minimum-error projection'. The idea is partly described by the archaic term 'balance of errors' used by Airy to describe the minimum-error projection called after him. We already know that a and b are the maximum and minimum particular scales at any point. Since we specify that the principal scale is equal to unity, it follows that the *scale errors* along the principal directions through a point may be expressed respectively as

$$e_1 = 1 - a \qquad (4.65)$$

$$e_2 = 1 - b \qquad (4.66)$$

The idea implicit in any minimum-error map projection is to balance these errors so that *the sums of the squares of the scale errors throughout the map as a whole are a minimum value.*

For example it is necessary to find expressions for (r, θ) which satisfy the condition that

$$\int_{z=0}^{z=\beta} \{ (1-a)^2 + (1-b)^2 \} \sin z . dz = \text{minimum} \qquad (4.67)$$

It is necessary to specify the limits of the area to be mapped in which these conditions must be satisfied. Thus (4.67) must be expressed as a *definite integral* which indicates the size of the area to be mapped. In (4.67) we have taken the simplest case of a map with a circular boundary and point of zero distortion at the centre of this circle. Then the definite integral indicates summation of the sums of the squares of the scale errors at all points from the centre ($z=0$) to the edge of the map ($z=\beta$). Clearly the expression of the minimum-error conditions for many projections is algebraically quite difficult to follow.

The practical use and interpretation of the distortion characteristics of a map projection

In this chapter we have derived algebraic expressions for the four important particular scales at any point. The additional parameters p and ω may be derived from these particular scales and the special properties of any map projection are also defined in terms of the particular scales and distortion parameters.

Table 3

Particular scales and distortion parameters for the Cylindrical Equal-area Projection (Lambert)

Latitude φ	Particular scales $k=a$	$h=b$	Area scale p	Maximum angular deformation ω
0°	1·0000	1·0000	1·0000	0°
15°	1·0353	0·9659	1·0000	3° 58′
30°	1·1547	0·8660	1·0000	16° 25′
45°	1·4142	0·7071	1·0000	38° 57′
60°	2·0000	0·5000	1·0000	73° 44′
75°	3·8637	0·2588	1·0000	121° 57′
90°	∞	0·0000	—	180°

Coordinate Systems and Map Projections

It is now desirable to show what value these characteristics have in helping us to describe a particular map projection. Even more important, they give us some clues about a logical and systematic way of choosing which map projection is suitable for a particular purpose.

Usually the values for the particular scales are calculated for a fairly widely spaced graticule, for example, 10° or 15° of latitude and longitude on a world or hemispheric map. There is no reason why the information should not be obtained for every 1° of latitude and longitude apart from the sheer labour of computation but if it is only done for every 20° or 30° some salient features of a given projection may be missed. The results of the computations may be listed in a form such as is illustrated in Table 3.

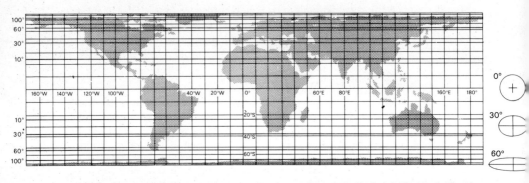

Figure 48 World map based upon the normal aspect of the Cylindrical Equal-area Projection (Lambert) (No. 1 in Appendix I) showing conventional representation of Tissot's Indicatrix for the parallels 0°, 30° and 60° and also showing isograms for maximum angular deformation (ω) for 10°, 30°, 60° and 100°.

This projection is illustrated by Fig. 48. Although we have not yet defined what we mean by a cylindrical projection, it can be seen that the world map is represented by a rectangular outline and both the parallels and meridians are represented by families of parallel straight lines. We might conduct interpretation of Table 3 in the following fashion:

(1) *We look for evidence of the location of the lines or points of zero distortion.* Since the principal scale is conventionally expressed as $\mu_0 = 1\cdot 0000$, we look for values corresponding to this in the columns for the particular scales. We find that both scales are equal to unity in the first line, corresponding to $\varphi = 0°$. We also note that $p = 1\cdot 0000$ and $\omega = 0°$. This confirms that the principal scale is preserved along the Equator which is therefore a line of zero distortion. We can also see that the particular scales do not equal unity elsewhere. Consequently the Equator is the only line of zero distortion.

(2) *We look for evidence about special properties.* This must be a relationship established for the whole projection. From the preceding section it is likely to be of the forms $a = b$, $a = 1/b$, $h = 1\cdot 0000$ or $k = 1\cdot 0000$. A conformal map projection will have $\omega = 0°$ throughout and an equal-area map projection will have $p = 1\cdot 0000$ throughout. We find the evidence that this is an equal-area projection from the constant value of p in column 4 of the table.

(3) *We look for evidence concerning the principal directions.* In this particular example the parallels and meridians form an orthogonal network and therefore the principal directions coincide with the graticule. Thus $k=a$ and $h=b$. It follows that a projection of this sort is much easier to study than one whose principal directions do not coincide with the graticule.

(4) *We look for evidence for singular points, characterised by particular scales equal to zero or infinity.* This is shown in the last line of Table 3, where $\varphi=90°$. Here $a=\infty$, $b=0\cdot0000$, p is indeterminate and the maximum angular deformation $\omega=180°$. All these clues lead us to suppose that the one-to-one correspondence of points does not apply at the geographical poles. This is confirmed in Fig. 48 by the representation of both poles by means of lines which are equal in length to the Equator.

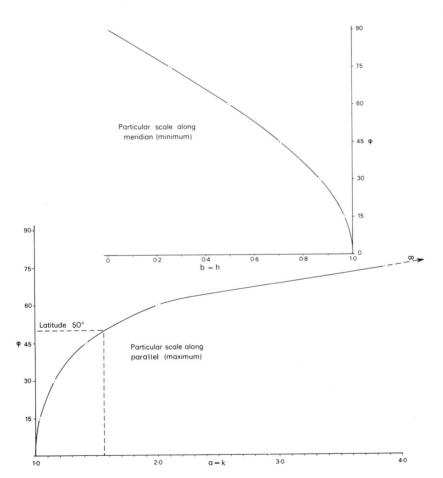

Figure 49 Graphs showing the variations in particular scales with latitude for the Cylindrical Equal-area Projection, illustrated by Fig. 48 and derived from the numerical values for the particular scales in Table 3, p. 71.

(5) *We may study the variation in particular scale with latitude.* This is done quite simply by plotting graphs for $a=f(\varphi)$ and $b=f(\varphi)$, as shown in Fig. 49. Each of the numerical values in the table have been determined for the infinitely small ellipse located at the intersections of the parallels with a meridian. Hence each numerical value refers to a point on the projection. If the map is a continuous representation of the spherical surface, as in the present example, and there are no gaps or interruptions such as are illustrated by Fig. 31, we are justified in making the interpretation that particular scales vary regularly and continuously between the numerical values which have been determined for discrete points. For example, if $k=1\cdot4142$ in latitude 45° and $k=2\cdot0000$ in latitude 60°, we may interpolate from the graph an approximate value $k=1\cdot55$ for latitude 50°. Simple graphs showing the particular scales plotted against latitude are very useful in assessing the relative merits of several different map projections which might be chosen for a particular job. The gradient and nature of each curve compared with others gives a useful visual appreciation about which projection provides least distortion in a particular part of the map. The same kind of graphs may also be drawn for p and ω.

(6) *We may also use spatial representation of the ellipses of distortion.* Thus, if we plot a and b to some arbitrary but convenient scale we can construct the ellipses corresponding to different points on the projection. These diagrams provide a generalised picture of deformation from place to place, as shown in Fig. 48. Several points about interpretation ought to be demonstrated. The first is that on the Equator the ellipse of distortion is a circle of radius $1\cdot0$ on the scale which has been adopted for the ellipses. This again confirms that the Equator is a line of zero distortion. Secondly, the ellipses vary in eccentricity but appear to be all of similar area. This is confirmed by the fact that this is an equal-area projection, characterised by $p=1\cdot0000$.

(7) *We may plot a series of isograms indicating constant values for any single parameter.* In this example, the variable selected for illustration by this means is the maximum angular deformation. By determining the positions of the isograms for $\omega=10°$, 30° etc., the way in which maximum angular deformation increases as latitude increases may be illustrated. The use of shading or patterns to emphasise the variations is also valuable.

In other map projections, where the particular scales vary with both latitude and longitude, information such as has been given in Table 3 would refer to a single meridian. Thus a table for 15° graticule intersections for the whole world might require up to 338 separate entries for each of the variables, a, b, p and ω.†
This kind of table is difficult to comprehend and graphical representation of the variables is practically essential. It could be done by showing ellipses at every graticule intersection, as shown in Fig. 50, but this is a laborious way of doing it.

---

† The actual number of entries depends upon the symmetry of the projection about certain parallels and meridians. Some, like the Cylindrical projections, are symmetrical about the Equator so that the tabulated values are valid for both hemispheres. A projection which is symmetrical about both the Equator and its central meridian only requires tabulated values for 79 graticule intersections in the quadrant north of the Equator and east of the central meridian. See also pp. 92, 114/126.

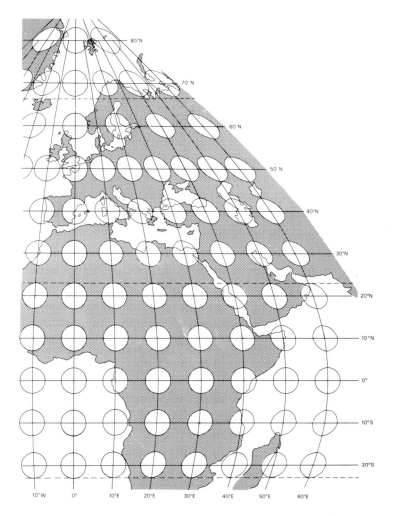

Figure 50 Part of the Sinusoidal Projection (No. 30 in Appendix I) showing diagrammatic representation of ellipses of distortion at the graticule intersections. This is an equal-area member of the Pseudocylindrical Class of projections in which the meridians are sine curves. The parallels are equally spaced along the central meridian.

Note: (1) That the ellipses along the Greenwich Meridian and Equator are circles, indicating that the principal scale is preserved along these lines.

(2) That all the ellipses have the same area, indicating that this is an equal-area projection.

(3) That there is an increasing ellipticity of the ellipses towards the north-eastern part of the map. Compare this figure with Fig. 56 (a), p. 90, in which isograms for maximum angular deformation are shown.

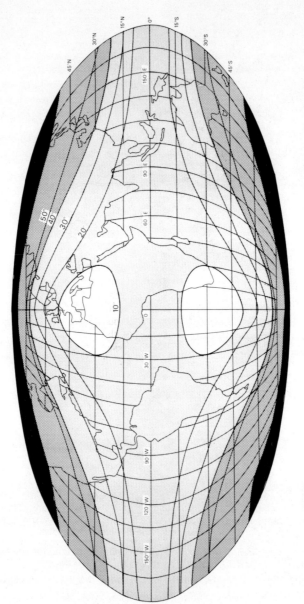

Figure 51 Mollweide's Projection for the whole World, showing isograms for maximum angular deformation, (ω), at 10°, 20°, 30°, 40° and 50°. Parts of the World map where ω > 80° are shown in black. This is an equal-area projection and therefore $p = 1·0$ throughout.

More commonly the distortion patterns are shown by means of isograms and shading. Figure 51 illustrates such a technique applied to a world map projection in which the isograms do not coincide with the graticule.

An important advantage in using these parameters to assess the distortion characteristics and relative merits of a map projection is that the parameters have been computed for the majority of useful map projections. For example, Reignier (Ref. 1) gives tables for many of the better known projections. Nevertheless it is important to note that some writers have maintained that a method of evaluation which is derived from the particular scales and therefore upon infinitesimal areas is unrealistic. Thus Hinks (Ref. 4) was critical of Tissot's methods and did not attempt to use them. This is the main reason why the methods outlined in this chapter are still little known in the English writings on map projections whereas they are commonplace in every other European language. Tobler (Ref. 5) has also made certain reservations about the validity of interpreting the distortion characteristics of map projections solely in terms of the ellipse of distortion. Both Hinks and Tobler have ignored the principle outlined in (5) above, that if *x* and *y* are continuous fuctions of φ and λ, the particular scales and derived parameters also grow in a continuous fashion and can therefore be mapped. Tobler's published alternative method, which involves the determination of the finite errors in computed triangles of different sizes in different parts of a map projection to be studied, is a more elaborate procedure which is only possible to accomplish with the aid of a large digital computer. Moreover the presentation of the results is tabular and statistical so that it is difficult to appreciate how distortion can vary from one part of a projection to another. The reader who can obtain access to the interesting *Atlas for the Selection of Map Projections* by Ginzburg and Salmanova (Ref. 6) published in Russia in 1957, will appreciate that simple graphics based upon the six variables which have been defined can be enormously helpful in deciding which projection is going to be the most useful to serve as the framework for a new map. After all, this is the chief practical reason for wishing to know about the spatial distribution of distortion in a projection. We return to this important subject in Chapter 9 where the principles of selecting a projection are considered in more detail. Theoretically it is also possible to apply the variations in particular scale as corrections to measurements of distance, angle and area made from maps. But the present author must frankly confess that he has never met anyone outside Russia who admitted to having done this.

A worked example showing how the equations in Chapter 4 may be used

After such a lengthy algebraic introduction to the theory of distortion it is desirable to demonstrate how the variables may be computed to find numerical values for the particular scales and distortion characteristics at a specific point in a projection. The example given here is for a point on the *Hammer-Aitoff Projection* (Fig. 52) in latitude 60°N, longitude 60°E. We have chosen this because the meridians and parallels are curved and do not intersect at right angles. Consequently no simplification is possible arising from the coincidence of the principal directions with the graticule and it is necessary to start by finding numerical values for *E*, *F* and *G* (Ref. 7).

The coordinates for a point on the Hammer-Aitoff Projection may be written in the form

$$x = 2\sqrt{2}\,\frac{\cos\varphi \cdot \sin\frac{1}{2}\lambda}{\sqrt{1+\cos\varphi \cdot \cos\frac{1}{2}\lambda}} \qquad (4.68)$$

$$y = \frac{\sqrt{2}.\sin \varphi}{\sqrt{1+\cos \varphi.\cos \frac{1}{2}\lambda}} \tag{4.69}$$

It is required to find the maximum and minimum particular scales for the point 60° North, 60° East and thereby determine the maximum angular deformation, ω, and confirm that this is an equal-area projection.

The first requirement is to differentiate equations (4.68) and (4.69) with respect to φ and λ. This is by far the most difficult mathematical stage and we do not expect the beginner to understand the algebraic derivation of the four following equations:

$$\frac{\partial x}{\partial \varphi} = -\sqrt{2}\,\frac{\sin \varphi.\sin \frac{1}{2}\lambda(2+\cos \varphi.\cos \frac{1}{2}\lambda)}{(1+\cos \varphi.\cos \frac{1}{2}\lambda)^{3/2}} \tag{4.70}$$

$$\frac{\partial y}{\partial \varphi} = \frac{\cos \varphi(2+\cos \varphi.\cos \frac{1}{2}\lambda)+\cos \frac{1}{2}\lambda}{\sqrt{2}(1+\cos \varphi.\cos \frac{1}{2}\lambda)^{3/2}} \tag{4.71}$$

$$\frac{\partial x}{\partial \lambda} = \frac{\cos \varphi.\cos \frac{1}{2}\lambda(2+\cos \varphi.\cos \frac{1}{2}\lambda)+\cos^2 \varphi}{\sqrt{2}(1+\cos \varphi.\cos \frac{1}{2}\lambda)^{3/2}} \tag{4.72}$$

$$\frac{\partial y}{\partial \lambda} = \frac{1}{2^{3/2}}\cdot\frac{\sin \varphi.\cos \varphi.\sin \frac{1}{2}\lambda}{(1+\cos \varphi.\cos \frac{1}{2}\lambda)^{3/2}} \tag{4.73}$$

Once these equations are available, the numerical solution is not difficult with the aid of a desk calculator. Note that the term $(2+\cos \varphi.\cos \frac{1}{2}\lambda)$ appears in three of the equations and $(1+\cos \varphi.\cos \frac{1}{2}\lambda)^{3/2}$, occurs in all four. These terms only have to be calculated once for each graticule intersection.

Substituting for $\varphi=60$, $\lambda=60$ in equations (4.70)–(4.73) provides the following values:

$$\frac{\partial x}{\partial \varphi} = -0\cdot8685$$

$$\frac{\partial y}{\partial \varphi} = 0\cdot8584$$

$$\frac{\partial x}{\partial \lambda} = 0\cdot5373$$

$$\frac{\partial y}{\partial \lambda} = 0\cdot0446$$

Then, from (4.20)

$$E = -0\cdot8685^2+0\cdot8584^2=1\cdot4911$$

and, from (4.25), the particular scale along the meridian is

$$h = \sqrt{E}=1\cdot2211$$

Similarly, from (4.22)

$$G=0\cdot5373^2+0\cdot0446^2=0\cdot2907$$

and, from (4.30), the particular scale along the parallel is

$$k = \sqrt{G}/\cos \varphi=0\cdot5391/0\cdot5=1\cdot0783$$

We obtain the third fundamental quantity, F, from (4.21), i.e.

$$F = -(0\cdot8584 \times 0\cdot0446) - (-0\cdot8685 \times 0\cdot5373)= -0\cdot4284$$

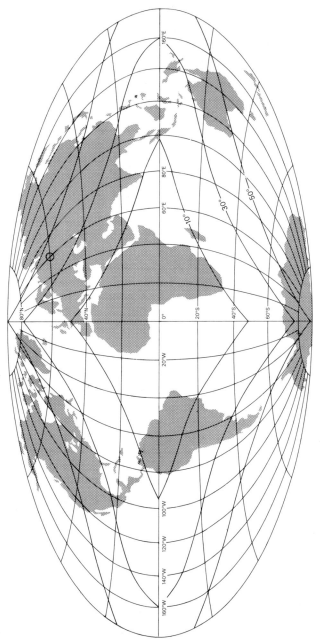

Figure 52 The Hammer-Aitoff Projection for the whole World showing isograms for maximum angular deformation, (ω), at 10°, 30° and 50°. The point in latitude 60° North, longitude 60° East indicated by means of a circle is that for which the particular scales and distortion characteristics have been determined in the worked example on pages 77–80. The Hammer-Aitoff Projection (No. 37 in Appendix I) is an equal-area member of the Polyconic Group of projections.

From (4.33),

$$\sin \theta' = F/(h.k.\cos \varphi)$$
$$= -0\cdot4284/0\cdot6584$$
$$= -0\cdot6507$$

it follows that $\cos \theta' = 0\cdot7594$.

From (4.51),

$$(a+b)^2 = h^2+k^2+2hk.\cos \theta'$$
$$= 4\cdot6536$$
$$(a+b) = 2\cdot1572$$

Similarly

$$(a-b)^2 = h^2+k^2-2hk.\cos \theta'$$
$$= 0\cdot6540$$
$$(a-b) = 0\cdot8087$$

Therefore

$$a+b = 2\cdot1572$$
$$a-b = 0\cdot8087$$

$$2a = 2\cdot9659$$
$$a = 1\cdot4830$$
$$b = 0\cdot6743$$

It follows that $ab=0\cdot999\,99$, indicating small errors in rounding off, but is close enough to $1\cdot0$ to confirm that the projection is equal-area.

Finally

$$\sin \frac{\omega}{2} = \frac{0\cdot8087}{2\cdot1572}$$

$$\frac{\omega}{2} = 22° \ 01'$$

Therefore

$$\omega = 44° \ 02'$$

We have obtained the following numerical values for the point $60°$ N, $60°$ E:

$$h = 1\cdot2211 \qquad k = 1\cdot0783$$
$$a = 1\cdot4836 \qquad b = 0\cdot6743$$
$$p = 0\cdot999\ 99 \qquad \omega = 44° \ 02'$$

In order to draw satisfactory isograms for ω, it would be necessary to derive these values for at least 50 points on the map. Because of the repetitive nature of this work it is best done by digital computer.

References

1 Reignier, F.: *Les Systèmes de Projection et leurs applications à la Géographie, à la Cartographie, à la Navigation, à la Topométrie, etc.*, Paris, 1957, Institut Géographique National, 2 volumes.
2 Fiala, F.: *Mathematische Kartographie*, Berlin, 1957, VEB Verlag Technik, 316 pp.
3 Maling, D. H.: 'The terminology of map projections', *International Yearbook of Cartography*, VIII, 1968, pp. 11–65.
4 Hinks, A. R.: *Map Projections*. Cambridge, 1912, The University Press, 126 pp.

5 Tobler, W. R.: *Geographical Coordinate Computations. Part II, Finite Map Projection Distortions*, 1964, The University of Michigan. Department of Geography, Technical Report No. 2. ONR Task No. 389–137.
6 Ginzburg, G. A. and Salmanova, T. D.: *Atlas dlya vybora kartograficheskikh proektsiy*. Trudy TsNIIGAiK, Vyp 110, Moscow, 1957, Geodezizdat, 240 pp.
7 Maling, D. H.: 'The Hammer-Aitoff Projection and some modifications', *Proceedings of the Cartographic Symposium held in the Department of Geography, University of Edinburgh, 21–24 September* 1962. Department of Geography, University of Glasgow, 1962, pp. 41–57.

CHAPTER 5

THE APPEARANCE, MODIFICATION AND CLASSIFICATION OF MAP PROJECTIONS

The whole subject of nomenclature of projection calls for settlement which should be on an international basis.

J. I. Craig: *The Theory of Map Projections*, 1910

Not only is the classification of projections unsatisfactory in English writings, but the nomenclature employed, both of the classification groups and of the individual projections, is in a state little short of chaotic.

L. P. Lee: *Empire Survey Review*, 1944

Introduction

Examination of the illustrations of different map projections which appear in this book indicates the great variety in the shape and detailed appearance of them. Some of the World maps are rectangular in outline, others are bounded by ellipses or more complicated curves. Some projections have rectilinear parallels or meridians; others have various combinations of curved graticule lines. In this chapter we introduce some of the terms which are commonly used to describe the *appearance* of map projections. These may be used in conjunction with distortion theory to *select* and *describe* suitable map projections for particular purposes or to *recognise* the projection used for a particular map.

The cartographer may have to decide which is the most suitable projection to use for an atlas map. This is a subject which we examine in detail in Chapter 9, pp. 159–82. The user of that atlas may have to make a reasoned guess about what projection has been employed if the cartographer has not done his job properly and has failed to indicate this information, or has described it in unfamiliar terms. The cartographer can communicate with the map user if both understand the same technical terms but confusion or misinterpretation result if they do not. Unfortunately the subject of map projections is embarrassingly rich in words which mean the same thing. Therefore the beginner who is already struggling to understand many new concepts is also confronted with and confused by many unnecessary alternative technical terms. Some of these are synonymous, such as the words 'autogonal' and 'orthomorphic' to mean *conformal* or the use of 'authalic' and 'orthembadic' instead of *equal-area*. Only two of the six words are necessary.† On the other hand, there are occasions when different words are needed to make fine but important distinctions. The different definitions for *azimuth* and *bearing* given in Chapter 3, pp. 36–37 illustrate the need for more than one word to describe angles on the spherical surface and the plane.

In many respects the richness of the terminology of map projections should create fewer problems than formerly. In 1964, the International Cartographic Association established a Commission to study the standardisation of technical

---

† Where alternative words are introduced, the preferred is given in italics and the unsuitable word is placed in inverted commas.

terms. This led to the creation of a British Working Group on Terminology and the publication of the *Glossary of Technical Terms in Cartography* (Ref. 1) in 1966. The present writer assisted this Working Group in their deliberations about map projections and published a specialised multilingual glossary of usage in the study of map projections in 1968 (Ref. 2). Both of these works indicate the preferred usage for future English contributions to the subject and these words are used throughout the present book.

In order to employ a satisfactory and succinct terminology we must also create some sort of classification system. The total number of map projections which can be described is infinitely great. From this population about four hundred projections have been described and used for some purpose or another. In order to distinguish between them it is desirable to group together those map projections which possess similar attributes or have related characteristics into some kind of ordered system. The student of the subject can then visualise how each projection is related to the others; to appreciate where each belongs within this vast collection of different kinds of transformation. Moreover a series of classification terms is helpful in giving each map projection a name or title which is more explanatory than merely calling it after the name of its author, or the title of the map, book or atlas in which it was first used.

In some respects the problem of recognising and giving a distinctive label to a map projection is analogous to the way of uniquely identifying the inhabitants of a small Welsh town. In Wales the number of surnames is limited to a handful, like Davies, Evans, Jones, Thomas and Williams. There are also few christian names. Thus to identify David Jones, the baker, and distinguish him from David Jones, the policeman, and all the other David Jones living in the town, it is necessary to introduce a third, descriptive, method of recognition ('Jones-the-bread' or 'Dai-book-and-pencil') which give apposite, poetical and frequently scandalous descriptions of the occupation, physical peculiarities or behaviour of each inhabitant. Just as three levels of recognition are needed in Wales, three methods of description and classification are required to identify a map projection. We will call these:

Aspect   Property   Class

The appearance and recognition of map projections

The following map projections are illustrated in this book:

Aitoff-Wagner Projection	Fig. 5, p. 6
Stereographic Projection	Fig. 7, p. 10
Mollweide's Projection	Fig. 10, p. 13 and Fig. 51, p. 76
Polyconic Projection	Fig. 32, p. 53
Cylindrical Equal-area Projection	Fig. 48, p. 72
Hammer-Aitoff Projection	Fig. 52, p. 79
Oblique Aspect Azimuthal Equidistant Projection	Fig. 53, p. 85
Transverse Aspect Cylindrical Equal-area Projection	Fig. 54, p. 87
Oblique Aspect Cylindrical Equal-area Projection	Fig. 55, p. 88
Sinusoidal Projection (different aspects)	Fig. 56, p. 90–91
Recentred Eckert VI Projection	Fig. 57, p. 96
Briesemeister's Projection	Fig. 61, p. 113
Normal Aspect Azimuthal Equal-area Projection	Fig. 75, p. 143
Transverse Aspect Azimuthal Equal-area Projection	Fig. 76, p. 145
Oblique Aspect Azimuthal Equal-area Projection	Fig. 77, p. 145
Equidistant Conical Projection with one standard parallel	Fig. 80, p. 150
Equidistant Conical Projection with two standard parallels	Fig. 81, p. 151

The reader will find it necessary to refer to these in following the discussion presented in this chapter.

This list indicates some of the methods which are commonly used to name individual projections. The meaning of some of the words occurring in these titles will become apparent as the reader proceeds. But before we consider the descriptive terminology and classification we must ask a simple question '*How do we recognise a map projection?*'

We offer here seven diagnostic features of a map projection which should be examined. We invite the reader to look at the World graticules listed above and make notes about the seven features as they appear on each map.

(1) Is the World mapped as a continuous feature or are there breaks in the continuity of the map?

Most of the projections illustrated in this book represent the whole Earth on a continuous map, but we find exceptions in Figs. 7, 57, 103 and also in Fig. 31 on page 52.

(2) What kind of geometrical figure is formed by the outline of the World or hemispherical map?

The examples illustrated include rectangular, circular, elliptical and more complicated outlines.

(3) How are the continents and oceans arranged with respect to the outline and axes of the map?

Many of the projections illustrated provide what we might loosely call a 'conventional' view of the World which is one to which we are accustomed because it has been used so many times in atlases, books and newspapers. It is the World map in which the Equator and Greenwich Meridian form axes and the geographical poles are situated at either end of the central meridian on the edges of the map. If the conventional arrangement is not apparent can you give any reason why this is not so? Possibly some meridian other than Greenwich has been used as the central meridian. Possibly the geographical poles are not located on the top and bottom edges of the map.

(4) Are the parallels and meridians rectilinear or curved?

(5) Do the parallels and meridians intersect everywhere at right angles or do oblique graticule intersections occur in some parts of the map?

(6) Are curved parallels or meridians composed of circular or higher order curves? If the arcs are circular are they also concentric?

(7) Is the spacing between successive parallels and meridians uniform or variable? If they are not uniformly equidistant does the separation between the parallels increase or decrease from the Equator towards the poles? Does the separation between meridians increase or decrease from the centre of the map towards its edges?

All of these variables can help us to identify a map projection and most of them will be used in some way or another as the basis of their classification. The appearance is of less value in helping us to decide the special property of a projection for visual inspection often only provides negative evidence. Thus we can state that a map projection with oblique graticule intersections *cannot* be conformal but this does not mean that all map projections having orthogonal graticules are necessarily con-

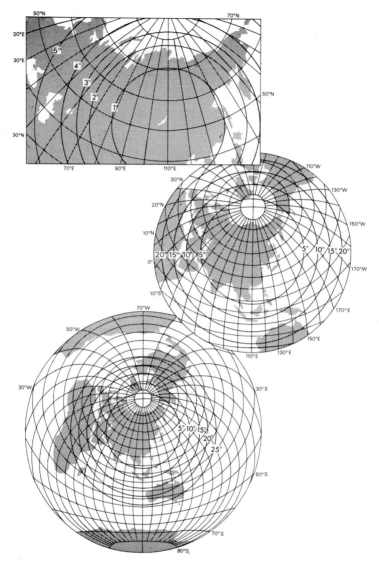

Figure 53 Three different versions of the same aspect of the Azimuthal Equidistant Projection (No. 11 in Appendix I). The bottom figure shows most of the World represented by means of an oblique aspect of this projection with the origin in latitude 52° N, longitude 110° E. The centre figure shows an hemisphere on the same projection and same origin. This is the best known way in which the Azimuthal projections are used. The top figure illustrates how the central portion of an azimuthal projection may also be used to depict a smaller area at a larger scale. In this example it is for an atlas map of the U.S.S.R. Note that this kind of use may create difficulties of identification of the projection used because the characteristic circular outline of an Azimuthal projection of an hemisphere is truncated by the neat lines of the map. Each of these maps shows isograms for maximum angular deformation (ω). On the two smaller scale maps the isograms are at intervals of 5°, 10°, 15°, 20° and 25°. Greater amounts of angular deformation on the World map are omitted for greater clarity. The larger scale map of the U.S.S.R. shows isograms for ω at 1° intervals to 5°.

formal. The way in which the parallels are spaced is often helpful in making a more positive guess about special property. Since the area on the Earth enclosed between two parallels and two meridians becomes smaller towards the poles, a map projection with small exaggeration in area must also represent this relationship. Comparison of Figs. 48 and 83 indicates that the first of the projections meets this requirement whereas the second does not.

The difficulty of recognition is greatly increased if only part of the World is shown on a map, which is arbitrarily bounded by the neat lines. Fig. 53 illustrates this principle with reference to a map of the USSR. Clearly the absence of the distinctive circular outlines of the World or hemispherical maps make it more difficult to identify the projection on which the largest scale map is based.

The fundamental properties of map projections

A further feature of many of the map projections illustrated in this book is the representation on them of isograms for equal values of maximum angular deformation, ω, of area scale, p, or particular scale μ. This information is not normally shown on maps produced for other purposes but it provides an alternative method of studying the merits of different projections. Using the methods of interpretation of the distortion characteristics of any map projection, outlined in Chapter 4, pp. 71–77, we may look again at some of these maps to study:

(1) The nature of the point or line of zero distortion and the location of it with respect to the World or hemispherical outline.
(2) The location of singular points on the map and how these appear. Usually a singular point is mapped as a line but sometimes it is removed infinitely far from the origin of the projection so that the map has no real boundary.
(3) The characteristic patterns formed by the isograms for ω, p or μ.

We may call these the *fundamental properties* of the projection. Look for similarity of pattern of different map projections (e.g. the comparison of Fig. 48, p. 72 with Fig. 83, p. 154 shows that both have rectilinear isograms which are parallel with the Equator). Look for precisely the same pattern appearing on maps with quite different graticules (e.g. Figs. 48, 54 and 55, or Figs. 75, 76 and 77).

The first comparison indicates that there are projections with related fundamental properties though different special properties. This suggests that they may serve as a basis for classification. The second comparison indicates that *the fundamental properties of a projection are independent of the graticule.*

We investigate the fundamental properties of three well-known classes of map projection through a description of them in these terms. This introduces us to the three collective names *Azimuthal*, *Cylindrical* and *Conical*, all of which figured in the titles of the map projections listed on page 83. In these descriptions we deliberately refrain from referring to the elements of the graticule (Equator, poles, parallels and meridians) because we wish to demonstrate that the three fundamental properties are always satisfied by all members of each class of projection, whereas the appearance of the maps may be quite different.

Azimuthal Projections are also sometimes called 'Zenithal Projections'. We prefer to use the first name, which has some meaning, and discourage use of the second, which has none. Some examples of Azimuthal Projections are illustrated by Figs. 7, 53, 75, 76 and 77.

These projections may be imagined as the transformation to a projection plane which is tangential to the generating globe, as illustrated in Fig. 37, p. 56, or intersecting the spherical surface, as in Fig. 40, p. 57. We consider the first example here.

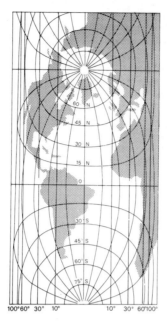

Figure 54 The transverse aspect of the Cylindrical Equal-area Projection (showing only part of the World), in which the line of zero distortion is the meridian 45° W and its antimeridian 135° E. The map shows isograms for maximum angular deformation (ω) at 10°, 30°, 60° and 100°. These are identical to the corresponding isograms shown in Fig. 48 on p. 72.

There is one point of zero distortion, corresponding to the point where the two surfaces meet and therefore all such projections have the common property that angles, or azimuths, are correctly represented at the central point. This indicates the reason for our preference for the word Azimuthal to be the collective name for this class of map projection.

The characteristic outline of an Azimuthal map of the hemisphere and, if possible, the whole World, is circular and since there is a single point of zero distortion at the centre of this circle, the particular scales increase radially outwards from it in all directions. Consequently the distortion isograms are also circular and concentric from the origin. The singular point of some Azimuthal projections is the antipodal point of the origin and this is mapped as the bounding circle of the World map. There are, however, some Azimuthal projections which can only be used to map smaller portions of the sphere because the singular points occur nearer the origin.

Cylindrical Projections are illustrated by Figs. 48, 54, 55 and 83. These projections may be imagined as the transformation to the plane if this is wrapped round the sphere in the form of a tangent cylinder, as illustrated by Fig. 35, p. 55. Ignoring the alternative possibility of the secant cylinder (Fig. 38) there is a single line of zero distortion corresponding to the great circle of contact and this is *always represented on the map by a straight line*. Singular points occur at 90° distance from the line of zero distortion on either side of it and these points are mapped as straight lines which are both parallel to it and of equal length. Consequently the character-

Coordinate Systems and Map Projections

istic outline for a World map on a Cylindrical projection is rectangular. Distortion isograms are always rectilinear and parallel to the line of zero distortion.

Conical Projections are also sometimes called 'Conic Projections'. We prefer the use of the first name because the word 'conic' has a different meaning in mathematics (the conic sections) which is totally unrelated to the cartographic usage. Some examples of Conical projections are illustrated by Figs. 80, 81 and 84. These projections may be imagined as the transformation to the plane if this is wrapped round the globe in the form of a cone, as illustrated by Fig. 36, p. 56. Ignoring the alternative possibility of the secant cone, illustrated by Fig. 39, p. 57, we have a single line of zero distortion corresponding to the small circle of contact and this is *always represented on the map by a circular arc*. The outline of the hemispherical map is fan-shaped. If the projection is extended far enough to include singular points, these are also mapped as circular arcs parallel to the line of zero distortion. The distortion isograms on Conical projections are also circular arcs concentric with the line of zero distortion.

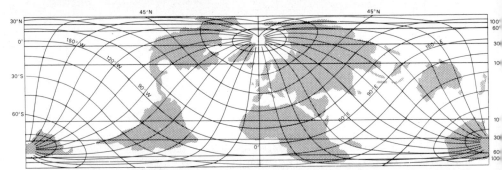

Figure 55 The oblique aspect of the Cylindrical Equal-area Projection, in which the line of zero distortion is the great circle passing through the points latitude 45° N, longitude 0° and latitude 45° S, longitude 180°. The map shows isograms for maximum angular deformation (ω) at 10°, 30°, 60° and 100°. These are identical to the corresponding isograms in Fig. 48 on p. 72 and Fig. 54 on p. 87.

The aspect of a map projection

In order to test the validity of these statements, the reader should study the three different versions of the Azimuthal Equal-area Projection illustrated by Figs. 75, 76 and 77 and the three different versions of the Cylindrical Equal-area Projection in Figs. 48, 54 and 55. Reference should also be made to Fig. 56, pp. 90–91 which illustrates seven different versions of the *Sinusoidal Projection*, a member of the *Pseudocylindrical* class, as yet undefined.

Each of the three Azimuthal Projections have the same principal scale and are therefore bounded by circles of equal radius. Figs. 48 and 55 for the Cylindrical Equal-area Projection are similarly of identical dimensions, but Fig. 54 is shorter in length because it does not show the whole World. Similarly all seven versions of the Sinusoidal Projection have identical dimensions, as defined by the lengths of the Equator and central meridian which are the axes of symmetry in Fig. 56 (a).

Thus every version of each projection may be regarded as having an identical outline. Similarly, the patterns of distortion isograms are the same for each projection. On the other hand the appearance of the parallels and meridians and therefore the continental outlines are different on every map.

We use the word *aspect* to indicate the appearance of the graticule. In much English writing on map projections the alternative word employed is 'case'. But the word *aspect* emphasises the essential ingredients of view and appearance, whereas the word 'case' does not. Moreover it has many other kinds of unrelated usage in medicine, law, travel and grammar. In order to use a systematic method of defining the different aspects of map projections it is desirable to relate the appearance of the graticule to the fundamental properties of them. We find it convenient to consider the threefold subdivision into

(1) The Normal Aspect
(2) The Transverse Aspect
(3) The Oblique Aspect

The Normal Aspect

Inspection of each group of illustrations of the same projection indicates that one of them is geometrically simpler than the others. Thus Fig. 48 has a rectilinear network of parallels and meridians, whereas Figs. 54 and 55 both show more complicated patterns of curved parallels and meridians. Moreover in Fig. 48 the distortion isograms coincide with parallels of latitude whereas in both Figs. 54 and 55 the isograms intersect the graticule. In Fig. 75, the geographical pole is at the centre of the map, coinciding, therefore, with the point of zero distortion. In this aspect of an Azimuthal projection the meridians are rectilinear and the parallels are concentric circles. Moreover the distortion isograms coincide with parallels of latitude. Figs. 76 and 77 indicate more complicated relationships between the isograms and the graticule. In Fig. 56 (a), the longer axis of the Sinusoidal Projection is represented by the Equator and the shorter axis by the central meridian. The principal scale is preserved along both of these axes, hence the asymptotic pattern of distortion isograms for ω illustrated in this map. We note that all the parallels are represented by parallel straight lines so that this version of the projection is simpler than any of the diagrams 56 (b)–56 (g). We call this the *Normal Aspect* of a projection because there is a direct relationship between the fundamental properties and the graticule.

The Transverse Aspect

We now consider the aspect of the three projections illustrated by Figs. 54, 56 (b) and 76. In the example of the Cylindrical Equal-area Projection, the central axis of the projection has become a meridian and this is the line of zero distortion. The singular points are the two points on the Equator 90° distant from the central meridian and these are mapped as two equidistant parallel lines of the same length. Thus the fundamental shape of the projection is retained, together with precisely the same pattern of distortion isograms which appeared in the normal aspect. The graticule is more complicated but we can see that it is symmetrical about both the central meridian and the Equator.

The example of the Azimuthal Equal-area Projection, shown in Fig. 76, indicates that the point of zero distortion has been selected on the Equator. This and the central meridian are represented by straight lines which are also two axes of symmetry.

Fig. 56 (b) illustrates the corresponding member of the group of Sinusoidal versions. The longer axis of the projection is a meridian together with its antimeridian. The Equator is formed by two curves which can be seen, by careful comparison of the two maps Figs. 56 (a) and 56 (b), to correspond to the two meridians 90° from the central meridian of the normal aspect. There are two axes of symmetry which are the two axes of the projection.

These versions may be called the *Transverse Aspect* of each projection. The term *Equatorial Aspect* is also used for this version of an Azimuthal projection.

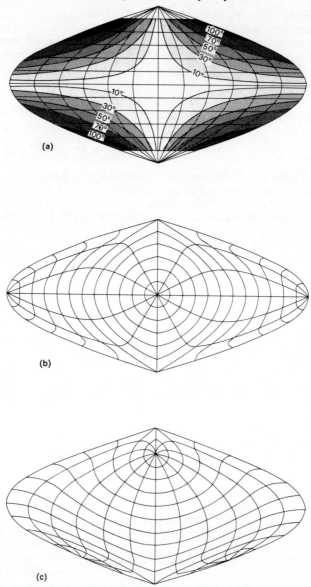

Figure 56 Seven different aspects of the Sinusoidal Projection (after Tobler). Figure 56 (a) is the normal aspect of the projection (No. 30 in Appendix I). This is an equal-area pseudocylindrical projection in which the parallels are equidistantly spaced and the meridians are sine curves. The map shows a 15° graticule and isograms for maximum angular deformation (ω) at 10°, 30°, 50°, 70° and 100°. The other examples, 56 (b) to 56 (g) represent transverse and oblique aspect versions of the same projection, each with the same 15° graticule.

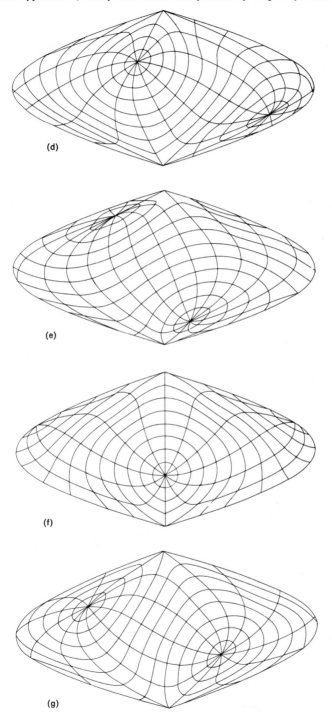

(d)

(e)

(f)

(g)

The Oblique Aspect

The third aspect is shown in Figs. 55, 77 and Fig. 56 (c)–(g). The large number of different versions illustrated in Fig. 56 indicates that there are limitless possibilities of variation. In the Cylindrical Equal-area Projection, the line of zero distortion, which is still the straight line forming the longer axis of the rectangle, corresponds to the great circle passing through the two points in latitude 45° N, longitude 0° and latitude 45° S, longitude 180°. The other axis of the projection is represented in part by the Greenwich Meridian and in part by the antimeridian, 180°. There are two singular points, in latitude 45° N, longitude 180° and latitude 45° S, longitude 0° which, as before, are mapped as parallel straight lines to form the two longer sides of the rectangle. The pattern of distortion isograms is the same as for the normal and transverse aspects of the projection. The graticule is symmetrical about only one axis, namely the central meridian.

Figure 77 illustrates this version of the Azimuthal Equal-area Projection with the origin in latitude 40° N, longitude 30° W. All the parallels and meridians are curved with the exception of the rectilinear central meridian which represents the single axis of symmetry.

The corresponding examples for the Sinusoidal Projection are shown by Figs. 56 (c) and (f). These show two different points of origin, the first in latitude 30° N and the second in 60° N. In both examples the central meridian is straight and forms an axis of symmetry. The remaining three examples, Fig. 56 (d), (e) and (g), are not symmetrical about a central meridian and should be referred to as *Skew Oblique* projections.

We have described the three aspects of these map projections in detail because we will find that this is an extremely important concept with considerable practical applications, not only for the design of World or hemispherical maps, as illustrated here, but also for maps of individual countries, as indicated by Fig. 53 and other examples described in Chapter 9. We repeat the principle that the only difference between a map projection in its different aspects is the pattern of the parallels and meridians and therefore in the location and appearance of the continents and oceans. The fundamental properties of the class of projection and the special properties of the projection itself remain unaltered. Thus we may think of the basic outline of a World map as being a fixed frame of reference, like the frame of a picture. Behind this frame the picture of the World can be shifted or rotated until a particular part of it occupies the central position. The patterns formed by the distortion isograms are (like cobwebs) related to the frame and not to the picture. Consequently these are not altered as the patterns of parallels and meridians are changed. It therefore follows that by careful planning of the aspect of any map we can locate the parts of the Earth which have immediate interest in a part of the projection where distortion is small. Conversely the unimportant parts of the World may be located where distortion is greater but does not materially influence interpretation of the map *for the purpose for which it was designed*. We develop these ideas further in Chapter 9, where we illustrate some practical examples.

In the description of each aspect of the projections studied we have drawn attention to the symmetry of the graticule about one or two axes. This, too, has practical significance when it is necessary to compute the coordinates of graticule intersections according to the methods described in Chapter 7. A map with a graticule having two axes of symmetry can be constructed from fewer points than a graticule with only one axis of symmetry and this, in turn is less troublesome to compute than a skew oblique projection for which the coordinates of every point in the entire graticule must be separately computed.

Modification of map projections

The selection of map projections for most practical purposes is preoccupied with methods of reducing distortion. We know, from Chapter 4, that some deformation is inevitable. Therefore we must use our ingenuity to keep it as small as possible in designing a map for a particular country and purpose. One method of doing this, just described, is to choose the aspect of a suitable projection which locates the area to be mapped in that part of the projection where distortion is least. There are, however, a variety of other techniques which may be used to reduce distortion and which transform the parent graticule to a greater or lesser extent. These are introduced at this stage in the book, but we do not make much use of them until the last three chapters. Some of the methods have immense practical value. Others are briefly described and then probably best forgotten.

The use of the word *modification* when applied to a map projection suggests a wide variety of possibilities. For example, one might argue, with a certain justification, that the change in the appearance of the graticule with change of aspect should be called modification.

The present writer does not like the use of the word (Ref. 2) but no alternative term would be generally understood. The following four concepts might reasonably be understood to represent modification of a projection, though it is preferable to retain the word modified to describe the first of these.

(1) Modification through redistribution of the particular scales and the creation of more than one line of zero distortion.
(2) Transformation through the introduction of constants which create singular points on the boundary of the map.
(3) Transformation by repetition of part of a map projection giving rise to a *recentred* or 'interrupted' projection.
(4) Transformation through the combination of different map projections to give the appearance of continuity.

Modification through redistribution of the particular scales

In the brief accounts of the fundamental properties of the Azimuthal, Cylindrical and Conical projections we have referred these to the tangent plane, cylinder and cone and have ignored the alternative geometrical concepts of the secant plane, cylinder and cone illustrated by Figs. 38, 39 and 40 on p. 57. It was shown there that the effect of making the plane, cylinder or cone intersect the spherical surface is to replace the single line of zero distortion by two such lines, or to substitute a *standard circle* for the single point of zero distortion. We now investigate the significance of these changes.

On a Conical or Cylindrical map projection with a single line of zero distortion the particular scales increase outwards from this line towards the edges of the map. This is exemplified by the numerical values for the maximum and minimum particular scales of the Cylindrical Equal-area Projection given in Table 3, p. 71, and illustrated graphically in Fig. 49 (a) and (b). If the single line of zero distortion is replaced by two, which are known as *standard parallels* in the normal aspect of both Conical and Cylindrical projections, the effect upon the particular scales is as follows:

(1) *Between the standard parallels and the edges of the map* the relationship between the maximum and minimum particular scales is similar to that for the unmodified projection. Thus in all normal aspect Cylindrical Equal-area projections the particular scale along the parallel is maximum and that along the meridian is minimum.

Coordinate Systems and Map Projections

(2) *On both standard parallels the principal scale is preserved.*

(3) *Between the two standard parallels* the directions of maximum and minimum particular scales are reversed. Thus, in the normal aspect modified Cylindrical Equal-area Projection the particular scale along the meridian is maximum and that along the parallel is minimum.

We may demonstrate this principle by giving the numerical values for the particular scales and distortion characteristics for the modified Cylindrical Equal-area Projection (Behrmann) with standard parallels in latitudes 30° North and 30° South. For a modern commentary on this and related projections see Ref. 3.

Table 4

Particular scales and distortion parameters for the modified Cylindrical Equal-area Projection (Behrmann) with standard parallels at 30°N and 30°S.

Latitude	Particular scales		Area scale	Maximum angular deformation
φ	k	h	p	ω
0°	0·8660	1·1547	1·0000	16° 26′
15	0·8966	1·1154	1·0000	12° 29′
30	1·0000	1·0000	1·0000	0°
45	1·2247	0·8165	1·0000	23° 04′
60	1·7321	0·5774	1·0000	60°
75	3·3461	0·2989	1·0000	113° 26′
90	∞	0·0000	—	180°

The following features should be noted. First, *modification should have no effect upon the special property of a projection.* Thus Behrmann's Projection is also equal-area. Secondly, *modification by the introduction of two standard parallels reduces the deformations towards the edges of the map.* We see that the maximum angular deformation in latitude 75° is more than 113°, whereas the corresponding value from Table 3 is nearly 122°. Third, *modification has no effect whatsoever at the singular points.* In all normal aspect Cylindrical projections the geographical poles are singular points where distortion theory is invalid. Consequently the numerical values for $\varphi = 90°$ in both Tables 3 and 4 do no more than indicate this fact. Fourth, we see the reversal in direction of the maximum and minimum particular scales at the standard parallel.

Precisely the same reasoning may be applied to Conical projections. In Chapter 8 we derive the formulae for the *Equidistant Conical Projection (Ptolemy) with one standard parallel* and the *Equidistant Conical Projection (de l'Isle) with two standard parallels.* The particular scales and distortion characteristics for these projections are given in Table 10, p. 149 and Table 11, p. 152, respectively. Examination of these indicates that the four principles apply equally to these projections.

Modification of this sort naturally has some effect upon the appearance of a projection. In the unmodified Cylindrical projections the principal scale is preserved along the Equator. Hence the distance between any two meridians separated by a difference in longitude $\delta\lambda$ is, from equation (3.18)

$$x = R \cdot \delta\lambda \qquad (5.01)$$

where $\delta\lambda$ is expressed in radians. The distance between the same pair of meridians in a projection which has the principal scale preserved along the standard parallels $\pm\varphi_0$ is, as shown by equation (3.17)

$$x = R \cdot \cos \varphi_0 \cdot \delta\lambda \qquad (5.02)$$

Obviously (5.02) is always less than (5.01) so that any normal aspect modified Cylindrical projection will have smaller East–West extent than the parent projection. To maintain equivalence in a projection like Behrmann's there must be corresponding alteration in the spacing of the parallels (Ref. 3). Modification of conformal Cylindrical and Conical projections is especially easy to apply because the particular scales at any point are the same in all directions. This follows from the definition of conformality by equation (4.60) on p. 69. It is therefore possible to transform the coordinates of points and obtain the particular scales by using a single numerical constant, or *scale factor*, as a common multiplier. The numerical value chosen for the scale factor represents the particular scale to be preserved where the line of zero distortion is located on the unmodified projection. The value of it is related to the positions of the two lines of zero distortion so that a change in one results in alteration of the other. This kind of modification is commonly used with the varieties of conformal projection (*Transverse Mercator Projection* and *Lambert Conformal Conical Projection*) which are used in surveying and topographical cartography, as described in Chapter 11, pp. 199–233.

Transformation of a projection by the creation of a pole-line

At first sight it may seem that the presence of a singular point on a map projection is inconvenient, for this means that either the map is abruptly terminated by a line or that there is no real edge to the map in that part. In the normal aspect Cylindrical Equal-area Projection the representation of the geographical poles by two lines of length equal to the Equator creates the squat rectangular shape which makes it unattractive for use as a World map. In contrast, the normal aspect Sinusoidal Projection looks better because the geographical poles are represented by points and the meridians converge to them.

However a defect of the Sinusoidal Projection, shared also by Mollweide's Projection (Fig. 51, p. 76) is the large amount of angular deformation towards the edges of the map. On the Sinusoidal Projection $\omega > 100°$ and on Mollweide's Projection $\omega > 80°$ and this deformation is also clearly evident from the obliquity of graticule intersections. It is easy to imagine that the substitution of a short *pole-line* would reduce angular deformation by making every graticule intersection closer to a right angle. This may be done by using constants which create singular points at the geographical poles in the normal aspect or the corresponding points in other aspects. The length of the pole-line depends upon the constants employed. A common choice is for the pole-line to be one half of the length of the Equator. The shape of the pole-line matches the parallels. Thus the Pseudocylindrical projections, like the Sinusoidal and Mollweide's, which have rectilinear parallels, have rectilinear pole-lines. Figure 57 illustrates this for a recentred version of the *Eckert VI Pseudocylindrical Projection*. American cartographers sometimes call these *flat polar projections*. Other classes of projections with curved parallels have curved pole-lines. The *Aitoff-Wagner Projection*, illustrated by Fig. 5, p. 6, represents this kind of modification applied to a projection in which the parallels are curved. We do not derive the algebraic expressions for this kind of modification in this book, though the coordinates needed to construct certain projections with pole-lines are given in Appendix I, pp. 234–45. The reader who wishes to investigate the general theory of this kind of transformation is referred to Wagner's book (Ref. 4).

Recentred map projections

Throughout Chapters 4 and 5 we have made the basic assumption that a projection is intended to represent the spherical surface continuously, without any of the gaps which were illustrated in Fig. 31, p. 52. However we have seen in Fig. 7 that there is

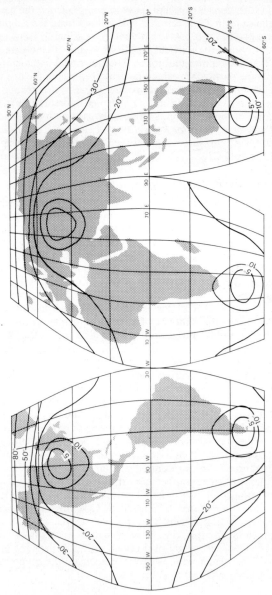

Figure 57 A recentred version of the Eckert (VI) Projection (No. 25 in Appendix I). This is an equal-area pseudocylindrical projection in which the meridians are sinusoidal and the geographical poles are represented by straight lines which are one-half of the length of the Equator. In addition the world map illustrated is recentred, having central meridians in longitudes 90° W, 70° W, 20° E, 60° E and 130° E. The isograms are for maximum angular deformation (ω) at 5°, 10°, 20°, 30°, 50° and 80°.

some merit in showing the World by means of two separate maps, either a pair to show one hemisphere each, or, as shown by Fig. 7 by two maps showing more than one hemisphere with a small overlap. There is also value in transforming other projections of the World by introducing artificial interruptions as shown in Fig. 57. In each method excessive angular deformation or exaggeration of area is checked by only using part of the World graticule *based upon different points of origin*. Hence we obtain the idea of using *recentred* map projections. The alternative term 'interrupted' relates to the appearance of the map. A considerable variety of these have been devised. Dahlberg (Ref. 5) is informative about the subject and attempts to classify them.

Figure 57 illustrates the recentred version of the normal aspect Eckert VI Projection which is also modified through the use of a pole-line. We see that the map is composed of five lobes or *gores* which are connected along the Equator. Each gore has a rectilinear central meridian (in longitudes 90° W and 60° E in the Northern Hemisphere; and in 70° W, 20° E and 130° E in the Southern Hemisphere). Hence this map has five different points of origin located along the Equator at the points of intersection with each of these meridians. The adjacent side of the five gores are bounded by three meridians, each of which is shown twice. Thus the meridian 30° W is common to both gores in the Northern Hemisphere and the Meridians 30° W and 90° E are both shown twice in the Southern Hemisphere. Examination of the isograms for maximum angular deformation indicates how the same pattern is repeated in each gore about the five points of zero distortion which occur on each central meridian in latitudes 50° N and 50° S. The problem of designing such a projection is to choose boundaries for each lobe which do not interfere with interpretation of the map. Thus to obtain a recentred map of the continents, as shown by Fig. 57, the boundaries should be selected to lie in the oceans. However the great land mass of Eurasia ought to be shown as a continuous feature. Consequently the corresponding lobe on the map must represent more than one-quarter of the entire sphere. Hence the angular deformation which occurs in Northern and Eastern Asia is the same which occurs on a continuous Eckert VI Projection of the World. Fig. 103, p. 201, shows a similar arrangement of a recentred Sinusoidal Projection.

Condensed map projections represent a further stage in the process of producing recentred maps. These are designed so that areas which are irrelevant to the purpose of the map have been excluded from the map altogether. For example, a map intended to show terrestial distributions in both the Old and New World may be designed so that the majority of the Atlantic and Pacific Oceans are not shown. The usual way of doing this, for example, in the *Oxford Projection* used for certain maps published in the Oxford Atlas, is to prepare two separate maps with different origins on the Equator and print these in juxtaposition with an irregular boundary through the Atlantic Ocean. The device is useful because it allows the presentation of certain terrestial distributions at a much larger scale than would be possible on a continuous World map. However the interpretation of such maps may be misleading if the unobservant user fails to appreciate the size of the gap between the two parts of the map. Misunderstanding of the convention might lead to stories like the one about the travel agent who insisted that the Shetland Isles were only fifty miles from Aberdeen because he had measured this on a map, himself. He had failed to realise that an inset map of the Shetland Islands, located for convenience in the Moray Firth, was not in its correct spatial relationship to the map of the mainland.

Composite map projections

The composite map projection is different from those modifications and transformations already described because it may appear to have continuity but in reality contains disconcerting breaks or changes in property. The composite map projection is created by the marriage of two or more projections along certain parallels or meridians where the agreement between them is quite good. For example, Goode devised the *Homolosine Projection* which is the fusion of the Sinusoidal and Mollweide Projections along the parallels which are the same length on each (latitudes 40° 44′ 11″.8 North and South). This is quite a useful combination because both projections are equal-area Pseudocylindrical Projections. Many of the star-shaped and lobular World maps which have been used from time to time in atlases and for advertisements belong to this category. The prize for sheer complexity in design of an elaborate composite projection must be awarded to the *Optimum Continental Projection* of the Old World (Ref. 6) which appears to have about twenty-four components. This map combines elements of the *Equidistant Conical Projection* (*Ptolemy*), the *Polyconic Projection* and *Bonne's Projection* which are fitted together along certain parallels and meridians to create an ingenious jig-saw puzzle.

The classification of map projections

It is desirable to formulate a system of classification which is, at the same time, collectively exhaustive and mutually exclusive. In other words, the system must include all possible kinds of map projection which have been, or which are likely to be described. Each projection ought, ideally, to occupy a unique position within the classification system, like every element in the Periodic System or each species within the Linnean classifications of the plant and animal kingdoms. No projections ought to be relegated to classes labelled 'Miscellaneous', 'Conventional' or 'Others' for this creates a kind of rubbish bin to hold all the varieties of map projection which cannot be conveniently accommodated elsewhere within the system. Reference is made in some books to map projections with 'arbitrary properties' (or 'aphylactic projections') which usually means that these are neither conformal nor equal-area projections. The use of such terms and the incorporation of such categories within a classification system is a negative approach with little to commend it.

Only two attempts at classification have really attempted to satisfy these desirable criteria. The first was the so-called 'Linnean System' described by Maurer in 1935 (Ref. 7) and the second is Tobler's *Parametric Classification* published in 1962 (Ref. 8).

Both of these have considerable merit. Maurer's system is the more complicated and is only useful to the advanced student of the subject. Tobler's method of classification has the great merit of being all-embracing yet quite simple to understand. But it does not go far enough. For the purposes of this book the present writer has taken Tobler's classification as the basis and extended it to produce an ordered hierarchy of *groups, classes* and *series*.

The subdivision of all map projections into five groups, A–E, is essentially Tobler's system. This makes use of different combinations of the functional relationships between the map, described in plane rectangular or polar coordinates and the geographical coordinates on the generating globe. Eight such pairs of combinations may be recognised, all of which map the spherical surface continuously. This gives rise to four possible kinds of continuous map. The fifth group represents those composite map projections in which there are changes in function and variation in the fundamental properties from place to place. We do not consider these creations further.

In order to simplify understanding of the system of classification we propose that, first, *every group, class and series is defined in terms of the normal aspect*. It could be undertaken in more general mathematical terms but it is easier for the beginner to comprehend its significance in respect to the graticule formed by geographical coordinates. Hence, we exclude all variations in aspect from the system. Secondly, we define every projection in terms of the simplest, unmodified version. Thus the modifications introduced by creating two standard parallels or a standard circle do not enter the classification system, nor do the transformations created by the introduction of pole-lines or recentred versions of a map. This may be unrealistic because many of the map projections bearing individual names are such modifications of another but inclusion of these as criteria of classification complicates the system.

In order to make the initial subdivision of all map projections into the four groups, A–D, we make use of the functional relationships between plane and geographical coordinates which were introduced at the beginning of Chapter 4. An understanding of this notation, as given in equations (4.01) – (4.04), p. 49, is essential. Therefore the reader who skipped that part of Chapter 4 should now refer to it. In order to explain the system in terms of the appearance of the graticule in each of the four groups we must also be explicit about the origins of the plane (x, y) and (r, θ) coordinate systems and also define the orientation of the axes or initial line with respect to parallels and meridians.

Plane representation by Cartesian coordinates

We specify that for a map projection to be defined by plane rectangular coordinates, the origin of the system is located on the Equator at its intersection with a selected central meridian. This may be the Greenwich Meridian, as shown in some of the illustrations in this book, but is not an essential condition. However we must specify that longitude is to be measured from the central meridian if this is not Greenwich. The abscissa of the plane coordinates coincides with the Equator and the ordinate with the central meridian. It therefore follows that x varies mainly with longitude whereas y varies mainly with latitude. In equations (4.01) and (4.02) both x and y vary with latitude and longitude. This is the general case which may be simplified in three different ways as follows:

$$\left.\begin{aligned} x &= f_1(\lambda) \\ y &= f_2(\varphi, \lambda) \end{aligned}\right\}(B)$$

$$\left.\begin{aligned} x &= f_1(\varphi, \lambda) \\ y &= f_2(\varphi, \lambda) \end{aligned}\right\}(A)$$

$$\left.\begin{aligned} x &= f_1(\lambda) \\ y &= f_2(\varphi) \end{aligned}\right\}(D)$$

$$\left.\begin{aligned} x &= f_1(\varphi, \lambda) \\ y &= f_2(\varphi) \end{aligned}\right\}(C)$$

The graphical appearance for these functions is illustrated in Fig. 58. Clearly (A) represents the general case expressed by (4.01) and (4.02) and (D) is the simplest case where x and y are functions of one variable only. (B) and (C) are the intermediate cases where either x or y is a function of one variable. Where x or y, or both coordinates vary with both latitude and longitude, each parallel or meridian must be represented by either an inclined straight line or a curve. The only exceptions to this rule are the axes of the plane coordinates where $f_1(\varphi, \lambda) = 0$ or $f_2(\varphi, \lambda) = 0$ and both the Equator and central meridians are represented by perpendicular straight lines. Hence a functional relationship of the sort

$$x = f(\varphi, \lambda)$$

indicates a curve, the exact nature and location of which is, as yet, unspecified.

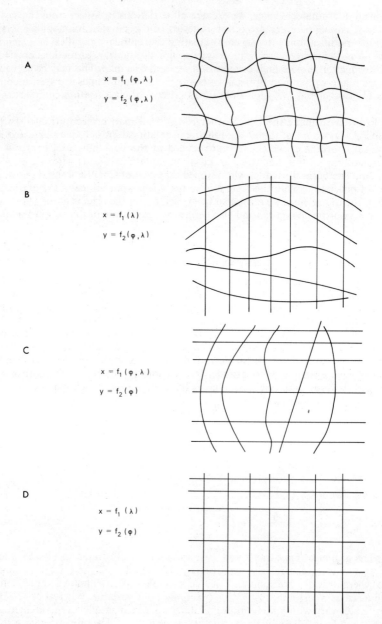

A

$$x = f_1(\varphi, \lambda)$$
$$y = f_2(\varphi, \lambda)$$

B

$$x = f_1(\lambda)$$
$$y = f_2(\varphi, \lambda)$$

C

$$x = f_1(\varphi, \lambda)$$
$$y = f_2(\varphi)$$

D

$$x = f_1(\lambda)$$
$$y = f_2(\varphi)$$

Figure 58 Diagrammatic representation of the geometrical meaning of the four possible functional relationships between geographical coordinates and plane Cartesian coordinates (after Tobler).

A parallel of latitude, by definition, represents the circumference of a small circle on the globe along which φ is constant. Similarly a meridian represents the great semicircle along which λ is constant. If we specify either that $x=f(\lambda)$ or that $y=f(\varphi)$, this means that any line depicting a constant value of λ or φ can only have one value for x or y. In other words, if $x=f(\lambda)$ each meridian will be represented by a straight line which is parallel to the central meridian. Similarly, if $y=f(\varphi)$ each parallel will be represented by a straight line which is parallel to the Equator.

We therefore have four basic types of map projection which may be defined by plane Cartesian coordinates.

Group A comprises the general case where both the parallels and meridians are composed of curves, as illustrated by Figs. 5, 32 and 52. This group is known to most writers as the *Polyconic* class of projections, although we must comment that this is an unfortunate choice of name because it is also applied to one projection.

Group B contains projections which have rectilinear meridians which are parallel to the central meridian, and curved parallels. This group has few named members and contains few projections which have any practical use in conventional cartography. The group does include certain projections which have other kinds of use, for example as graphic aids to the solution of spherical triangles in astronomical navigation.

Group C contains projections which have curved meridians and parallels composed of parallel straight lines. These are the Pseudocylindrical projections illustrated by Figs. 10, 45, 56 and 57.

Group D is the simplest of the four and must comprise projections which are composed of two families of parallel straight lines. These are the Cylindrical projections already introduced on p. 87.

Plane representation by polar coordinates

We employ similar arguments to subdivide the possible varieties of map projections which are more conveniently described in terms of plane polar coordinates. We specify that the origin of the system is situated at or near one of the geographical poles and that the initial line coincides with the central meridian. Thus the radius vector, r, represents the distance from the origin to a parallel of latitude and is therefore a measure of colatitude. However this is a function of latitude so we may retain the convention that $r=f(\varphi)$. The vectorial angle, θ, is related to the spherical angle measured at the geographical pole and therefore θ is predominantly a measure of longitude. However we have created some uncertainty in this specification by stating that the origin of the coordinate system is located 'at or near' one of the poles. This creates further complication which means that for each of the four possible pairs of functions there exist two possibilities. The first is where the origin of polar coordinates is at the geographical pole; the second is where it is located at some *vertex* which is a point on the prolongation of the polar axis beyond the spherical surface. Bearing in mind this dual interpretation, the four pairs of functions may be written in the form:

$$\left.\begin{matrix} r=f_1(\varphi, \lambda) \\ \theta=f_2(\lambda) \end{matrix}\right\}(B)$$

$$\left.\begin{matrix} r=f_1(\varphi, \lambda) \\ \theta=f_2(\varphi, \lambda) \end{matrix}\right\}(A)$$

$$\left.\begin{matrix} r=f_1(\varphi) \\ \theta=f_2(\lambda) \end{matrix}\right\}(D)$$

$$\left.\begin{matrix} r=f_1(\varphi) \\ \theta=f_2(\varphi, \lambda) \end{matrix}\right\}(C)$$

H

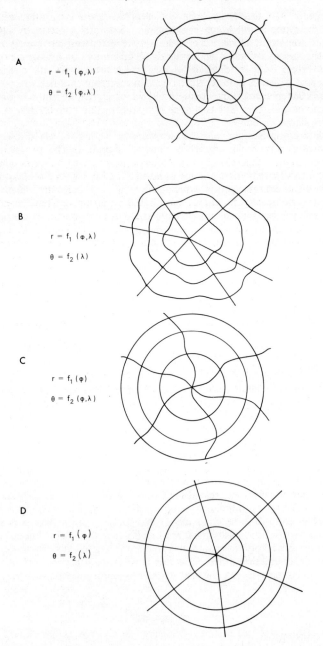

A

$r = f_1 (\varphi, \lambda)$

$\theta = f_2 (\varphi, \lambda)$

B

$r = f_1 (\varphi, \lambda)$

$\theta = f_2 (\lambda)$

C

$r = f_1 (\varphi)$

$\theta = f_2 (\varphi, \lambda)$

D

$r = f_1 (\varphi)$

$\theta = f_2 (\lambda)$

Figure 59 Diagrammatic representation of the geometrical meaning of the four possible functional relationships between geographical coordinates and plane polar coordinates (after Tobler).

As before, $f(\varphi, \lambda)$ indicates a curved parallel or meridian. Where r is a function of latitude only the parallels are represented by concentric circular arcs. Where θ is a function of longitude only the meridians are straight lines converging at the origin of the coordinate system. The functions represented by (A) correspond to projections in which both the parallels and meridians are curved and may be allocated to the Group A of Polyconic projections. The intermediate functions of Group B have rectilinear meridians and curved parallels which may be equated with Group B of cartesian coordinates. The two remaining groups (C) and (D) both have $r = f(\varphi)$ and therefore have parallels represented by concentric circular arcs. If the origin is located at the geographical pole, the parallels are represented by the circumferences of circles which have their common centre at this point. In Group D, the meridians radiate as straight lines from the origin, defining the Azimuthal class of projections. In Group C, the meridians are curved and may be known as *Pseudoazimuthal* projections. For an example of these curiosities, see Ref. 9. On the other hand, if the origin of the polar coordinates is located at some vertex, the parallels are again represented by concentric circular arcs but cannot form a complete circumference. The resulting shape of the projection depends upon the shape of the meridians. In Group D, the meridians are rectilinear, giving rise to the characteristic fan-shaped Conical projections. In Group C, the meridians are curved, producing the bell-shaped *Pseudoconical* projections.

We have now created four Groups A–D with combinations of functions which include all possible ways in which the spherical surface can be mapped continuously

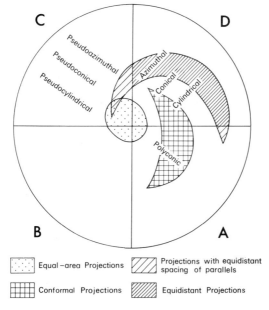

Figure 60 Venn diagram illustrating the relationship between Tobler's four groups, A-D, the subdivision of the groups into classes and indicating the relationship of certain special properties of map projections to the system of classification. Study of this diagram indicates, for example, that conformal map projections are confined entirely to groups A and D and that equidistant map projections are confined to group D. The student will find it instructive to plot the location of the projections listed in Appendix I upon an enlarged copy of this diagram.

upon a plane. Within these groups there are seven named classes, three of each in Groups C and D together with the word Polyconic which is applied to the entire Group A. This stage of classification may be illustrated diagramatically, as in Fig. 60.

Separation of the parallels

Thus far we have not specified any particular conditions concerning the spacing of the parallels, we have only stated that y is some function of latitude. However if the reader has studied the World map projections, as suggested at the outset of this chapter it will be appreciated that this can vary in three different ways:

(1) The separation between the parallels *decreases* with increasing latitude from the Equator towards the poles.
(2) The separation between the parallels *remains constant* for all equal increments of latitude.
(3) The separation between the parallels *increases* with increasing latitude from the Equator towards the poles.

(1) and (3) can vary in an infinitely large number of different ways but (2) cannot change.

For the Cylindrical and Pseudocylindrical classes, these variations may be conveniently expressed in terms of trignometric functions of latitude. For example, the sine of an angle varies in such a way that the difference between the sines of two angles close to $0°$ is greater than the difference between the sines of two corresponding angles near $90°$. This can be seen from the numerical variations to be found in the interpolation columns of a table of Natural Sines in any set of trigonometric tables. Thus, for the first case of decreasing separation we may write

$$y = f(\sin \varphi) \qquad (5.03)$$

and we will study the specific example of the Cylindrical Equal-area Projection (Fig. 48) in which the parallels crowd together in high latitudes.

For this projection we may write

$$y = R \cdot \sin \varphi \qquad (5.04)$$

and determine numerical values for the ordinate for the condition that $R = 1$.

Table 5

Values for the ordinate and the difference between successive values for y. Cylindrical Equal-area Projection.

Latitude	y	δy
0°	0·0000	
		0·2588
15	0·2588	
		0·2412
30	0·5000	
		0·2071
45	0·7071	
		0·1289
60	0·8660	
		0·0999
75	0·9659	
		0·0341
90	1·0000	

Since we have put $R=1$, the values for y represent the natural sines of the angle φ. The column headed δy lists the difference between successive values of y. This column shows that for a difference in latitude of $15°$, the distance between the parallels $\varphi=0°$ and $\varphi=15°$ is $0\cdot2588$ units but the distance between $\varphi=75°$ and $\varphi=90°$ is only $0\cdot0341$ units.

The converse case is

$$y = f(\tan \varphi) \qquad (5.05)$$

which indicates that the spacing between the parallels increases from the Equator towards the poles. Using a set of natural tangents the reader is invited to construct a table corresponding to Table 4 which demonstrates this increase (it is the ordinate for the 'Central Perspective Cylindrical Projection' of no practical value). Since $\tan 90° = \infty$ it follows that the geographical poles cannot be shown because they are infinitely far from the Equator on this projection.

The intermediate case is where the parallels have equidistant spacing. Then we may write

$$y = R.c.\varphi \qquad (5.06)$$

where c is some constant and φ is measured in radians.

If $c=1$ the separation of the parallels corresponds to the arc distance between them on the globe because this is just another way of expressing equation (3.10). Moreover, in certain classes of map projection, such as those in Group D this also corresponds to making the particular scale $h=1$ and creating the special property of equidistance. However we must note that equal separation of the parallels does not necessarily ensure that the projection is equidistant. Pseudocylindrical projections frequently have equidistantly spaced parallels (e.g. Fig. 56 (a)) but $h=1$ on the central meridian only. All other meridians are curved and therefore h varies from point to point on the map.

We employ the three principles relating to the spacing of the parallels in the classification. However the *Sine Series* and *Tangent Series* cannot be applied as descriptive terms for all classes of projections. Therefore we use *Decreasing Separation, Increasing Separation* and *Equidistant Parallels* as being an all-embracing form of subdivision. In each case we mean the change in separation of the parallels proceeding from the Equator towards the Poles.

Table 6 indicates the proposed system of classification including the projections which have been illustrated and those which are given in Appendix I.

The naming of map projections

A variety of different map projections have been mentioned in this chapter. Some of them are named after the supposed inventor or originator of the projection, such as *Mollweide's Projection, Aitoff-Wagner Projection, Bonne's Projection, Mercator Projection*. Less commonly projections are named after the book, map or atlas in which they were first used. The *Oxford Projection* is an example of this usage. A third group are named according to specific mathematical features of the graticule. The *Sinusoidal Projection* is so named because the meridians of the normal aspect are sine curves. Many projections have alternative names (*Sanson Flamsteed's Projection = Sinusoidal Projection*) and many have no proper name.

The problem of nomenclature have been examined by Lee (Ref. 10) and by the present writer (Ref. 2) who have suggested that the following rules should be followed:

Table 6

Classified List of the principal map projections.

This classification is based upon (1) Tobler's Groups, (2) Named classes, (3) Series formed by spacing of parallels.
It refers to the normal aspect in each Group and Class and does not include modified projections.
See Appendix I for these.

GROUP	CLASS	SERIES		
		Decreasing Separation	*Equidistant Spacing of Parallels (Q)*	*Increasing Separation*
D	CYLINDRICAL $x = f_1(\lambda)$ $y = f_2(\varphi)$	Cylindrical Equal-area (Lambert) Projection (E)	Plate Carrée Projection (Q)	Mercator Projection (C, L) Miller's Cylindrical Projections Braun's Perspective Cylindrical Projection
	AZIMUTHAL $r = f_1(\varphi)$ $\theta = f_2(\lambda)$	Stereographic Projection (C) Gnomonic Projection (O) Minimum-error Azimuthal Projection (Airy) (M) Breusing's (Geometrical) Azimuthal Projection Breusing's (Harmonic) Azimuthal Projection (M)	Azimuthal Equidistant Projection (Postel) (Q)	Azimuthal Equal-area Projection (Lambert) (E) Orthographic Projection
	CONICAL $r = f_1(\varphi)$ $\theta = f_2(\lambda)$	Conical Equal-area Projection with truncated pole (E) Conical Equal-area Projection with point pole (Lambert) (E)	Equidistant Conical Projection with one standard parallel (Ptolemy) (Q) Equidistant Conical Projection with point pole (Mendeleev) (Q) Minimum-error Conical Projection (Murdoch III) (M)	Conformal Conical Projection with one standard parallel (Lambert) (C)

C	PSEUDOCYLINDRICAL $x = f_1(\varphi, \lambda)$ $y = f_2(\varphi)$	Mollweide's Projection (E) Ps Equal-area Projection with elliptical meridians (Fournier II) (E) Parabolic Projection (E) Eumorphic Projection (Bogs) (E)	Sinusoidal Projection (E) Ps Projection with elliptical meridians (Apianus II) Polyhedric Projection	
	PSEUDOAZIMUTHAL $r = f_1(\varphi)$ $\theta = f_2(\varphi, \lambda)$			Equal-area Pseudoazimuthal Projection (Wiechel) (E)
	PSEUDOCONICAL		Bonne's Projection (E)	
A	POLYCONIC $x = f_1(\varphi, \lambda)$ $y = f_2(\varphi, \lambda)$	Hammer-Aitoff Projection (E)	Simple Polyconic Projection Aitoff's Projection Tripel Projection (Winkel)	

Key to special property: E = Equal-area; Q = Equidistant; C = Conformal; M = Minimum-error (of that class); L = Rectilinear rhumb-lines; O = Rectilinear great circles.

(1) Certain names are inviolate because of their long history of international use. These include the names of the Azimuthal projections originally described by the Greek geometers, such as *Stereographic*, *Gnomonic* and *Orthographic*. It further includes some extremely well-known projections with a long history and considerable practical importance, like *Mercator's Projection*, *Bonne's Projection* and *Cassini's Projection*.

(2) The great majority of map projections ought to be referred to in terms of:
    (a) Aspect (if other than normal)
    (b) Class,
    (c) Special Property,
    (d) Name of originator,
    (e) Nature of any modifications.

Thus we may distinguish between the *Cylindrical Equal-area* (*Lambert*) and the *Cylindrical Equal-area* (*Behrmann*) *with standard parallels in* 30° *N and S*. However Ref. 2 indicates examples when even this amount of information is insufficient to distinguish between several projections.

References

1 — *Glossary of Technical Terms in Cartography*, London, 1966, The Royal Society, 84 pp.

2 Maling, D. H.: 'The terminology of map projections', *International Yearbook of Cartography*, VIII, 1968, pp. 11–65.

3 Maling, D. H.: 'Some notes about the Trystan Edwards Projection', *The Cartographic Journal*, 3, 1966, pp. 94–96.

4 Wagner, K-H.: *Kartographsche Netzentwürfe*, Leipzig, 1957, Bibliographisches Institut, 263 pp.

5 Dahlberg, R. E.: 'Evolution of interrupted map projections', *International Yearbook of Cartography*, II, 1962, pp. 36–54.

6 Macdonald, R. R.: 'An optimum continental projection', *The Cartographic Journal*, 5, 1968, pp. 46–47.

7 Maurer, H.: *Ebene Kugelbilder*, Petermanns Mitteilungen, Ergänzungsheft Nr 221, 1935, Gotha, 87 pp.

8 Tobler, W. R.: 'A classification of map projections', *Annals of the Association of American Geographers*, 52, 1962, pp. 167–175.

9 Arden-Close, Sir Charles: 'A forgotten pseudo-zenithal projection', *Geographical Journal*, 118, 1952, p. 237.

10 Lee, L. P.: 'The nomenclature and classification of map projections', *Empire Survey Review*, 7, 1944, pp. 190–200.

CHAPTER 6

PRACTICAL CONSTRUCTION OF MAP PROJECTIONS

'Why,' said the Dodo, 'the best way to explain it is to do it.'
Lewis Carroll: *Alice in Wonderland*

Introduction

At the beginning of this chapter it is necessary to emphasise that there is a considerable difference between the 'methods of construction' described in most of the elementary textbooks on map projections published in the English language and the techniques which should be used by professional cartographers. No doubt the geometrical methods described in the textbooks are used from time to time, but this is generally because information about the alternative methods is practically nonexistent in English. It is only the cartographer who has had the opportunity to study the methods used in continental Europe, or who can read the appropriate literature in French, German or Russian, who is aware of the profound difference in cartographic practice.

The compilation of every map starts with plotting some kind of grid or graticule, for this is the framework on which it is based and which determines the quantitative or positional accuracy of everything shown upon it. At the level of map use the network of lines forms an important frame of reference which can be used to define position and even make a crude estimate of distance, direction or area. Other requirements such as ascertaining by measurement the amount of distortion of the paper upon which a map has been printed can also be satisfied by measuring known distances between the grid or graticule intersections.

At the larger scales, i.e. at 1/10,000 or larger, the framework of the map is usually a grid. Nowadays most large-scale maps have neat lines which are grid lines and the sheet numbering system is also based upon the grid. At the smaller scales, i.e. at 1/1,000,000 or smaller, only the graticule is shown and often the neat lines of the map are pairs of parallels and meridians. At scales intermediate between these extremes, corresponding to most topographical map series, both the grid and graticule are probably shown. Where the grid and graticule both appear on the map, the draughting specification usually calls for the representation of certain grid lines in full. The graticule is only indicated by small crosses at the points of intersection of selected parallels and meridians and by subdivisions of the margin round the neat lines of the map. Often the crosses are omitted in parts of the map where they coincide with and might confuse other detail.

Choice about spacing of the grid lines and graticule depends upon the scale of the map. Table 7 shows the kind of intervals which are commonly found on land maps and in atlases. Nautical and other navigation charts which are used for precise plotting of position and direction frequently have a closer network of parallels and meridians than are found on other maps of equivalent scale.

On a multicoloured map the graticule is generally printed in the colour of the base plate (margins, marginal letterpress, settlement and boundaries) which is either black or dark brown. The graticule is nearly always represented by continuous lines of gauge $0 \cdot 1 - 0 \cdot 2$ mm. (4–6, measured in thousandths of one inch). On national

109

topographical maps the grid is also often represented in the colour of the base plate. Grid lines may be continuous, or depicted as a *rouletted grid* in which the lines are composed of small, closely-spaced dots. The draughting specification may also require emphasis of certain integer grid lines (usually at every 10 km. or 100 km.) at a wider gauge than the remainder.

Table 7

Spacing of grid and graticule commonly found on published maps at different scales. Data for large scale and topographical map scales indicates Ordnance Survey practice.

Scale	Grid separation (km)	Graticule separation (Degrees and minutes)
1/2,500 and larger	0·1	—
1/10,000	1·0	1′ (margin only)
1/25,000	1·0	†
1/50,000 – 1/63,360	1·0	1′ (margin)
		5′ (optional crosses)
1/250,000	10·0	1′ (margin)
		30′ (optional crosses)
1/625,000	10·0	10′ (margin only)
1/1,000,000	—	1°
		1′ (margin)
1/2,000,000	—	1°
1/5,000,000	—	2°
1/10,000,000	—	5°
1/20,000,000	—	5°–10°
1/50,000,000	—	10°–15°
1/100,000,000	—	10°–20°
Smaller than 1/100,000,000	—	15°–20°

† The only graticule information on the 1/25,000 O.S. series is a statement of the geographical coordinates of the sheet corners.

On military maps the grid is frequently printed in some colour other than black. The use of a different colour facilitates rapid location of grid lines with respect to other map detail. Moreover the use of a distinct colour for each grid zone provides a means of distinguishing between two overlapping grids where these have to be shown on the same map sheet.

Since the grid or graticule represents the mathematical framework upon which the whole of the rest of the map is based, it follows that grid or graticule inter- sections should be plotted with great accuracy and the component lines ought to be fair-drawn with considerable care. Most of the map accuracy specifications which have been drawn up for the purposes of legal contract or guarantee refer to *plani- metric error* as the displacements of map detail compared with their surveyed positions, both measured relative to the grid or graticule. The graphical work of navigation is done with reference to the parallels and meridians on the printed chart. It follows, therefore, that the grid or graticule of a map ought to be plotted 'without sensible error' corresponding to a standard error in position of about $\pm 0·1$ mm. This is an exceedingly high standard to achieve and it is therefore necessary to examine the practical ways in which it can be accomplished.

Reference to the illustrations of map projections which appear in this book indicates that certain lines are straight; others are arcs of circles, ellipses and other conic sections. Some projections contain higher order curves and these may have reverse curvature or even cusps, where the curvature is discontinuous at a point. Only a few instruments are available for drawing these lines. Obviously a straight-edge assists drawing of straight lines and a half-set or beam compass can be used to construct circular arcs, but this is practically the limit to the instruments which can be used to draw curves to a particular specification. More complicated kinds of *trammel* have been designed and manufactured to draw the other conic sections (ellipses, parabolae and hyperbolae) but these are quite rare and they are not particularly reliable. Thus, in order to draw any curve of higher order than a circle it is necessary to use some kind of template to guide the ruling pen or scribing tool. These may be flexible, known as *splines* or flexicurves, or they are rigid drawing aids known as *French Curves, Ship Curves* or *Copenhagen Curves*. We will use the word 'curves' to mean any of these rigid varieties. Splines and curves have to be fitted by trial and error until part of a ruling edge passes through a succession of plotted points. Consequently a graticule composed of curves can only be drawn after the individual graticule intersections have been located on the plotting sheet. Hence the first stage in constructing any map projection is to plot the positions of the graticule intersections at the required scale. The second stage is to draw the individual parallels and meridians through these points.

Location of graticule intersections

A variety of graphic and semi-graphic techniques can be devised to locate the points where the parallels intersect one meridian or vice versa. For some projections the methods of plotting can be carried out entirely with ruler and compasses and the wholly geometrical constructions can be accomplished without having to make any calculations apart from the initial determination of the scale of the intended map. However, the construction for each projection is unique and therefore it must be learned. The elementary textbooks are full of such recipes and many students of the subject are led to believe that the study of map projections comprises learning these by rote. The present author believes that this approach to the subject is wrong and it is a waste of time. Moreover there are three additional reasons why the wholly geometrical methods of construction are unsatisfactory.

(1) Geometrical construction tends to be progressive so that the work proceeds 'from the part to the whole' without much opportunity for checking the accuracy of construction and is almost always concerned with graphical *enlargement* (with all its attendant shortcomings). This means that inevitable small errors of plotting introduced at the initial stages of construction accumulate to quite large errors in the final positions of parallels and meridians. Elsewhere in this chapter (pp. 119–22) we examine some of these kinds of problems in the discussion of suitable methods for constructing a master grid when this has to be done graphically.

(2) Geometrical construction is often limited to the preparation of very small scale maps. This is because there are few straight edges, beam compasses and splines of length greater than 1 metre and even quite small scale maps require construction arcs which are longer than this. Instruments such as beam compasses are quite impractical and lack precision when used for distances exceeding 2 metres. Some points used in the construction may have to be located beyond the boundary of the map, often a long way from the centre of the projection. This requires a very large plotting table and can be extremely wasteful in consumption of draughting film.

(3) The final and most important objection of all is that most of the really useful map projections cannot be constructed by geometrical methods.

The correct professional approach to the task is to locate and plot the graticule intersections by means of their coordinates upon a master grid

This has been current practice in continental cartography since the nineteenth century and it is also used in topographical map production in all countries. It is argued here that the methods are equally applicable to the construction of all maps and that once the technique is understood it can be used to construct any map projection at any scale. Consequently there is no further need for the useless clutter of knowledge concerning the details of geometrical construction of a variety of map projections which are never used in practice.

Construction of a map projection by plotting coordinates

Let us suppose that it is required to plot a fairly complicated map projection, for example *Briesemeister's Projection* of the whole World, at scale 1/40,000,000 showing parallels and meridians at 15° intervals. A smaller scale version of this projection with a 20° graticule is illustrated in Fig. 61 and the coordinates required for the construction are given in Appendix II on page 246.

The required equipment and data are:

(1) A master grid showing 5 mm. rectangular coordinates on a sheet of plastic of suitable dimensions.
(2) Tabulated values of the rectangular coordinates for the 15° graticule intersections for this projection.
(3) A slide rule or calculator for converting the tabulated coordinates into the values required for plotting at the required map scale.
(4) Ordinary draughting instruments, including splines or curves and a fine needle mounted in a pin vice for pricking the positions of all points.

The procedure for plotting the intersections and fair drawing the graticule is as follows:

(1) Select the range of coordinates which represents the maximum extent of the proposed map in each direction and determine the distance in millimetres corresponding to this range.
(2) Choose an origin on the master grid which will permit the whole graticule to be plotted upon it and number the selected axes in millimetres from this origin.
(3) Take each pair of coordinates from the tables and convert their values into millimetres at the intended scale. Repeat this for each graticule intersection to complete a list of all coordinates converted into metric units.
(4) Plot these coordinates on the master grid to locate each graticule intersection. Repeat until all the graticule intersections have been plotted.
(5) Lay a spline or curve through the succession of plotted points corresponding to the same parallel or meridian and draw a smooth curve through the points. This stage is repeated until the whole graticule has been drawn.

We now examine each of these steps in detail.

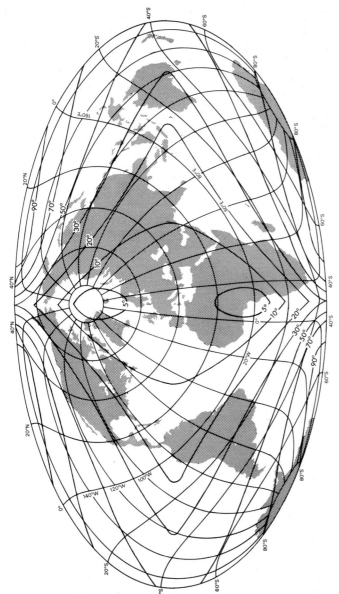

Figure 61 Map of the World on Briesemeister's Projection (No. 37 b in Appendix I). This is an equal-area projection from Group A of Polyconic projections. It is devised specifically for oblique aspect representation with the origin in latitude 45° N and longitude 10° E, so that the major land areas of the northern hemisphere lie close to the centre of the map. The isograms are for maximum angular deformation (ω) at 5°, 10°, 20°, 30°, 50°, 70° and 90°. Note that the graticule shown on this figure is for 20° intervals of latitude and longitude whereas the tabulated coordinates in Appendix II are for a 15° graticule. The choice is deliberate so that a student required to construct the projection by tables cannot trace the graticule from this diagram.

The nature of the projection tables

Our example is a small scale World map for which the spherical assumption is justified. Consequently these are simpler tables to use than the kind required in topographical cartography which must be used to derive the positions of graticule intersections for the *Transverse Mercator Projection* and other projections used for large-scale and topographical maps. The design of the projection tables used in topographical cartography is described in Chapter 11, pp. 226–33. In this chapter we only consider the construction of small-scale map projections of the sphere.

Inspection of the table of rectangular coordinates of Briesemeister's Projection (p. 246) indicates that the range of tabulated latitude is from the North Pole to the South Pole but the range of tabulated longitude is only from the Greenwich Meridian to 180° East. This is because the projection is symmetrical about the central meridian. Consequently the graticule intersections in the western hemisphere can be obtained from the table by simply changing the sign of x. For example, the point $\varphi = 60°$ North, $\lambda = 30°$ East has coordinates $x = +0 \cdot 23933$, $y = +0 \cdot 33204$. The coordinates of the point $\varphi = 60°$ North, $\lambda = 30°$ West are $x = -0 \cdot 23933$, $y = +0 \cdot 33204$. The range in coordinate values is from $x = 0 \cdot 00000$, $y = 0 \cdot 00000$ for the point $\varphi = 45°$ North, $\lambda = 0$ to the following extreme values (Fig. 62).

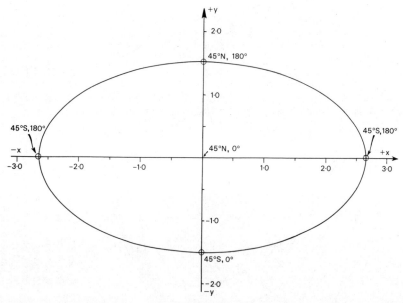

Figure 62 Initial specification of the coordinates for the extreme points needed to construct a World map on Briesemeister's Projection. The axes are divided in units of Earth radius, R, and the four points defining the major and minor axes of the bounding ellipse have been plotted directly from the coordinates tabulated in Appendix II.

Northern limit of map: $\varphi = 45°$ N, $\lambda = 180°$
$x = 0 \cdot 00000$, $y = 1 \cdot 51188$

Southern limit of map: $\varphi = 45°$ S, $\lambda = 0°$
$x = 0 \cdot 00000$, $y = -1 \cdot 51188$

Eastern limit of map: $\varphi = 45°$ S, $\lambda = 180°$ E
$x = 2 \cdot 64579$, $y = 0 \cdot 00000$

Western limit of map: $\varphi = 45°$ S, $\lambda = 180°$ W
$x = -2 \cdot 64579$, $y = 0 \cdot 00000$

At this stage it is useful to make a rough plot of some of the points (e.g. the 45° graticule intersections) on graph paper using some convenient scale such as 100 mm. = 1·0 tabulated unit, which corresponds to a representative fraction of 1/63,711,000. This is useful to find out how the tables have been compiled, for example, to ascertain which direction is denoted by x. Moreover a rough plot of this sort indicates immediately how much of the World map can be plotted from the tabulated coordinates and how much has to be plotted using the opposite sign for either x or y. The diagram also serves as a useful check against making gross errors in location of the first few points which are plotted on the master grid.

From the extreme values tabulated above it can be seen that the World map will extend $2 \times 1 \cdot 5118 = 3 \cdot 0237$ units in the direction of the ordinate and $2 \times 2 \cdot 6458 = 5 \cdot 2916$ units in the direction of the abscissa.

Scale conversion of the tabulated coordinates

The values of x and y are given in units of Earth radius. In other words, if we put $R = 1 \cdot 0$ cm., the width of the map at that scale would be $5 \cdot 29$ cm.

In order to use the tabulated coordinates to plot a map of any desired scale it is necessary to convert from units of R into the values of r, which we saw in Chapter 4, corresponds to the radius of a generating globe whose scale is the principal scale of the map. For example, we are required to plot Briesmeister's Projection at 1/40,000,000. From equation (4.06).

$$\frac{1}{40,000,000} = \frac{r}{6,371,100}$$

and

$$r = 0 \cdot 1592 \text{ metres or } 159 \cdot 2 \text{ millimetres.}$$

This value is now used as a constant multiplier to convert all the tabulated values of x and y into millimetres at the scale of plotting. Thus, as in (2.12) and (2.13),

$$x' = r \cdot x \tag{6.01}$$

$$y' = r \cdot y \tag{6.02}$$

which is an application of the scale transformation to Cartesian coordinates described in Chapter 2 (p. 26). We will refer to the (x', y') system as the *Master Grid Coordinates*.

Thus the transformed values for the four extreme points of Briesmeister's Projection are:

φ	λ	x' (mm.)	y' (mm.)
45° N	180°	0·0	+240·8
45° S	0°	0·0	−240·8
45° S	180° E	+421·4	0·0
45° S	180° W	−421·4	0·0

This indicates that the map requires a master grid with dimensions greater than 0·843 metres × 0·482 metres in order to plot the whole map of the World at 1/40,000,000.

To avoid making the calculation of the constant multiplier, *r*, we give these values in Table 8 for many commonly used map scales within the range 1/5,000,000 to 1/250,000,000. The upper limit corresponds to the largest scale at which the spherical assumption is justified. The lower limit corresponds to the smallest scale used for World maps in most atlases. In addition we give the representative fractions for maps in which *r* is an integer within the range 30 mm. through 70 mm. and for *r* = 100 mm.

Table 8

Values of the radius of the generating globe, r, to be used as a constant multiplier for conversion of coordinates in projection tables to plot the coordinates in millimetres. This table employs the spherical assumption for R=6371.1 km.

Scale	*r* (mm.)	Scale	*r* (mm.)
1/250,000,000	25·484	1/60,000,000	106·185
1/212,366,666	30·00	1/50,000,000	127·422
1/200,000,000	31·856	1/40,000,000	159·278
1/159,277,500	40·00	1/30,000,000	212·370
1/150,000,000	42·474	1/25,000,000	254·844
1/127,422,000	50·00	1/20,000,000	318·555
1/125,000,000	50·969	1/15,000,000	424·470
1/106,185,000	60·00	1/12,500,000	509·688
1/100,000,000	63·711	1/10,000,000	637·110
1/91,015,714	70·00	1/9,000,000	707·900
1/90,000,000	70·790	1/8,000,000	796·388
1/80,000,000	79·639	1/7,000,000	910·157
1/70,000,000	91·016	1/6,000,000	1061·850
1/63,711,000	100·00	1/5,000,000	1274·220

Most electrical desk calculating machines have the facility for constant multiplication as part of the operating system so that the conversion of the tabulated coordinates can usually be made as quickly as their values can be inserted on the keyboard.

Construction of the master grid

We have already seen that certain classes of map projections such as the Azimuthal, Conical, Pseudoazimuthal and Pseudoconical projections of Groups C and D are more conveniently defined as functions of polar coordinates. However it is more difficult to construct a reliable master grid in polar coordinates than in rectangular coordinates by graphical methods because there are no polar coordinatographs available which compare in working range with large Cartesian coordinatographs. Hence we find that *the master grid is always a system of rectangular coordinates and even when a map projection has been initially derived in polar coordinates, these are transformed into rectangular coordinates for purposes of plotting.* This is easily done by using equations (2.01) and (2.02), as will be shown in the next chapter.

The plotting stage requires a sheet of dimensionally stable draughting film (probably polyester plastic) with dimensions greater than the maximum extent of the projection. Unless a coordinatograph is used to plot the coordinates, a precise (x', y',) grid must be drawn or reproduced upon the plotting sheet. There are four different ways in which a suitable master grid may be prepared. These are, in preferred order of choice:

Plate 1 Coradi coordinatograph with effective plotting dimensions 1000 mm. in both x and y.

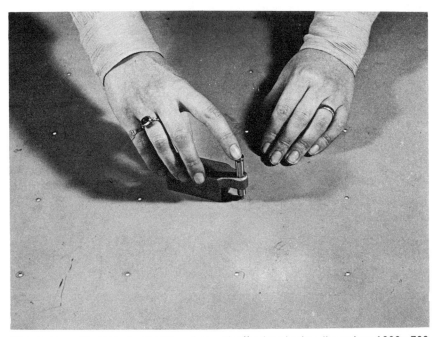

Plate 2 Haag-Streit Master Grid Template with effective plotting dimensions 1000 × 700 mm. and holes at 100 mm. intervals.

Plate 3 Aristo small size coordinatograph for use with a Master Grid Template.

Plate 4 Scribing curved lines with the aid of a French Curve.

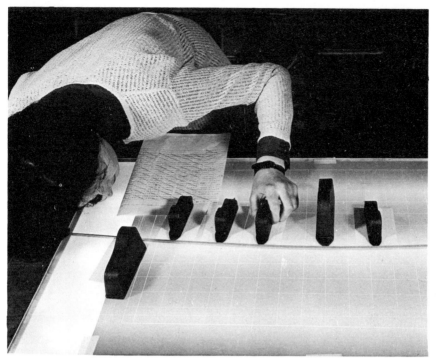

Plate 5 Alignment of a conventional lancewood spline held in position with ship weights.

Plate 6 Scribing curved lines with the aid of a plastic spline held in position with weights and modelling clay.

(1) To use a large coordinatograph as the master grid,
(2) To use a master grid template and small coordinatograph for plotting the individual graticule intersections,
(3) To reproduce the master grid from one obtained by method (1) or, alternatively purchase a precision grid printed on plastic,
(4) To construct the master grid graphically.

(1) *Use of a coordinatograph*

In many cartographic establishments the whole of the plotting and drawing stages of constructing a map projection can be done by coordinatograph (Plate 1). This instrument creates the two orthogonal axes of rectangular coordinates by means of one fixed steel beam and a travelling steel gantry which has a moving plotting head attached to it. Linear displacements of the gantry and the plotting head may be transferred to scales by means of lead screws or a rack-and-pinion drive. With the aid of verniers or micrometers attached to each movement it is possible to read or plot coordinates to a least count of 0·1 mm. on the majority of instruments. Some of them even give scale readings to a least count of 0·01 mm. If the fixed beam is regarded as the *y*-axis, values of the ordinate may be obtained by moving the gantry along this axis to the appropriate scale reading. Values of the abscissa are changed by moving the plotting head along the gantry. The precision of plotting is usually claimed to be a standard error of about ±0·05 mm. on each axis.

The great advantage of using a large coordinatograph to plot a map projection is that no preliminary construction is needed. Thus a virgin sheet of plastic can be mounted on the drawing table of the instrument and can be left there until all the graticule intersections have been plotted. Moreover, if it is required to plot a grid or graticule composed entirely of orthogonal straight lines, the fair drawing of the component lines can be done entirely on the instrument, using a special ruling pen or scribe tool holder which can be attached to the plotting head. This eliminates a great deal of slow careful work such as the alignment of a straight edge through pairs of points, which would be necessary if the lines were drawn by conventional methods.

The addition of servo-motors and electronic control to a coordinatograph further extends the efficiency of the equipment because it can be used in conjunction with a card or tape reader, or even on-line to a digital computer, so that plotting of graticule intersections can be accomplished automatically as their coordinates are computed. Moreover a variety of interpolation programmes have been written which will control a coordinatograph connected on-line to a computer as it draws or scribes smooth curves through the plotted points. Thus the whole work of plotting and drawing a map projection can be done automatically if this sophisticated equipment is available. For example, automatic plotting is now done as a standard production routine at the Hydrographic Department, where all new charts have the projection and marginal subdivisions of the graticule plotted and scribed without any manual intervention. Lattice charts (p. 183) are also prepared by these means.

The only objection to the use of a coordinatograph for plotting graticule intersections is that a large format precision instrument with a working range of about 1 metre on each axis is expensive. Consequently not every cartographic establishment has access to even a manually operated instrument. Therefore we suggest some cheaper ways of obtaining the master grid.

(2) *Master grid template and small coordinatograph*

A master grid template (Plate 2) is a flat sheet of metal with dimensions 1 m. × 0·7 m.

or thereabouts. This sheet is drilled with a network of holes at uniform spacing, usually 50 mm. × 50 mm. or 100 mm. × 100 mm. Each hole is identical and a special tool which fits them exactly is used to mark points by pricking the surface of the plotting sheet lying under the template. Although the equipment seems crude compared with the use of a large format coordinatograph, the master grid template is a precision instrument and those points which can be located with it have accuracy equivalent to those plotted by coordinatograph. The job of plotting grid intersections by master grid template is extremely quick, for there are no scales to be read or set. Consequently the seventy or more points drilled in a typical template can be transferred to the plotting sheet in no more time that it takes to set the coordinatograph to plot half a dozen of them. The only disadvantage of the method is that the grid points plotted are rather far apart. This means that further subdivision of the master grid by graphical methods may be needed before the required graticule intersection can be located. However a careful draughtsman who is willing to make a few additional calculations during the work of plotting ought to be able to work within the 50 mm. or 100 mm. grid as precisely and efficiently as within the 5 mm. grid suggested earlier.

Plotting of graticule intersections can be done entirely with ordinary drawing instruments, such as bowspring dividers, and a steel scale. There is also a variety of small size coordinatographs which can be used with a master grid template to make it practically as efficient as a large format coordinatograph. The small coordinatograph usually has an operating range of 200 mm. or less along each axis and therefore corresponds to a miniature version of the big instrument (Plate 3) which can be placed upon the surface of the plotting sheet and orientated to the points already located by master grid template. The combination of the master grid template and small size coordinatograph is both efficient and cheap.

(3) *Use of a preprinted grid*

We use a preprinted grid every time we plot on graph paper. However the typical sheet of graph paper is not particularly accurately printed and it has been reproduced upon the dimensionally unstable base of cartridge or detail paper. For use in cartography, as a substitute for a coordinatograph or master grid template, we need a precision grid reproduced on polyester plastic. These can be bought from some of the manufacturers of drawing office equipment but such grids have to be tested carefully (see p. 120) for there are a number of indifferent products available. In a department where different projections have to be constructed fairly often, the quickest and least expensive method of producing master grids is by photomechanical reproduction of positive copies from a precision grid which is used solely as a master copy. This could be scribed by coordinatograph to the department's own specification.

(4) *Graphical methods of plotting the master grid*

In an ill-equipped drawing office, or under special working conditions, such as at sea or when the gridded sheet must be larger than the coordinatograph table, it may be necessary to construct a master grid graphically. Although we believe that the use of a preprinted grid is the more economical method to use in practice, we describe two methods of making the graphical construction. This is because useful lessons can be learnt from comparison of the two methods. One provides valuable independent checks whereas the other does not and this important principle can be applied to the comparative study of many other kinds of graphical work.

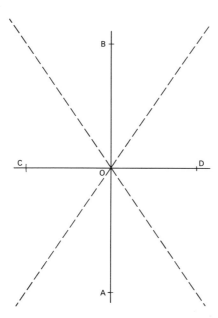

Figure 63 Graphical construction of a master grid by Method I. Stages 1–4 showing the location of the centre of the plotting sheet by drawing diagonals, the construction of the axes *AOB* and *COD* and the location of the points *A, B, C* and *D* by arcs drawn from *O*.

Method I   See Figs. 63, 64, 65.

(1) The approximate centre of the plotting sheet is located by drawing diagonals through the sheet corners. From the centre, *O*, thus defined, the axes *AB* and *CD* are drawn at right angles to one another and approximately parallel to the edges of the plotting sheet. The construction of the right angle at the centre is important for if the two axes are not perpendicular, the whole grid will turn out to be a parallelogram and not a rectangle.

(2) The distances along the axes to the edges of the grid are set upon two beam compasses. For example, $OB = OA = 500 \cdot 0$ mm. and $OC = OD = 350 \cdot 0$ mm. are the settings needed to plot a grid with overall dimensions $1 \cdot 0$ m. $\times$ $0 \cdot 7$ m. The use of two beam compasses saves having to reset the measurements during the next two stages of construction.

(3) The beam compass with the setting *OC* is centred at *O* and the arcs *OC* and *OD* are constructed on one axis.

(4) The beam compass with the setting *OB* is centred at *O* and the arcs *OA* and *OB* are constructed on the other axis.

(5) The beam compass with the setting *OB* is centred at *C* to construct the arcs *CQ* and *CR*.

(6) The beam compass with the setting *OB* is centred at *D* to construct the arcs *DS* and *DT*.

(7) The beam compass with the setting *OC* is centred at *A* to construct the arcs *AQ* and *AT*.

(8) The beam compass with the setting *OC* is centred at *B* to construct the arcs *BR* and *BS*. The intersections of arcs at *Q*, *R*, *S* and *T* locate the four corners of the grid. At this stage it is desirable to check that the lengths of the diagonals *QS* = *RT*. This is a necessary geometrical requirement of a rectangle.

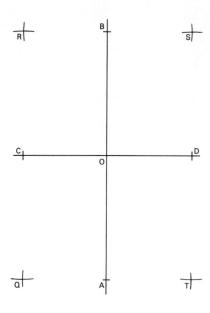

Figure 64 Graphical construction of a master grid by Method I. Stages 5–8, showing the location of the corner points *Q*, *R*, *S* and *T* by the intersection of arcs drawn from *A*, *B*, *C* and *D*.

(9) The grid is now subdivided as required, e.g. into 5 mm. units, along each side. This has to be done by setting the appropriate measurements upon the beam compasses and plotting each subdivision from the two most convenient control points of the eight (*A*, *B*, *C*, *D*, *Q*, *R*, *S*, *T*) which have been located. It is most undesirable to use the drawing office methods of subdividing a line by parallel ruler, set squares or by stepping off equal divisions by bowspring dividers set to a separation of 5 mm. Each of these methods can introduce systematic errors into the construction and, by definition, the master grid should be sensibly free from error. Location of a large number of subdivisions by beam compass is excessively tedious, but it has to be done.

(10) Corresponding points along the edges of the grid are joined by ruling straight lines between them.

(11) The accuracy of the work may be tested by laying a straight edge diagonally across the grid, e.g. between the points D and U, T and V, etc. If all the grid intersections coincide with the straight edge, the construction may be accepted.

The weakness of this method is that no check is made upon the quality of the work after stage (8), when the diagonals are measured, until after the grid has been subdivided. Since stage (9) is the most laborious part of the whole job, the preparation of a grid which proves to be unacceptable has wasted much time and effort.

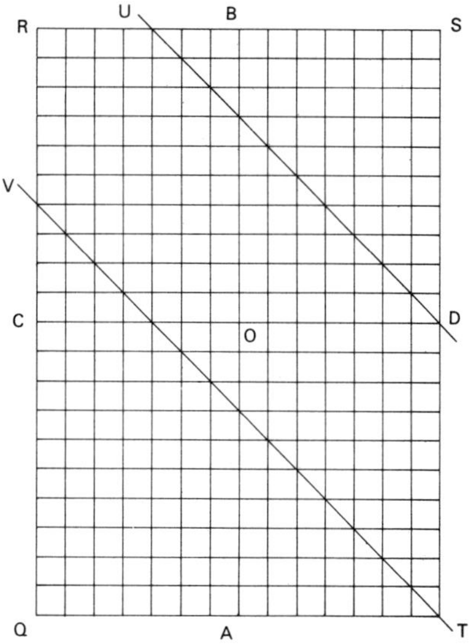

Figure 65 Checking the accuracy of plotting and drawing a master grid by laying a ruling edge through points such as *UD* and *VT*. Note that all grid intersections along these lines coincide with the ruling edge.

Method II   See Figs. 66, 67

(1) The first step is to calculate the length of the diagonal of the grid ($QS = RT$) and the bearing which the diagonal makes with one side of the grid. This is done by plane trigonometry. For example, in Fig. 66,

$$\tan \theta = x/y \qquad\qquad (6.03)$$

$$QS = x \cdot \operatorname{cosec} \theta \qquad\qquad (6.04)$$

Thus, for a grid with dimensions 1000 mm. × 700 mm.,

$$\tan \theta = 1000/700 = 1 \cdot 42857$$
$$\theta = 55° \cdot 008$$
$$QS = 1000 \times 1 \cdot 22066$$
$$= 1220 \cdot 66 \text{ mm.}$$

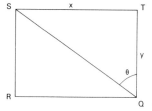

Figure 66 Graphical construction of a master grid by Method II. Stage 1, showing the definition of the angle θ and determination of the length of the diagonal, *QS*.

(2) We commence construction from an arbitrary point near one corner of the plotting sheet which we decide to call the point Q. A line corresponding to the diagonal QS is drawn from the point, making the approximate angle θ with the shorter side of the grid. This is to ensure that the sides of the grid will be more or less parallel with the edges of the plotting sheet when the construction has been completed.

(3) With a beam compass set to the calculated length of the diagonal and centred at Q, the arc QS is constructed on the diagonal line. This locates the point S.

(4) With a beam compass set to the distance $ST=QR$, construct two arcs in the vicinity of the two remaining grid corners from Q and S respectively.

(5) With a beam compass set to the distance $QT=RS$, construct two arcs to cut the arcs made in stage (4) from Q to S respectively. The intersection of the two pairs of arcs from Q and S locates the points T and R.

(6) Using the beam compass still set to the length of the diagonal, test that $QS=RT$. If this comparison is exact the four points define the corners of a rectangular grid. If one diagonal is longer than the other, the figure is a parallelogram and the construction must be repeated.

(7) Join RT.

(8) Join the four corners of the grid and bisect each side. This defines the four points A, B, C, and D.

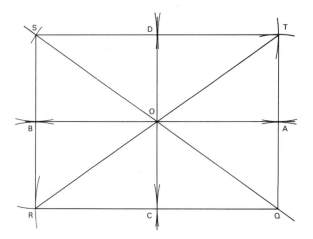

Figure 67 Graphical construction of a master grid by Method II at the completion of Stage 9. This shows all the arcs needed to locate the four corner points Q, R, S, T and the midpoints A, B, C and D of each side. Note that the four lines which pass through the point O all intersect at this point.

(9) Join AB and CD. If the four lines AB, CD, QS and RT all meet at the point O the construction is correct. The presence of a *cocked hat* formed by certain lines failing to pass through the centre indicates some error in construction which must be eliminated.

(10) Subdivision of the grid is carried out in the same way as stage (9) of Method I.

(11) Testing of the final construction is carried out in the same way as stage (10) of Method I.

The advantage of Method II is that this contains two independent checks upon the quality of the work before the tedious task of subdividing the grid is attempted. This means that comparatively little time is wasted if the first few attempts fail to produce a grid of sufficient standard.

Drawing the graticule

We need not comment in detail about plotting within the master grid apart from noting that this is most easily done by linear measurement, using bow-spring or similar dividers and plotting each point by means of four measurements made from each corner of the grid square in which the point is to be located. Only two of these measurements are needed to locate a point but four are used to overcome the possibility of both gross and systematic errors in plotting. Graticule intersections are plotted on topographical maps by the *arc and tangent method*, described in Refs. 1 and 2.

Where the draughting specification calls for parallels and meridians to be drawn in full, and these are curved, it is necessary to use splines or curves as draughting aids. The curves representing the parallels and meridians on a map are lines which satisfy specific mathematical functions and these functions must be satisfied not only at the graticule intersections which have been plotted but at all intervening points along each curve. Hence the smooth curve joining the plotted points has mathematical significance and it will not suffice to draw them in any arbitrary fashion. Bearing in mind that the standard error in the location of a graticule intersection ought to be about $\pm 0 \cdot 1$ mm., this suggests that considerable care must be taken in selecting how each line passes through the points.

One important aid to construction is to plot more graticule intersections than need be shown on the completed map. For example, if the final map is to show $20°$ separation of parallels and meridians it is worth plotting graticule intersections at every $10°$ on the plotting sheet. Although this example involves a threefold increase in the work of computing graticule intersections and plotting, it is also a valuable aid to compilation because the closer graticule affords more control in transferring map detail from one scale and projection to another.

It is difficult to lay down any formal rules concerning the use of splines or curves for completing the drawing of a graticule. The difficulty of this part of the work depends very much upon the complexity of the lines which have to be drawn. Clearly a map projection composed of straight lines and circular arcs can be completed more easily than one like the Briesemeister Projection illustrated in Fig. 61. However the following advice may be useful.

Curves (See Plate 4)

The procedure is to test different parts of different curves to find which of them best suits the plotted distribution of points. It is not sufficient to find a curve which appears to pass through only two or three intersections. The ruling edge of the curve must pass through about four or five consecutive points in order to draw only a short part of the required line. The reason for this is illustrated in Fig. 68.

In order to draw a smooth curve through the plotted points, *a, b, c, d, e, f* and *g* it will be necessary to fit various curves in different positions. To draw the line it may be necessary to fit a curve to the points *a, b, c* and *d* in order to draw the part *bc*; to fit it through *b, c, d* and *e* to draw *cd* and so on. If a ruling edge can be found to fit points *a, b, c* and *d* in one position, followed by a setting through *d, e, f* and *g* in a second position, it is likely that the two lines drawn to meet at *d* would produce an unintended discontinuity at that point.

A further difficulty is that the ruling pen or scribing tool held in the optimum position for drawing is slightly offset from the edge of the curve. Consequently the ruling edge of the curve has to be slightly offset from the points so that the nib or sapphire passes through every point correctly. Thus, in addition to trying to make the curve fit a sequence of points it is also desirable to imagine it tracing a line parallel to that required. All this calls for considerable skill.

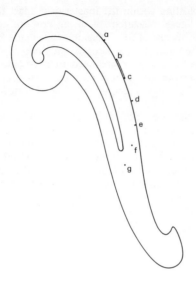

Figure 68 The alignment of a French Curve through four plotted points in order to draw the part of the curve *bc*.

Splines (*See Plates* 5 *and* 6)

The draughtsman's spline is a flexible rod about 1 m. in length. Traditionally this was made of lance-wood, though nowadays a variety of other flexible materials can be used. The rod may be square or rectangular in section. It may taper towards the ends or towards the middle. Only experiment shows how much curvature can be obtained from a rod of particular length and cross section and therefore how many weights will be needed to hold it in position. The location of the ship weights is important from the point of view of stability and continuity of drawing. Usually it is better to have the weights aligned on the inside (concave) surface of the spline and to draw along the outer or convex edge. Ultimately, however, there must be at least two weights on the outer edge to hold the spline in position (Plate 5). Stability in position of the ruling edge is important for it is obviously unsatisfactory if the spline undulates with the slight lateral pressure as the pen moves along its side. In ink draughting this invariably causes smudging of the freshly drawn line. In any case it reduces the accuracy of the drawing.

A different technique for anchoring the spline to the fair drawing may be used when the work is done by scribing. Since the opaque surface of scribe coating is unaffected by materials which would ruin an ink drawing we may use modelling clay, such as Plasticene, to replace some of the ship weights. The spline for this job can be cut from heavy-gauge plastic, for example 1 mm. thick Cobex, in a strip of width 5 mm. to any desired length.

This spline is set in the upright, or edge-on, position on the manuscript and temporarily held by ship weights. The modelling clay is packed along the inside edge throughout its length as shown in Plate 6. For large-radius curves it is sufficient to use only two ship weights at the ends of the spline and the whole of the rest is held sufficiently firmly by the clay. A small-radius curve or a complicated curve with reverse curvature will need a few additional ship weights to keep the spline in position.

References

1 — *Military Engineering, Vol. XIII—Survey, Part XII Cartography*, London, 1962, The War Office, 323 pp.
2 — *A Guide to the Compilation and Revision of Maps*, Department of the Army Technical Manual TM 5-240, Washington, 1955, Department of the Army, 167 pp.

CHAPTER 7

COMPUTATION OF PROJECTION COORDINATES

It is unworthy of excellent men to lose hours like slaves in the labour of calculation which could safely be relegated to anyone else if machines were used.

Leibnitz, 1671

Introduction

If we recommend that a map projection should be constructed by plotting the plane coordinates of every graticule intersection, we must assume that these tables have already been calculated and tabulated. Although tables of these are given in many of the standard foreign textbooks, such as Reignier (Ref. 1) and Wagner (Ref. 2), few of them have ever been published in the English language. Consequently they are less well known than they ought to be. Space does not allow us to give a comprehensive collection of tables in this book apart from those for Briesmeister's Projection (which have never been published) in Appendix II. In any case, no published set of projection tables could give coordinates for every oblique aspect version of even the commonly used projections. Therefore it is necessary for the cartographer to be able to compute the coordinates should the occasion ever arise that some new version of a projection is required.

The kind of computations to be described ought not to present any difficulties to the student who has learnt to execute the simpler kinds of surveying calculations by means of logarithms or using a desk calculating machine. The majority of coordinate expressions which are derived in Chapter 8 or listed in Appendix I are not difficult to solve numerically but a great obstacle is the repetitive nature of the work. A map projection of the whole World having a graticule spacing of 10° comprises 631 separate points of graticule intersection. If the determination of the coordinates of each point takes only 10 minutes, the amount of computing time which is needed to obtain all the coordinates to plot the whole map will be more than 105 hours or about three weeks' work for one man. This is an extreme case, exemplified by a skew oblique aspect projection (like those shown in Fig. 56, d, e, and g) in which there is no symmetry about the axes and each point has to be computed separately. We have seen that many map projections are symmetrical about one or two axes. Therefore it is normally only necessary to compute the coordinates of the graticule intersections in one hemisphere (317 points), or even one quadrant (173 points) with corresponding reductions in time. Nevertheless these figures indicate that the kind of computations needed to plot a map projection are best done by digital computer. We will refer to some of the special problems which arise in writing a programme elsewhere in the chapter.

However just as we cannot assume that every cartographer has access to a large format coordinatograph, we cannot assume that a digital computer is available. Consequently we must also describe the older, but slower methods of making the computations by logarithms or by desk calculator and with the aid of tables. In any case, the production of a satisfactory programme for use with a digital computer requires a proper understanding of all the arithmetical steps which are involved. Therefore it is essential to understand the older methods.

A typical kind of computation which has to be done in the field of practical work with map projections is the derivation of an oblique aspect graticule to satisfy the particular requirements for a new map. This kind of computation involves three different coordinate transformations which have to be carried out consecutively for every graticule intersection.

(1) The transformation from geographical coordinates (φ, λ) to Bearing and Distance coordinates (z, a) on the sphere,

(2) The transformation from bearing and distance coordinates into projection coordinates (x, y) or (r, θ) on the plane,

(3) The transformation from projection coordinates into master grid coordinates (x', y') for plotting.

The third part of the transformation corresponds to *scale conversion of the tabulated coordinates* described in Chapter 6 (pp. 115–16).

Bearing and distance coordinates

This system of spherical polar coordinates was mentioned briefly in Chapter 3 as an alternative to geographical coordinates. From the practical point of view of constructing oblique aspect map projections they are a valuable aid because use of them generally overcomes the need to determine and evaluate complicated algebraic expressions to relate (φ, λ) to the plane. By introducing bearing and distance coordinates, we split the transformation from the spherical surface to the plane into two separate parts.

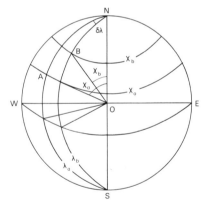

Figure 69 Points *A* and *B* on the spherical surface and their definition by means of colatitude and longitude (χ, λ) coordinates.

Consider the part of the spherical surface illustrated in Fig. 69. We are accustomed to define the positions of the two points *A* and *B* by means of their geographical coordinates but we could also define them by the (χ, λ) coordinates of colatitude and longitude. The only difference between this system and conventional geographical coordinates is that colatitude (χ) is measured from the pole in a plane containing the axis of rotation rather than from the plane of the Equator. In other words we use the angle *NOA*. The (χ, λ) graticule differs from the conventional system of geographical (φ, λ) coordinates in only one respect. The numerical values assigned to parallels of colatitude increase from the Pole towards the Equator.

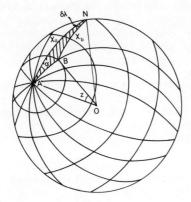

Figure 70 The bearing and distance coordinates (z, α) of a point B from a pole at A.

Suppose, however, that we wish to refer the point B to the point A instead of the Pole N as shown in Fig. 70. We may imagine the ordered sequence of small circles and great circles to which A is the pole as being the result of shifting the entire pattern of (χ, λ) coordinate lines from N to A. In this system the position of B is related to that of A by means of the angular distance $AOB=z$, measured at the centre of the sphere, together with another angle, such as NAB measured between the planes NOA and OAB. By analogy with geographical coordinates the second angle is also represented by the spherical angle NAB. If we refer back to the spherical triangle illustrated in Fig. 24 (p. 37), we find that the angle NAB is the true bearing, α of B from A. Combining these two measures to form an alternative system of coordinate reference upon the spherical surface, we have defined the (z, α) system of *Bearing and Distance Coordinates*.

Thus we may define the position of any point on the curved surface with respect to any other point which has been selected as the pole for the (z, α) system. If this pole happens to be the geographical pole, then $z=\chi$ and $\alpha=\lambda$ so that the small circles representing $z=$ constant become parallels of colatitude and the circles denoting $\alpha=$ constant become meridians.

The transformation from geographical coordinates into bearing and distance coordinates is accomplished by the solution of the spherical triangle NAB. This has already been done in Chapter 3 and it is only necessary to convert the algebraic notation into the form which is usually encountered in practice. We denote the coordinates of the point A as (φ_0, λ_0) and those of any other point B as (φ, λ). The difference in longitude is $\lambda_0 - \lambda = \delta\lambda$. Then, substituting these terms in equations (3.20) and (3.24),

$$\cos z = \sin \varphi_0 . \sin \varphi + \cos \varphi_0 . \cos \varphi . \cos \delta\lambda \qquad (7.01)$$

$$\sin \alpha = \cos \varphi_0 . \sin \delta\lambda . \operatorname{cosec} z \qquad (7.02)$$

Hence the first transformation from (φ, λ) to (z, α) involves the numerical solution of equations (7.01) and (7.02).

Numerical evaluation of z and α

We can solve equations (7.01) and (7.02) by using logarithms, a desk calculating machine or a digital computer. We may also use special tables which have been prepared for integer values of φ_0, λ_0, φ and λ.

The first, and most important, difficulty which arises from the use of equations (7.01) and (7.02) is that z, φ_0, φ and $\delta\lambda$ all appear in equation (7.01) in the argument of their cosines. Also cos φ_0 appears in equation (7.02). If any of these angles exceeds 90°, the cosine of the angle will be a negative quantity. In the case of φ_0 and φ this arises when either A or B lie in the southern hemisphere but the spherical triangle is solved with respect to the North Pole so that the sides corresponding to χ_0 or χ are greater than 90°. Although the presence of negative cosines will not be troublesome to the experienced computer who is working with a desk calculating machine and tables of natural trigonometric functions, this may be a serious difficulty to the beginner, especially if he is also using the logarithmic solution. Under these circumstances a fair amount of attention is needed to ensure the correct interpretation of z. If $\delta\lambda$ and z are much greater than 90°, then the correct solution ought to be fairly obvious, even to the beginner. It is where z lies close to 90° that great care must be taken to ensure that the correct answer has been obtained.

An important additional factor in the selection of a foolproof method of computing is that the work is repetitive. We have already referred to the number of individual solutions which have to be made to derive 10° graticule intersections for the sphere, hemisphere and quadrant. Any method of calculation which avoids time-consuming entry to tables (and interpolation therein) as well as possible ambiguity in the computed result will be preferred to a solution which requires greater use of tables and pause for thought.

The problem is akin to that of the navigator who may have to solve a spherical triangle to find certain of its parts quickly, accurately and under conditions of stress. It is therefore not surprising to find that the methods of computation used in navigation are both economical and reliable. A convenient solution of both equations (7.01) and (7.02) is through the medium of the *haversines* of certain parts of the spherical triangle. By virtue of the form of the left-hand side of the equation, the modification of equation (7.01) to find z is known as the *Natural Haversine Formula*.

The *versine* of any angle may be derived from the cosine as

$$\text{vers } \theta = 1 - \cos \theta \tag{7.03}$$

The haversine is one-half of this quantity, or

$$\text{hav } \theta = \tfrac{1}{2}(1 - \cos \theta) \tag{7.04}$$

Conversely

$$\cos \theta = 1 - 2 \text{ hav } \theta \tag{7.05}$$

It can also be shown that

$$\text{hav } \theta = \sin^2 \frac{\theta}{2} \tag{7.06}$$

As θ increases from 0 to π, hav θ increases from 0 to $+1$. Since the limiting size of any side or angle of a spherical triangle is 180° (or π radians), any part of any spherical triangle may be expressed through its haversine as a positive quantity.

The derivation of the natural haversine formula simply involves substitution of the haversine for those sides and angles expressed in (7.01) by their cosines. We do not give the proof here. It may be found, for example, in numerous textbooks on navigation. Using the notation that the colatitude of $A = \chi_0$ and that of $B = \chi$, we find that

$$\text{hav } z = \text{hav}(\chi \sim \chi_0) + \sin \chi \cdot \sin \chi_0 \cdot \text{hav } \delta\lambda \tag{7.07}$$

The symbol $\sim$ denotes the positive difference between the colatitudes (larger minus smaller).

The Natural Haversine Formula has long been used in navigation. Cotter (Ref. 3) attributes the first publication of tables for $\sin^2 \theta/2$ to James Andrews in his *Astronomical and Nautical Tables* published in 1805. Because of its considerable

K

practical importance in sight reduction for astronomical navigation there are many different published sets of five-figure tables of natural and logarithmic haversines and these are arranged in a form which is convenient for quick reference without much interpolation (Refs. 4, 5 and 6). Five-figure values for these trigonometric functions provide adequate accuracy for practical work for this allows determination of z to the nearest $0' \cdot 1$ (6 secs) of arc. Assuming a spherical Earth of radius $6371 \cdot 1$ km. this corresponds to an uncertainty of about $0 \cdot 2$ km. in the length of z and at the scales for which the spherical assumption is justified this distance is negligible.

In order to demonstrate the different methods of solving equation (7.01) numerically and to demonstrate the practical advantage of using the Natural Haversine Formula, we will solve the same problem by four different methods. We solve the Cosine Formula (7.01) by logarithms and by desk calculating machine followed by solution of the Natural Haversine Formula (7.07) by each method. The example demonstrates the difficult case where z is slightly greater than 90° so that negative cosines enter into the argument.

We specify that A lies in latitude 45° North, longitude 20° West, and that the point B lies in latitude 30° North, longitude 130° East. We wish to determine the angular distance, z, between the points.

(a) *Solution of the Cosine Formula by logarithms to find z*

$$\delta\lambda = \lambda - \lambda_0 = 150°$$

log sin $\varphi_0 = 9 \cdot 849$ 49   log cos $\varphi_0 = 9 \cdot 849$ 49
log sin $\varphi = 9 \cdot 698$ 97   log cos $\varphi = 9 \cdot 937$ 53
                                             log cos $\delta\lambda = 9 \cdot 937$ 53 ($-$)

___

                                             log second term $= 9 \cdot 724$ 55 ($-$)
First term $= 0 \cdot 353$ 56   Second term $= -0 \cdot 530$ 33
          cos $z = -0 \cdot 176$ 77
          $z = 180° - 79^\sigma 49' \cdot 1 = 100° \ 10' \cdot 9$

Note the use of the sign of cos $\delta\lambda$ in the calculation of the second term. The beginner would probably subtract log cos $\delta\lambda$ from the sum of log cos φ_0 and log cos φ. This would produce the erroneous value of $-0 \cdot 150$ 51 for this term, which, converted to a natural value and combined with the first term would give an impossible value for cos z. Alternatively he might ignore the fact that cos $\delta\lambda$ was a negative quantity, obtain $0 \cdot 883$ 89 for cos z and find that z was the absurd value $27° \ 53'$. The sign of log cos $\delta\lambda$ is put in brackets to indicate that the second term must be treated as a negative quantity when it is converted into its natural value. Finally, if the right answer were obtained but the sign of cos z ignored, the length of the side AB would be taken to represent $79° \ 49' \cdot 1$ whereas this is the supplement of the true value. Clearly there is much scope for confusion in this solution.

(b) *Solution of the Cosine Formula by desk calculating machine to find z*

$$\delta\lambda = \lambda - \lambda_0 = 150°$$

sin $\varphi_0 = 0 \cdot 707$ 11   cos $\varphi_0 = 0 \cdot 707$ 11
sin $\varphi = 0 \cdot 500$ 00   cos $\varphi = 0 \cdot 866$ 03
                                         cos $\delta\lambda = -0 \cdot 866$ 03

___

First term $= 0 \cdot 353$ 55
                                         Second term $= -0 \cdot 530$ 34
          cos $z = -0 \cdot 176$ 79
          $z = 180° - 79° \ 49' \cdot 1 = 100° \ 10' \cdot 9$

The only precaution needed here is to attribute the correct sign to cos $\delta\lambda$ in the second term so that the product of cos $\varphi_0 \cdot$ cos $\varphi \cdot$ cos $\delta\lambda$ is negative.

(c) *Solution of the Natural Haversine Formula by logarithms to find z*

$$\delta\lambda = \lambda - \lambda_0 = 150°, \ \chi_0 = 90° - \varphi_0 = 45°, \ \chi = 90° - \varphi = 60°, \ \chi - \chi_0 = 15°$$

$$\log \sin \chi_0 = 9\cdot849 \ 49$$
$$\log \sin \chi = 9\cdot937 \ 53$$
$$\log \text{hav } \delta\lambda = 9\cdot969 \ 89$$

$$\log \text{second term} = 9\cdot756 \ 91$$
$$\text{second term} = 0\cdot571 \ 36$$
$$\text{hav}(\chi \sim \chi_0) = 0\cdot017 \ 04$$

$$\text{hav } z = 0\cdot588 \ 40$$
$$z = 100° \ 11'.0$$

(d) *Solution of the Natural Haversine Formula by desk calculating machine to find z*

$$\delta\lambda = \lambda - \lambda_0 = 150°, \ \chi_0 = 90° - \varphi_0 = 45°, \ \chi = 90° - \varphi = 60°, \ \chi - \chi_0 = 15°$$

$$\sin \chi_0 = 0\cdot707 \ 11$$
$$\sin \chi = 0\cdot866 \ 03$$
$$\text{hav } \delta\lambda = 0\cdot933 \ 01$$

$$\text{Second term} = 0\cdot571 \ 35$$
$$\text{hav}(\chi \sim \chi_0) = 0\cdot017 \ 04$$

$$\text{hav } z = 0\cdot588 \ 39$$
$$z = 100° \ 10'.9$$

In both of the solutions of the Natural Haversine Formula there is no possibility of ambiguity in reading the value of z from tables of natural haversines.

The number of computation steps involved in these four solutions of the same problem may be summarised as follows. Each solution includes the preliminary steps of determining $\delta\lambda$, χ_0, χ and $(\chi_0 \sim \chi)$

Method	(a)	(b)	(c)	(d)
Entry to tables	8	6	6	5
Addition and				
subtraction	5	2	6	5
Multiplication	0	3	0	2

The advantage of solution (d) is clearly demonstrated here. Although it needs one more arithmetical step than any of the other solutions it is more economical in the use of tables. As has already been noted, this is the principal cause of delay in obtaining the result.

We now consider the solution of equation (7.02) to obtain the bearing a. In this expression, $\cos \varphi_0$ can be a negative quantity and there may be ambiguity in the result because both $\delta\lambda$ and z may be greater than 90°.

Substitution of haversines in this equation leads to the alternative expression

$$\text{hav } a = \text{hav } \chi - \text{hav}(\chi_0 \sim z) \cdot \text{cosec } \chi_0 \cdot \text{cosec } z \qquad (7.08)$$

This will give a value for a which lies between 0° and 180° and which is therefore either the clockwise or the anticlockwise angle measured from the meridian through A to the great circle AB. The fact whether this is the angle which is required or the angle $360° - a$ can be verified from the longitudes of the two points A and B. If B lies to the East of A, then the calculated value of a is the true bearing. If B lies to the West of A, then the required true bearing is $360° - a$.

We repeat the procedure for calculating a by three different methods, using the same data as were used to find z. The three solutions are:

(*a*) Solution of the Cosine Formula (7.02) by desk calculating machine,
(*b*) Solution of the Haversine Formula (7.08) by logarithms,
(*c*) Solution of the Haversine Formula by desk calculating machine.

Note that we do not attempt solution of the Cosine Formula by logarithms. We believe that we have already demonstrated that the method is too slow and inefficient to be considered further.

(*a*) *Solution of the Cosine Formula by desk calculating machine to find a*

$$\delta\lambda = \lambda - \lambda_0 = 150°, \ z = 100° \ 10'.9$$
$$\cos \varphi = 0\cdot866 \ 03$$
$$\sin \delta\lambda = 0\cdot500 \ 00$$
$$\operatorname{cosec} z = 1\cdot016 \ 00$$

$$\overline{}$$

$$\sin a = 0\cdot439 \ 94$$
$$a = 26° \ 06'.0$$

(*b*) *Solution of the Haversine Formula by logarithms to find a*

$$z = 100° \ 10'.9, \ \chi_0 \sim z = 55° \ 10'.9$$
$$\operatorname{hav} \chi = 0\cdot250 \ 00$$
$$\operatorname{hav}(\chi_0 \sim z) = 0\cdot241 \ 51$$

$$\overline{}$$

$$\text{Difference} = 0\cdot035 \ 49$$
$$\log \text{difference} = 8\cdot550 \ 11$$
$$\log \operatorname{cosec} \chi = 0\cdot150 \ 51$$
$$\log \operatorname{cosec} z = 0\cdot006 \ 89$$

$$\overline{}$$

$$\log \operatorname{hav} a = 8\cdot707 \ 51$$
$$a = 26° \ 06'.1$$

(*c*) *Solution of the Haversine Formula by desk calculating machine to find a*

$$z = 100° \ 10'.9, \ \chi_0 \sim z = 55° \ 10'.9$$
$$\operatorname{hav} \chi = 0\cdot250 \ 00$$
$$\operatorname{hav}(\chi_0 \sim z) = 0\cdot241 \ 51$$

$$\overline{}$$

$$\text{Difference} = 0\cdot035 \ 49$$
$$\operatorname{cosec} \chi_0 = 1\cdot414 \ 21$$
$$\operatorname{cosec} z = 1\cdot016 \ 00$$

$$\overline{}$$

$$\operatorname{hav} a = 0\cdot050 \ 99$$
$$a = 26° \ 06'.0$$

The relative merits of the three different methods of obtaining a may be tabulated as follows:

Method	(*a*)	(*b*)	(*c*)
Entry to tables	4	6	5
Addition and subtraction	1	4	2
Multiplication	2	0	2

From this table it is clear that the most convenient solution is by means of the Cosine Formula using natural trigonometric functions and a desk calculator, for the method requires less reference to the tables than do either of the other methods. However the Cosine Formula gives an ambiguous solution so that time might be wasted in deciding about the proper quadrant for α. The use of haversines avoids all ambiguity apart from the need to make the simple check whether A lies to the East or West of B.

Solution of the spherical triangle by digital computer

The advantage of finding the bearing and distance coordinates of several hundred points by solving the equations by digital computer are obvious. It is therefore desirable to comment briefly upon the relative merits of the different kinds of solution which may be done by automatic data processing. Obviously the logarithmic solution is not required for all computers can multiply and divide. Hence the real choice lies between the use of either the Cosine Formula or the Haversine Formula to find z and α.

The trigonometric functions are generally available to the user of a computer through the standard *subroutines* stored in the machine at all times. These provide numerical values for $\sin \theta$, $\cos \theta$, $\tan \theta$ (and usually the other three trigonometric functions in most modern machines) by inserting a suitable statement in the programme. However the use of these subroutines requires all angles to be defined in radians so that an essential preliminary stage in any programme is to convert all angles from degree measure into radians. Similarly the values of z and α determined by digital computer will be expressed in radians and may have to be converted into output in sexagesimal units for subsequent use.

Another most important problem is to know how angles in different quadrants are handled by the subroutines for the trigonometric functions. This is also associated with the mathematical convention about the sign of an angle, described in Chapter 2 (p. 23). Consequently it is usually necessary to test each of the input values (φ_0, φ, $\delta\lambda$) to ascertain which of these lie in the first and which lie in the second quadrant and a sequence of conditional statements must be introduced to ensure that every possible combination of these variables is correctly processed. This difficulty appears to suggest an overwhelming case in favour of using the haversine solutions. However the solution of the equations is in terms of hav z and hav α. Consequently it is necessary to convert the computed results into the angles z and α expressed first as radians and then as sexagesimal units. This involves the use of the sub-routines for the inverse trigonometric functions ($\sin^{-1} \theta$ and $\cos^{-1} \theta$). In order to allocate the computed result for z and α to the correct quadrant it is necessary to introduce the sequence of tests and conditional statements which would permit correct processing of the six possible results (z in two quadrants, α in four quadrants). Since these are equivalent to testing the input, there seems to be no advantage to be gained from using the haversine solutions. Examples of the use of digital computers to solve the transformation from geographical to bearing and distance coordinates have been described in Refs. 7 and 8.

Solution of the spherical triangle by tables

If a digital computer is not available, the job of finding the values of z and α for a large number of graticule intersections is an extremely laborious task. It is not surprising, therefore, that tables have been published which circumvent this part of cartographic computation. Unfortunately none of the tables specifically intended for cartographic use have ever been published in the English language, but this matters little because the arrangement of the tables is usually quite simple and the notation differs little from that used in this book.

The first tables of this kind appear to have been calculated by Professor E. Hammer during the nineteenth century. These first appeared in his book, published in 1889, and are therefore often called 'Hammer's Tables'. However copies of the original version of them are exceedingly rare in Britain. Thus we cannot cite them as a useful source for practical purposes. However two other sets of almost identical tables have been published during the last twenty-five years and provide a substitute. These are:

(1) *Wagner's Tables*, 1949 (*German*)

The tables appear as an appendix to the book *Kartographische Netzentwürfe* by Karl-Heinz Wagner (1st Edition, 1949, Bibliographisches Institut, Leipzig).

They comprise tables for δ ($=z$) and α for 5° intervals of φ and λ, for 5° intervals of φ_0 from 0° to +75°. The tables terminate where $\delta > 90°$.

(2) *TsNIIGAiK Tables*, 1960 (*Russian*)

The tables have been prepared and published by the Central Research Institute for Geodesy, Aerial Survey and Cartography (whose initials are TsNIIGAiK) in Moscow as volume 132 of the 'Trudy', or works, of that Institute. Earlier editions of the same tables were published in the 1930's and shortly after World War II. These are tables for z and α for 5° increments in φ and λ, arranged for 5° values of φ_0 from 0° to +85°. Additional values of z and α are also given for the Arctic Circle and the Tropic of Cancer. The tables are also terminated where $z > 90°$.

Although these appear to be the only tables which have been published specifically for cartographic purposes, the list does not exhaust the range of tables which may be adapted for this work. In navigation an important method of reduction of astronomical sights is the *Marq St. Hilaire Method* which requires computation of the altitude and azimuth of a star for some known position close to where the navigator thinks that he is. The labour of computation is much reduced by using tables of computed altitude and azimuth. Since the spherical triangle to be solved is equivalent to the triangle *NAB* in Fig. 70 such tables can be used to find the bearing and distance prepared for 30' intervals of declination (corresponding to χ_b) and 1° intervals of hour angle (corresponding to $\delta\lambda$). Consequently they occupy much more space than the cartographic tables already described. For example, Ref. 9 comprises six volumes of altitude and azimuth tables to cover all latitudes from the Equator to the Pole. A further disadvantage of astronomical tables is that because their primary use is for astronomical navigation, the values of computed altitude and azimuth only commence at altitudes greater than 5° above the horizon. Translated into terms of great circle distance, this means that the tables are limited to use for $z < 85°$.

The use of tables to determine z and α where z > 90°

All the tables which have been described are for $z \leqslant 90°$. We therefore have to find a procedure which gives the bearing and distance coordinates for more than the hemisphere. It is remarkable that none of the cartographic tables explain how this may be done. The solution is quite simple, though not immediately obvious. One cannot help feeling that many thousands of man hours have been wasted in making special calculations for the remaining graticule intersections, all for the lack of the following explanation.

In Fig. 71, the arc *AB* is greater than 90°. If we extend the arc *BA* and the arc *BN*, these will meet at the point *B'* to form the lune *BAB'N*. By definition, the

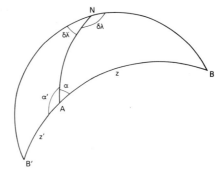

Figure 71 The solution of the spherical triangle *NAB* by tables where *AB=z* is greater than 90°.

arcs *BAB'* and *BNB'* are both equal to 180° of angular distance. Thus $AB'=z'=180°-z$.

Since our problem states that $z>90°$, it follows that $z'<90°$.

At the point *A*, the great circle *BAB'* makes the spherical angle of 180°. It therefore follows that $NAB'=a'=180°-a$.

If, therefore, we can find the (z', a') coordinates for the point *B'*, the required (z, a) coordinates of *B* are the supplement of them.

Since *B'* is 180° from *B* it is the antipodal point of *B*. If we define its geographical coordinates as $B'=(\varphi', \lambda')$, these may be obtained from the geographical coordinates of *B* by means of

$$\varphi' = -\varphi \qquad (7.09)$$

$$\lambda' = 180° - \lambda \qquad (7.10)$$

The procedure for finding the (z, a) coordinates from tables when z is greater than 90° may be summarised as follows:

(1) Given the geographical coordinates of $A=(\varphi_0, \lambda_0)$ and $B=(\varphi, \lambda)$, we find the coordinates of $B'=(\varphi', \lambda')$ from equations (7.09) and (7.10). We calculate the difference in longitude between *A* and *B'* to be $\delta\lambda'=\lambda_0-\lambda'$.

(2) Entering the tables with the arguments φ_0, φ' and $\delta\lambda'$ we find the tabulated values of z' and a'.

(3) Then

$$z=180°-z' \qquad (7.11)$$

$$a=180°-a' \qquad (7.12)$$

which are the required coordinates for *B*. The chief difficulty which arises in this solution is finding the correct value of $\delta\lambda'$. It is useful to have a globe to hand, especially when returning to these computations after a lapse of months or years.

As an example of the method described, we use the same values which were computed by various methods. Therefore $\varphi_0=45°$ N, $\lambda_0=20°$ W, $\varphi=30°$ N and $\lambda=130°$ E.

The antipodal point *B'* has geographical coordinates

$$\varphi' = 30° \text{ S}$$

$$\lambda' = 180° - 130° = 50° \text{ W (check this on a globe)}$$

Entering the tables for $\varphi_0 = 45°$, $\varphi' = -30°$ and $\delta\lambda' = 50° - 20° = 30°$, we find

$$z' = 79° \ 49' \ 04''.5 \text{ or } z = 100° \ 10' \ 55''.5$$

$$a' = 153° \ 53' \ 59''.5 \text{ or } a = 26° \ 06' \ 00''.5$$

which corresponds to the values obtained by calculation.

Transformation from bearing and distance coordinates to projection coordinates and master grid coordinates

In Chapters 4 and 5 we have made use of the general functions to relate the geographical coordinates of a point to its position on the plane by means of the (x, y) or (r, θ) systems.

In Chapter 8 we derive certain other map projections by analytical methods. The first of these is the Azimuthal Equal-area Projection (Lambert), the derivation of which illustrates the use of polar coordinates. Equation (8.19), p. 144 has the form

$$\left. \begin{aligned} r &= 2 \cdot \sin \frac{\chi}{2} \\ \theta &= \lambda \end{aligned} \right\} \tag{7.13}$$

where χ is the colatitude, and $R = 1$.

The description of bearing and distance coordinates has emphasised that the (χ, λ) system is just a particular case of the (z, a) system where the point A is at the geographical pole. It follows that where a projection is described in terms of colatitude and longitude, the transformation to bearing and distance coordinates requires no more than substitution of z for χ and a for λ. Therefore (7.14) expressed for the normal aspect Azimuthal Equal-area projection may be written in the form

$$\left. \begin{aligned} r &= 2 \cdot \sin \frac{z}{2} \\ \theta &= a \end{aligned} \right\} \tag{7.14}$$

and any transverse or oblique aspect of the projection can be derived once the transformation of every graticule intersection to the (z, a) system has been carried out.

However a third stage of transformation is required before the map can be constructed. It was noted in Chapter 6 that map projections are invariably constructed on a master grid of rectangular coordinates. Hence it is required to transform the polar coordinates of (7.13) and (7.14) to a cartesian system.

In the normal aspect of the Azimuthal Equal-area Projection the geographical pole is the origin of the (r, θ) system of polar coordinates. Therefore we make this point also the origin of the (x', y') system of master grid coordinates. We further specify that the Greenwich Meridian coincides with the $-y'$ axis, as illustrated in Fig. 72.

Then any point whose polar coordinates have been expressed by (7.13) may be located on the master grid by the equations

$$\left. \begin{aligned} x' &= 2r \sin \frac{\chi}{2} \cdot \sin \lambda \\ y' &= 2r \sin \frac{\chi}{2} \cdot \cos \lambda \end{aligned} \right\} \tag{7.15}$$

where r is the common multiplier obtained from Table 8, p. 116 or by solution of equation (4.06).

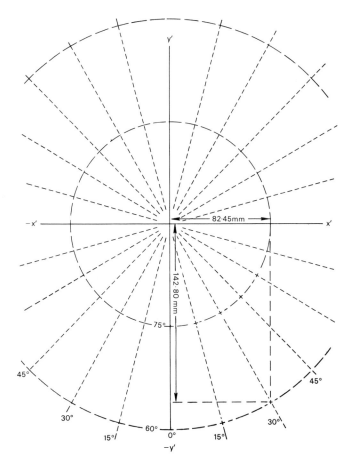

Figure 72 The construction of a normal aspect Azimuthal Equal-area Projection by master grid coordinates.

For example, if the point B has geographical coordinates 60° N, 30° E and the scale of the map is 1/20,000,000, so that $r = 318 \cdot 55$ mm., the master grid coordinates of this point are

$$x' = 2 \times 318 \cdot 55 \times \sin 15° \times \sin 30°$$
$$= 82 \cdot 45 \text{ mm}.$$

$$y' = -2 \times 318 \cdot 55 \times \sin 15° \times \cos 30°$$
$$= -142 \cdot 80 \text{ mm}.$$

The position of this point is shown in Fig. 72.

In the oblique aspect of the Azimuthal Equal-area Projection illustrated by Fig. 77, p. 145, the origin of the polar coordinates is the point (φ_0, λ_0) which we specify as $\varphi_0 = 40°$ N, $\lambda_0 = 0°$. We make this the origin of the master grid coordinates and further specify that the central meridian southwards from this point coincides with the $-y'$ axis. Equation (7.14) may now be transformed to

$$x' = 2r \sin \frac{z}{2} \cdot \sin \alpha$$

(7.16)

$$y' = 2r \sin \frac{z}{2} \cdot \cos \alpha$$

This time the point $B = (60° \text{ N}, 60° \text{ E})$ must be related to the origin by its bearing and distance coordinates. By calculation or from tables, we find $z = 41° 34' 01''$ and $\alpha = 40° 44' 23''$. Therefore the master grid coordinates are

$$x' = 2 \times 318 \cdot 55 \times \sin 20° 47' 00'' \times \sin 40° 44' 23''$$
$$= 147 \cdot 54 \text{ mm}.$$

$$y' = 2 \times 318 \cdot 55 \times \sin 20° 47' 00'' \times \cos 40° 44' 23''$$
$$= 171 \cdot 29 \text{ mm}.$$

The position of this point is shown in Fig. 73.

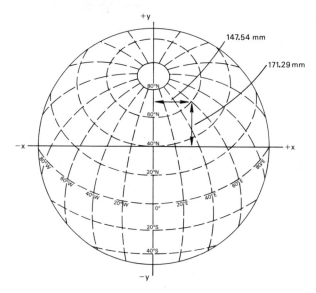

Figure 73 The construction of an oblique aspect Azimuthal Equal-area Projection by master grid coordinates.

References

1 Reignier, F.: *Les Systèmes de Projection et leurs applications . . .* , Paris, 1957, Institut Géographique National, 2 vols.

2 Wagner, K-H.: *Kartographische Netzentwürfe*, Leipzig, 1949, Bibliographisches Institut, 263 pp.

3 Cotter, C. H.: *A History of Nautical Astronomy*, London, 1968, Hollis and Carter, 387 pp.

4 Norie, J. W.: *A Complete Set of Nautical Tables . . .* , London, 1963 and numerous earlier editions, Imray, Laurie, Norie and Wilson.

5 Inman, J.: *Nautical Tables designed for the use of British Seamen*, London, 1940 and numerous earlier editions, Potter.

6 — *Useful Tables from the American Practical Navigator*, H.O. No. 9, Part II, Washington, 1932, U.S. Hydrographic Office.

7 Ward, K. W. and Bateman, C.: 'The Oblique Zenithal Equidistant Projection', *The Cartographic Journal*, 4, 1967, pp. 127–137.

8 Maling, D. H.: 'The Hammer-Aitoff Projection and some modifications', *Proceedings of the Cartographic Symposium*, Edinburgh, 1962, pp. 41–57.

9 — *Tables of Computed Altitude and Azimuth*, 6 vols., Hydrographic Publication H.D. 486, London, 1951, Hydrographic Department.

CHAPTER 8

THE ANALYTICAL DERIVATION OF SOME MAP PROJECTIONS

Geography is not alone in the embarrassing abundance of its material; the mammalia are only one, and not the largest, of sixteen classes of animals and there are about 5,000 species of mammals alone; merely to read a list of their names would waste about three lecture hours, yet with all this vast unexplored field of mammalian zoology awaiting investigation the zoology student spends about sixty hours dissecting the rabbit—and with profit. There is something here for us to ponder. Should we not be gaining more valuable discipline if we took much of the routine description for granted and employed our time in dissecting the anatomy of the map as thoroughly and as exhaustively as he dissects his rabbit, and like him, in getting down to the guts of the matter?

A. A. Miller: Presidential Address to
The Institute of British Geographers, 1948.

Introduction

Throughout this book we have been preoccupied with principles and with practical techniques. Although we have referred to, and illustrated, a variety of different map projections, we have not yet attempted to derive any of the coordinate expressions needed to define and construct them. An exception might be made of the *Cylindrical Equal-area* which has been described in some detail in Chapters 4 and 5. But even with this example it was taken on trust that the Cylindrical Equal-area Projection satisfies the special property in its title. The reader has had to accept the fact that this is so simply because we have made this statement. This is a fundamental weakness in most descriptive studies of map projections where the method of presentation is primarily geometrical. Almost as an afterthought we are told that a particular projection is conformal, or equal-area, or more commonly, that it has 'arbitrary properties'. To the beginner this means that names and properties have to be correctly equated and committed to memory, for many of the most popular projections are not conveniently described like *Lambert's Conformal Conical Projection*, but give no clue to their special property. It is therefore necessary to memorise the facts that the *Stereographic* and *Mercator* projections are conformal; that *Bonne's* and *Mollweide's* are equal-area. To the intelligent beginner, or the outsider who is a scientist or engineer, it may seem that the subject of map projections is an empirical collection of facts which seem to have been collected almost accidentally and that there is no particular thread of continuity in the processes of reasoning through which they have been derived.

We therefore believe that it is both desirable and necessary to demonstrate the *analytical approach* to the study of map projections. In other words, we must show how it is possible to derive a map projection which satisfies a particular property within the limitations imposed by the Group and Class to which it belongs. Thus we start by specifying certain initial mathematical constraints and finish with the coordinate equations for the map projection which satisfies them.

We do not intend to give a comprehensive analysis of all the special properties which can be derived in every class of projection. We may learn much about the

140

analytical approach from the study of a few well known examples from Group D of the classification system.

Example I The Azimuthal Equal-area Projection (Lambert)

The first example illustrates how an Azimuthal projection may be derived which satisfies the special property of equivalence. This projection is attributed to Lambert (1772).

We have already seen, in Chapter 5, that the Azimuthal class is one of the sub-divisions of Group D. Moreover it has been specified that the Azimuthal projections can be defined in terms of polar coordinates according to the special condition that the origin of these coordinates is the point of zero distortion at the centre of the projection. In the normal aspect, this point is the geographical pole.

These conditions have the geometrical significance of being the transformation of the spherical surface to a plane which is tangential to it at the geographical pole, as shown in Fig. 37, p. 56. It follows from the definition of a spherical angle in Chapter 3, p. 35, as well as from the creation of the point of zero distortion at the origin of the polar coordinates, that any plane angle θ at that point is equal to the corresponding spherical angle on the globe. At the pole, this spherical angle represents longitude and therefore we may write the first of the essential equations to define any Azimuthal projection in its normal, or polar aspect, as

$$\theta = \lambda \qquad (8.01)$$

From the functional relationships which have been established in Chapter 5, we also know that in a normal aspect Azimuthal projection the meridians are represented by straight lines and the parallels by concentric circles with common centre at the pole. Since the parallels of latitude must satisfy the functional relationship of Group D that $r = f_1(\varphi)$ and since θ has already been determined, it follows that the only way in which we can derive an Azimuthal projection to satisfy a special property is to seek a suitable expression for the radius of each parallel.

We may also write

$$r = f(\chi) \qquad (8.02)$$

where χ is the colatitude. We have made this change because it is algebraically simpler to derive an expression for the radius vector in terms of colatitude. Moreover it facilitates conversion from equations derived for the normal aspect into those needed to construct the projection in any aspect.

Since the graticule intersections of the normal aspect are orthogonal, it follows that the principal directions coincide with the graticule and therefore the particular scales along the meridians and parallels coincide with the maximum and minimum particular scales.

Consequently we have the alternative conditions that

Either

$$h = a \text{ and } k = b \qquad (8.03)$$

Or

$$k = a \text{ and } h = b \qquad (8.04)$$

The analysis of the particular scales can be made from comparison of the infinitely small corresponding figures $ABCD$ on the spherical surface and $A'B'C'D'$ on the plane. In Chapter 4 we developed these arguments for the general case of any map projection. Now we modify them according to the special conditions common to any Azimuthal projection. Figure 74 (a) illustrates the portion of the spherical surface in which the two parallels are φ and $\varphi + d\varphi$ and the meridians are λ and $\lambda + d\lambda$. The radii of the parallels on the map, Fig. 74 (b), are $N'A' = r$ and $N'B' = r - dr$. The vectorial angle $A'N'D' = d\theta$.

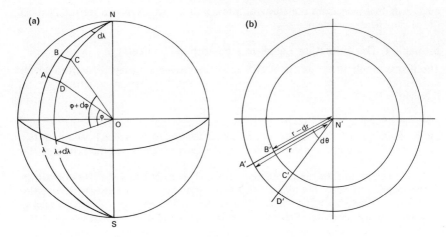

Figure 74 (a) and (b) An infinitely small quadrilateral, *ABCD*, on the spherical surface and its plane representation *A'B'C'D'* by means of an Azimuthal Projection.

The scale along the meridian at A' is the relationship $A'B'/AB$ or

$$h = \frac{-\mathrm{d}r}{R.\mathrm{d}\varphi} \tag{8.05}$$

$$= \frac{\mathrm{d}r}{R.\mathrm{d}\chi} \tag{8.06}$$

Note that if we use the expression for latitude we must allocate the negative sign to dr, because r increases as latitude decreases. In (8.06) dr is positive because r increases with χ.

The scale along the parallel through A' is the relationship $A'D'/AD$ or

$$k = \frac{r.\mathrm{d}\theta}{R.\cos\varphi.\mathrm{d}\lambda} \tag{8.07}$$

$$= \frac{r.\mathrm{d}\theta}{R.\sin\chi.\mathrm{d}\lambda} \tag{8.08}$$

Since we have already specified that $\theta = \lambda$, we may also state that d$\theta =$ dλ and therefore (8.08) is simplified to

$$k = \frac{r}{R.\sin\chi} \tag{8.09}$$

We have already noted that the principal directions coincide with the graticule. Therefore

$$p = h.k$$

$$= \frac{\mathrm{d}r}{R.\mathrm{d}\chi} \cdot \frac{r}{R.\sin\chi} \tag{8.10}$$

and

$$\sin\frac{\omega}{2} = \frac{h\sim k}{h+k} \tag{8.11}$$

to give the equation for maximum angular deformation. In equation (8.11) we use the symbol $\sim$ in the same sense as it was used in Chapter 7. It denotes the positive difference between the larger and smaller values h and k which are, as yet, unspecified. The use of this symbol is identical to the expression $\mid h-k \mid$.

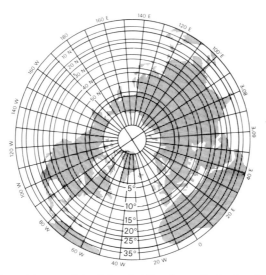

Figure 75 The Normal Aspect of the Azimuthal Equal-area Projection (Lambert) (No. 12 in Appendix I). The origin of the projection is the North Pole. The isograms represent equal values of maximum angular deformation (ω) at 5°, 10°, 15°, 20°, 25° and 35°. These are identical to the isograms shown in Figs. 76 and 77, except that the 30° isogram has been omitted for greater clarity.

Equations (8.01)–(8.11) *apply equally to all normal aspect Azimuthal projections.* We wish to obtain an equal-area projection. From equation (4.61) this is the condition that $a.b=1$. However we have shown that in the normal aspect Azimuthal projections, $h.k=a.b$ and therefore we can satisfy the property of equivalence by making the right-hand side of equation (8.10) equal to unity, i.e.

$$\frac{dr}{R.d\chi} \cdot \frac{r}{R.\sin \chi} = 1 \qquad (8.12)$$

or

$$r.dr = R^2.\sin \chi.d\chi \qquad (8.13)$$

This must be solved by integration of r with respect to χ, i.e.

$$\frac{r^2}{2} = R^2 \int_0^\chi \sin \chi.d\chi \qquad (8.14)$$

From elementary calculus, the integral $\int \sin \theta.d\theta = -\cos \theta + C$ (Abbott/ Calculus §110). C is known as the integration constant.
Therefore

$$r^2 = -2R^2.\cos \chi + C$$
$$= C - 2R^2.\cos \chi \qquad (8.15)$$

In the normal aspect Azimuthal projection, where $\chi=0$, $r=0$, $\cos \chi=1\cdot0$, i.e. $C-2R^2=0$ and $C=2R^2$.

Consequently

$$r^2=2R^2(1-\cos \chi) \qquad (8.16)$$

In Chapter 7, p. 129, we derived the expression vers $\theta=1-\cos \theta$ and we noted, moreover, that $1-\cos \theta=2 \sin^2 \theta/2$. Therefore (8.16) may be expressed in the form

$$r^2=4R^2 \sin^2 \frac{\chi}{2} \qquad (8.17)$$

so that, finally,

$$r=2\cdot R\cdot\sin \frac{\chi}{2} \qquad (8.18)$$

Equations (8.01) and (8.18) are the polar coordinate equations needed to define the normal aspect Azimuthal Equal-area Projection. For a spherical Earth of unit radius, these may be rewritten as

$$\left.\begin{array}{c} r=2 \sin \dfrac{\chi}{2} \\ \theta=\lambda \end{array}\right\} \qquad (8.19)$$

We have already converted these equations into master grid coordinates to plot both the normal and oblique aspects of the projection in Chapter 7, pp. 136–8.

Once a value for r has been determined, this may be substituted in the general expressions for the particular scales. Thus, replacing r in equations (8.06) and (8.09) by the right hand side of (8.18) we obtain

$$h=\cos \frac{\chi}{2} \qquad (8.20)$$

$$k=\sec \frac{\chi}{2} \qquad (8.21)$$

Substituting these expressions in equation (8.11) we obtain numerical values for ω. Table 9 gives the results of these calculations.

Table 9

Normal aspect Azimuthal Equal-area Projection (Lambert). Table of radii of parallels, particular scales and distortion characteristics of 15° increments of latitude.

Latitude	Radius	Particular scales		Area scale	Maximum angular deformation
φ	r	h	k	p	ω
0°	1·4142	0·7071	1·4142	1·0000	38° 57′
15°	1·2175	0·7934	1·2605	1·0000	26° 17′
30°	1·0000	0·8660	1·1547	1·0000	16° 26′
45°	0·7654	0·9239	1·0824	1·0000	9° 04′
60°	0·5176	0·9659	1·0353	1·0000	3° 58′
75°	0·2611	0·9914	1·0086	1·0000	0° 59′
90°	0·0000	1·0000	1·0000	1·0000	0°

This table only shows numerical values for an hemispherical map. The projection can be extended to show the entire World. In this case the boundary represents the antipodal point (South Pole in the normal aspect with origin at the North Pole). This is a singular point which is mapped as the circumference of a circle of radius 2 *R*.

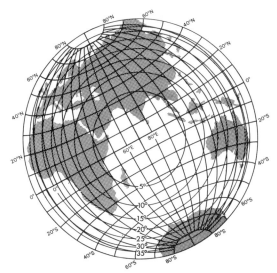

Figure 76 The Equatorial, or Transverse Aspect of the Azimuthal Equal-area Projection. The origin of the projection is on the Equator in longitude 70° E. The isograms represent equal values of maximum angular deformation (ω) at 5° intervals. These are identical to the isograms shown in Figs. 75 and 77.

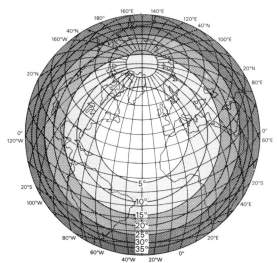

Figure 77 The Oblique Aspect of the Azimuthal Equal-area Projection. The origin of the projection is in latitude 40° N, longitude 30° W. The isograms represent equal values of maximum angular deformation (ω) at 5° intervals. These are identical to the isograms shown in Figs. 75 and 76.

L

As demonstrated in Chapter 7, the Transverse and Oblique aspects of the Azimuthal Equal-area projection may be derived simply by substituting z for χ and α for λ in all the foregoing equations. The three aspects of the projection are illustrated in Figs. 75, 76 and 77.

Example II The Conical Equidistant Projection (Ptolemy) with one standard parallel and the Conical Equidistant Projection (de l'Isle) with two standard parallels

From Chapter 5 we know that the Conical Class of projections also belongs to Group D and, like the Azimuthal Projections, these may also be derived in polar coordinates. The differences between these two classes are, first, that the origin of the polar coordinates used to define any Conical projection in the normal aspect is not the geographical pole. Secondly, a fundamental property of all conical projections is that the line of zero distortion is the arc of a small circle. In the normal aspect this is a parallel of latitude, known as the Standard Parallel. From the brief description of the class given in Chapter 5, we already know that the meridians of the normal aspect are represented by straight lines which converge to the origin of polar coordinates. This point is usually situated some distance beyond the geographical pole, as illustrated in Fig. 79 where it is represented by the vertex, V. This has the important effect of altering the relationship between the vectorial angle, θ, and longitude, so that there is a constant $n < 1$ of the form

$$\theta = n . \lambda \qquad (8.22)$$

This is known as the *Constant of the Cone*.

The parallels of the normal aspect conical projection are concentric circular arcs with common centre at the vertex. It follows that in many, though not all, conical projections the geographical pole is represented by a short circular arc instead of a point. Such projections are sometimes described as *truncated conical*

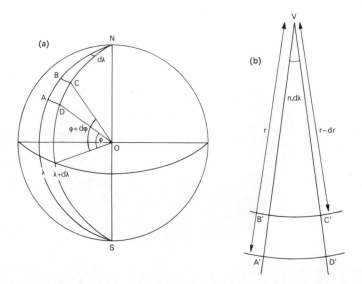

Figure 78 (a) and (b) An infinitely small quadrilateral, *ABCD*, on the spherical surface and its plane representation *A'B'C'D'* by means of a Conical Projection.

projections to distinguish them from those examples where the pole is a point. In all the truncated conical projections the pole is a singular point. Both of the examples examined here belong to the truncated category.

Derivation of the particular scales for the conical projections follows arguments similar to those already employed on pages 141–3. Fig. 78 (a) and (b) represent the slightly different meanings of r and θ. This time we derive the equations in terms of φ though, of course, this could also be done through the argument of colatitude. We note that the conditions expressed by equations (8.04) and (8.04) still apply so that if we can derive the particular scales along the meridian and parallel through A', we have also obtained the maximum and minimum particular scales.

As in (8.05)

$$h = \frac{-dr}{R.d\varphi} \tag{8.23}$$

and like (8.07)

$$k = \frac{r.d\theta}{R.\cos \varphi.d\lambda} \tag{8.24}$$

However, following (8.22), we must write $d\theta = n.d\lambda$ so that the expression for the scale along the parallel now becomes

$$k = \frac{n.r}{R.\cos \varphi} \tag{8.25}$$

It is now desirable to evaluate the constant of the cone.

The first condition which defines it is that we have specified that the principal scale is preserved along the standard parallel. Thus, denoting the scale along the standard parallel by k_0 we must fulfil the condition that

$$k_0 = \frac{r.d\theta}{R.\cos \varphi_0.d\lambda} = 1 \tag{8.26}$$

where r_0 is the radius of the standard parallel in latitude φ_0.

Therefore

$$d\theta = \frac{R.\cos \varphi_0}{r_0} d\lambda \tag{8.27}$$

or

$$\theta = \frac{R.\cos \varphi_0}{r_0} \lambda \tag{8.28}$$

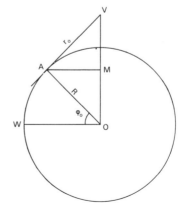

Figure 79 The determination of the radius of the standard parallel, r_0, of a conical projection with one standard parallel.

The second condition which defines the constant of the cone is the geometrical requirement that the surface of a cone which is tangential to the spherical surface must be perpendicular to the radii along the small circle of contact. Hence in the triangle VAO illustrated in Fig. 79, the angle OAV is a right angle.

Therefore

$$AM = r_0 . \sin \varphi_0 \qquad (8.29)$$

But AM corresponds to the radius of the standard parallel which on the sphere is equal to $R . \cos \varphi_0$. Substituting the right hand side of (8.29) in (8.28)

$$\theta = \frac{r_0 . \sin \varphi_0}{r_0} \lambda \qquad (8.30)$$

$$\theta = \sin \varphi_0 . \lambda \qquad (8.31)$$

Substituting this in equation (8.22)

$$n = \sin \varphi_0 \qquad (8.32)$$

We wish to preserve the special property of equidistance, i.e. $h = 1$. Substituting this in (8.23)

$$h = \frac{-\mathrm{d}r}{R . \mathrm{d}\varphi} = 1$$

and therefore

$$\mathrm{d}r = -R . \mathrm{d}\varphi \qquad (8.33)$$

Integration of this equation yields the expression

$$r = C - R . \varphi \qquad (8.34)$$

where C is the integration constant which may be interpreted as follows. In equation (8.34) we put $\varphi = O$. Then $R.\varphi = O$ and therefore $r = C$. In other words, this constant represents the radius of the Equator on the projection. If we had proceeded, as in the study of the Azimuthal Equal-area Projection, to derive the Equidistant Conical Projection in terms of colatitude we would have obtained as the integration constant a value corresponding to the radius of the circular arc representing the geographical pole.

It now remains to relate the radius of any parallel to that of the standard parallel. This may be done analytically but is also easily found from Fig. 79 where it can be seen that the angle $AVO = MAO = AOW = \varphi_0$ and therefore the radius, VA, of the standard parallel is

$$r_0 = R . \cot \varphi_0 \qquad (8.35)$$

We can now express the constant C in terms of the radius of the standard parallel because if C represents the radius of the Equator

$$C = r_0 + R . \varphi_0 \qquad (8.36)$$

$$= R . \cot \varphi_0 + R . \varphi_0 \qquad (8.37)$$

From (8.34), therefore, the radius of any parallel may be written

$$r = R . \cot \varphi_0 + R(\varphi_0 - \varphi) \qquad (8.38)$$

This expression, together with (8.31) gives the polar coordinates for any point in this projection. For $R = 1$, therefore, the equations defining the Equidistant Conical Projection (Ptolemy) are

$$\left. \begin{array}{l} r = \cot \varphi_0 + (\varphi_0 - \varphi) \\ \theta = \sin \varphi_0 . \lambda \end{array} \right\} \qquad (8.39)$$

The particular scales may be determined by substitution of the equation for r in the general expression for the particular scale along the parallel.

Thus

$$h = 1$$

$$k = \frac{\cos \varphi_0 + (\varphi_0 - \varphi) \sin \varphi_0}{\cos \varphi} \tag{8.40}$$

Because this is an equidistant projection,

$$p = k$$

and the maximum angular deformation may be evaluated from the equation

$$\sin \frac{\omega}{2} = \frac{k-1}{k+1} \tag{8.41}$$

Table 10 gives numerical values of these parameters for the particular case of a projection with the standard parallel in latitude 45°.

Table 10

Equidistant Conical Projection (Ptolemy) with one standard parallel. Numerical values for radii of parallels, particular scales and distortion characteristics for 15° graticule with standard parallel, $\varphi_0 = 45°$.

Latitude	Radius of parallel	Particular scales		Area scale	Maximum angular deformation
φ	r	h	k	p	ω
0°	1·7854	1·0000	1·2625	1·2625	13° 19′
15	1·5236	1·0000	1·1153	1·1153	6° 15′
30	1·2618	1·0000	1·0303	1·0303	1° 42′
45	1·0000	1·0000	1·0000	1·0000	0°
60	0·7382	1·0000	1·0440	1·0440	2° 28′
75	0·4764	1·0000	1·3015	1·3015	15° 03′
90	0·2146	1·0000	∞	—	180°

This projection is often called the *Simple Conical Projection with One Standard Parallel*. It is illustrated in Fig. 80.

An important modification to any of the Conical projections is to replace the single standard parallel with two. This is equivalent to the geometrical concept of the secant cone illustrated in Fig. 39, which has the effect of redistributing the particular scales because the principal scale is now preserved along two parallels of latitude. This means that a greater extent in latitude may be mapped without excessive distortion.

In order to demonstrate this important principle to the projection which has already been described, we explain the derivation of the *Equidistant Conical Projection (de l'Isle) with two standard parallels*, which is also known as the *Simple Conical Projection with two standard parallels*. Since there are other equidistant conical projections which may be described (Ref. 1), it is necessary to state the important condition for the de l'Isle projection that *the two standard parallels are located in latitudes which are midway between that of the centre of the map and its bounding parallels*. Thus, if we desired to prepare a map of the Northern Hemisphere with bounding parallels $\varphi_s = 0°$ and $\varphi_N = 90°$, the central parallel, φ_0, is latitude 45° N and the two standard parallels would be in latitudes $\varphi_1 = 67° 30′$ N and $\varphi_2 = 22° 30′$ N.

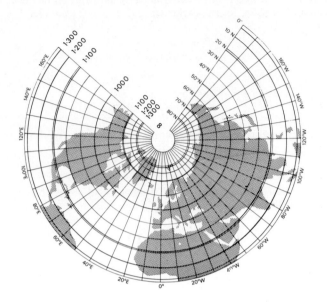

Figure 80 The Normal Aspect of the Equidistant Conical Projection with One Standard Parallel (Ptolemy). In this map of the northern hemisphere the standard parallel is latitude 50° N. The isograms represent equal values of particular scale along the parallels and since the particular scale along the meridians is everywhere equal to unity the numerical values for the isograms also represent area scale (*p*).

Algebraically we may express these conditions as follows:

$$\varphi_1 = \varphi_N - 1/4(\varphi_N - \varphi_S) \tag{8.42}$$

$$\varphi_2 = \varphi_S + 1/4(\varphi_N - \varphi_S) \tag{8.43}$$

Since φ_1 and φ_2 are standard parallels, the particular scales along them are equal to unity. Thus

$$k_1 = k_2 = 1 \cdot 0 \tag{8.44}$$

We may obtain an equation containing k and the two constants n and C by combining equations (8.25) and (8.34)

$$k = \frac{n(C - R \cdot \varphi)}{R \cdot \cos \varphi} \tag{8.45}$$

For the two standard parallels this may be written as

$$\frac{n(C - R \cdot \varphi_1)}{R \cdot \cos \varphi_1} = \frac{n(C - R \cdot \varphi_2)}{R \cdot \cos \varphi_2} = 1 \tag{8.46}$$

This gives us the two solutions

$$C = R \cdot \varphi_1 + \frac{R \cdot \cos \varphi_1}{n} \tag{8.47}$$

$$C = R \cdot \varphi_2 + \frac{R \cdot \cos \varphi_2}{n} \tag{8.48}$$

Subtracting (8.48) from (8.47) and putting $R=1$,

$$(p_1 - p_2) = \frac{\cos \varphi_2 - \cos \varphi_1}{n} \tag{8.49}$$

or

$$n = \frac{\cos \varphi_2 - \cos \varphi_1}{\varphi_1 - \varphi_2} \tag{8.50}$$

From (8.46) it can also be shown that

$$\frac{C - R \cdot \varphi_1}{R \cdot \cos \varphi_1} = \frac{C - R \cdot \varphi_2}{R \cdot \cos \varphi_2} \tag{8.51}$$

which may be solved for C as

$$C = \frac{(\varphi_1 \cdot \cos \varphi_2 - \varphi_2 \cdot \cos \varphi_1)}{\cos \varphi_2 - \cos \varphi_1} \tag{8.52}$$

These new values for n and C may be used with equations (8.22) and (8.34) to construct the de l'Isle Projection and determine its distortion characteristics. Numerical values for these are given in Table 11 and the projection is illustrated in Fig. 81.

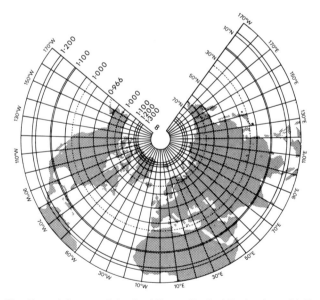

Figure 81 The Normal Aspect of the Equidistant Conical Projection with Two Standard Parallels. In this map of the northern hemisphere the standard parallels occur in latitudes 35° N and 65° N. The isograms represent equal values of particular scale along the parallels and since the particular scale along the meridians is everywhere equal to unity the numerical values for the isograms also represent area scale (p).

Table 11

Equidistant Conical Projection (de l'Isle) with two standard parallels. Numerical values for radii of parallels, particular scales and distortion characteristics for 15° graticule with standard parallels $\varphi_1=67°\ 30'$ N and $\varphi_2=22°\ 30'$ N. $n=0.68907$; $C=1.73346$.

Latitude	Radius of parallel	Particular	Scales	Area scale	Maximum angular deformation
φ	r	h	k	p	ω
0°	1·7335	1·0000	1·1945	1·1945	10° 10′
15°	1·4717	1·0000	1·0499	1·0499	2° 47′
22° 30′	1·3408	1·0000	1·0000	1·0000	0°
30°	1·2099	1·0000	0·9627	0·9627	2° 11′
45°	0·9481	1·0000	0·9239	0·9239	4° 32′
60°	0·6863	1·0000	0·9458	0·9458	3° 12′
67° 30′	0·5554	1·0000	1·0000	1·0000	0°
75°	0·4245	1·0000	1·1301	1·1301	7° 0′
90°	0·1627	1·0000	∞	—	180°

Example III The Conformal Cylindrical, or Mercator Projection

We now examine the derivation of one of the most important of all map projections which, in the normal aspect is the basis of most nautical charts and in the transverse aspect is equally important for topographical mapping. We defer examination of how the projection is used for these purposes until Chapters 10 and 11 and here confine our attention to the derivation of it as the conformal member of the Cylindrical class. Figure 82 (a) illustrates the representation of an infinitely small quadrilateral on the spherical surface and Fig. 82 (b) illustrates the corresponding figure on the

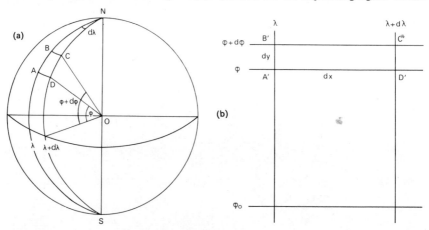

Figure 82 (a) and (b) An infinitely small quadrilateral, *ABCD*, on the spherical surface and its plane representation *A′B′C′D′* by means of a Cylindrical Projection.

plane. Using the kind of argument to which the reader should now be accustomed, we may define the particular scale along the meridian at A' as

$$h = \frac{dy}{R.d\varphi} \qquad (8.53)$$

and the particular scale along the parallel is

$$k = \frac{dx}{R \cdot \cos \varphi \cdot d\lambda} \qquad (8.54)$$

The value of dx depends upon the spacing of the meridians on the map. Since the normal aspect of a Cylindrical projection has one line of zero distortion at the Equator, this means that the meridians must be correctly spaced along the Equator. In other words, the equation

$$x = R \cdot \lambda \qquad (8.55)$$

is true for all normal aspect Cylindrical projections. Substituting the corresponding expression for infinitely small increments of longitude in equation (8.54)

$$k = \frac{R \cdot d\lambda}{R \cdot \cos \varphi \cdot d\lambda} \qquad (8.56)$$

which simplifies to

$$k = \frac{1}{\cos \varphi} \qquad (8.57)$$

$$= \sec \varphi \qquad (8.58)$$

In other words, the scale along the parallel varies according to the secant of the latitude. This, too, *is common to all normal aspect cylindrical projections.*

It follows from the pattern of parallels and meridians of the normal aspect Cylindrical projection, which we remember is composed of two families of straight lines intersecting orthogonally, that the conditions described by equations (8.03) and (8.04) remain valid. Thus we may simplify the algebraic condition for conformality, that $a = b$, with the expression

$$h = k \qquad (8.59)$$

In other words, we put

$$\frac{dy}{R \cdot d\varphi} = \frac{dx}{R \cdot \cos \varphi} \qquad (8.60)$$

and solve this equation for y.

Equation (8.60) may be written in the form

$$\frac{dy}{dx} = \frac{d\varphi}{\cos \varphi} \qquad (8.61)$$

so that

$$y = \int \sec \varphi \cdot d\varphi \qquad (8.62)$$

The solution of this integral is well known in elementary calculus (e.g. Abbott/Calculus §120) and therefore we may write

$$y = \log_e \tan\left(\frac{\pi}{4} + \frac{\varphi}{2}\right) + C \qquad (8.63)$$

In the normal aspect Cylindrical projection the origin of the plane coordinates is located somewhere on the Equator. Therefore, where $\varphi = 0$, $y = 0$ and the integration constant $C = 0$. Consequently the projection coordinates defining the Mercator Projection of a sphere of unit radius are

$$\left. \begin{aligned} x &= \lambda \\ y &= \log_e \tan\left(\frac{\pi}{4} + \frac{\varphi}{2}\right) \end{aligned} \right\} \qquad (8.64)$$

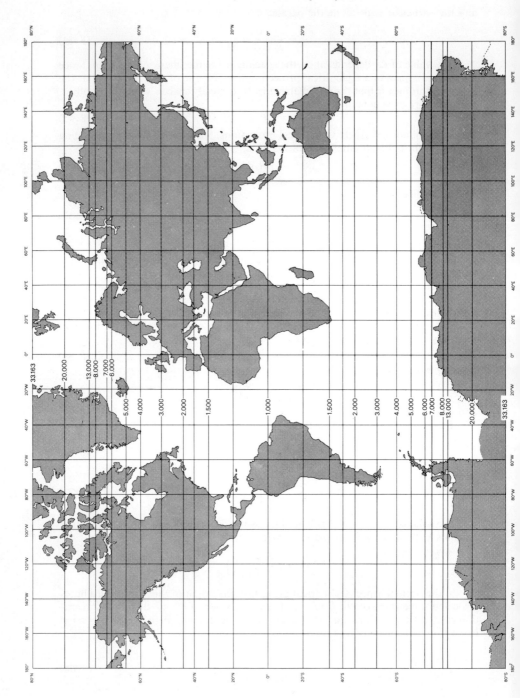

In this case, where the Equator is the single line of zero distortion, the particular scales are

$$h = k = \sec \varphi \qquad (8.65)$$

$$p = \sec^2 \varphi \qquad (8.66)$$

$$\omega = 0 \qquad (8.67)$$

Numerical values for these are given in Table 12. The projection is illustrated in Fig. 83.

Table 12

Mercator Projection. Values for the ordinate, particular scales and distortion characteristics for 15° graticule.

Latitude	Ordinate	Particular scales	Area scale	Maximum angular deformation
φ	y	$h = k$	p	ω
0°	0·0000	1·0000	1·0000	0°
15	0·2649	1·0353	1·0719	0°
30	0·5493	1·1547	1·3333	0°
45	0·8814	1·4142	2·0000	0°
60	1·3170	2·0000	4·0000	0°
75	2·0276	3·864	14·931	0°
90	∞	∞	—	180°

Because of the practical importance of this projection we must also consider the effect of the modification caused by the introduction of a standard parallel. This is frequently used for navigation charts which bear statements such as 'Scale 1/2,000,000 at 56° N'. If we denote the standard parallel as φ_0, then the particular scale here is

$$k_0 = \frac{dx}{R . \cos \varphi_0 . d\lambda} = 1 \qquad (8.68)$$

or

$$\frac{x}{R . \cos \varphi_0 . \lambda} = 1 \qquad (8.69)$$

and therefore

$$x = R . \cos \varphi_0 . \lambda \qquad (8.70)$$

Elsewhere on the map we have

$$k = \frac{R . \cos \varphi_0}{R . \cos \varphi} \qquad (8.71)$$

so that the condition for a conformal projection must now be

$$\frac{dy}{R . d\varphi} = \frac{R . \cos \varphi_0}{R . \cos \varphi} \qquad (8.72)$$

Figure 83 (opposite) The Normal Aspect of the Mercator Projection. The isograms represent equal values of area scale (p). For illustration of other properties of the Mercator Projection see Figs. 92 p. 177, 93 p. 179, 96 p. 186, 99 p. 191, 100 p. 193, 101 p. 195 and 102 p. 196.

From this we obtain the projection coordinates for the modified form of Mercator Projection

$$\left. \begin{array}{l} x = \cos\,\varphi_0 . \lambda \\[2mm] y = \cos\,\varphi_0 . \log_e\,\tan\!\left(\dfrac{\pi}{4} + \dfrac{\varphi}{2}\right) \end{array} \right\} \tag{8.73}$$

Example IIIA Derivation of the Mercator Projection of the spheroid

The third stage in our study of this important projection is to show how the normal aspect Mercator Projection can be derived for charts at scales where the spheroidal assumption must be made.

From equation (3.34) p. 46 we already know that an infinitely short meridional arc on the spheroid may be expressed in the form

$$\mathrm{d}s_m = \rho . \mathrm{d}\varphi \tag{8.74}$$

From equation (3.33) we may further derive the corresponding expression for an infinitely short arc of the parallel

$$\mathrm{d}s_p = \nu . \cos\,\varphi . \mathrm{d}\lambda \tag{8.75}$$

We substitute these expressions in the equations (8.53) and (8.54) defining the particular scales along the meridian and parallel. Thus

$$h = \frac{\mathrm{d}y}{\rho . \mathrm{d}\varphi} \tag{8.76}$$

$$k = \frac{\mathrm{d}x}{\nu \cos\,\varphi . \mathrm{d}\lambda} \tag{8.77}$$

For the projection of the spheroid, equation (8.55) may be written in the form

$$x = a . \lambda \tag{8.78}$$

Therefore

$$k = \frac{a . \mathrm{d}\lambda}{\nu \cos\,\varphi . \mathrm{d}\lambda}$$

$$= \frac{a}{\nu \cos\,\varphi} \tag{8.79}$$

The condition for a conformal projection is now satisfied by the equation

$$\frac{\mathrm{d}y}{\rho . \mathrm{d}\varphi} = \frac{a}{\nu \cos\,\varphi} \tag{8.80}$$

Substituting for ρ and ν their respective values according to equations (3.30) and (3.31), equation (8.80) becomes

$$\mathrm{d}y = a\,\frac{(1 - e^2)\mathrm{d}\varphi}{(1 - e^2\,\sin^2\,\varphi)\cos\,\varphi} \tag{8\cdot81}$$

Integration of this equation leads to

$$y = a . \ln\,\tan\!\left(\frac{\pi}{4} + \frac{\varphi}{2}\right)\left(\frac{1 - e . \sin\,\varphi}{1 + e . \sin\,\varphi}\right)^{e/2} + C \tag{8.82}$$

In equations (8.82)–(8.84) we have used 'ln' to denote common logarithms rather than use the better known convention of writing '$\log_e$'. This is because confusion can arise in the interpretation of these equations employing two different uses of e. In these equations, e represents eccentricity of the spheroid.

As in the derivation of the Mercator Projection for the sphere, the integration constant, $C=0$. The part of the right-hand side of equation (8.82)

$$q = \ln \tan\left(\frac{\pi}{4} + \frac{\varphi}{2}\right) \left(\frac{1 - e \cdot \sin \varphi}{1 + e \cdot \sin \varphi}\right)^{e/2} \qquad (8.83)$$

is called the *Isometric Latitude*. This is so-called because a system of (q, λ) coordinates upon the curved surface of the spheroid subdivides it into a network of small squares. The system of *Isometric Coordinates* thus defined may be employed to derive other conformal projections and is therefore extremely useful in the advanced study of conformal projections.

A variety of different methods may be used to convert equation (8.82) into a form which is convenient for practical computation. The method commonly found in British and American works is to expand the term

$$\left(\frac{1 - e \cdot \sin \varphi}{1 + e \cdot \sin \varphi}\right)^{e/2}$$

in *series*. This subject is briefly described in Chapter 11, pp. 209–10. Here it leads to the equation

$$y = a \cdot \ln \tan\left(\frac{\pi}{4} + \frac{\varphi}{2}\right) - a\left(e^2 \cdot \sin \varphi + \frac{e^4}{3} \cdot \sin^3 \varphi + \frac{e^6}{5} \cdot \sin^5 \varphi + \frac{e^8}{7} \cdot \sin^7 \varphi + \dots\right)$$
$$(8.84)$$

Values for the ordinate of the Mercator Projection can usually be obtained from tables without having to calculate (8.63) for the sphere and (8.84) for the spheroid. For use with the spherical assumption there are numerous published tables of *Meridional Parts* (or *Mercatorial Parts*). Since the abscissa of the Mercator Projection varies only with longitude, the tables are usually compiled in arguments of minutes of longitude at the Equator, giving the distance from the Equator to any parallel, φ, in these units of measurement. If a line to represent the Equator is drawn and carefully subdivided at the required scale of a chart, the remainder of the construction can be done by setting a compass to separations corresponding to the tabulated Meridional Parts. Cotter (Ref. 2) and textbooks on navigation describe this technique in detail. Tables of Meridional Parts are used for various calculations in navigation and therefore appear in sets of tables for nautical use (Refs. 3 and 4). There are at least two sets of published tables for Meridional Parts of the spheroid (Refs. 5 and 6). Both of these are for the Clarke 1880 Figure of the Earth ($f = 1/293 \cdot 5$) so that we must presume that hydrographic charts produced in English-speaking countries are all based upon this reference spheroid.

References

1 Maling, D. H.: 'A review of some Russian map projections', *Empire Survey Review*, 15, 1960, pp. 203–215, 255–266, 294–303.

2 Cotter, C. H.: *The Astronomical and Mathematical Foundations of Geography*, London, 1966, Hollis and Carter, 244 pp.

3 Norie, J. W.: *A Complete Set of Nautical Tables . . .*, London, 1963 and numerous earlier editions, Imray, Laurie, Norie and Wilson.

4   Inman, J.: *Nautical Tables designed for the use of British Seamen*, London, 1940, and numerous earlier editions, Potter.
5   —   *Useful Tables from the American Practical Navigator*, H.O. No. 9 Part II, Washington, 1932, U.S. Hydrographic Department.
6   —   *Tables used in the Construction of Charts*, H.D. 470, London, Hydrographic Department.

CHAPTER 9

THE CHOICE OF A SUITABLE MAP PROJECTION

> There is much to be said for the belief that the best way of judging a world-projection is to look at it.
>
> A. R. Hinks: *Geographical Journal*, 1934

Introduction

In certain fields of cartography, notably in the production of topographical and other series of large-scale sheet maps, and in the preparation of navigation charts, there is little possibility of exercising any choice about the kind of projection to be used as the base for the map or chart. The most suitable projections for these purposes have been evolved alongside the methods of map or chart use, and the needs of the user. Often, too, the specification of the projection to be used for related map sheets or map series produced by different organisations have been agreed internationally, by organisations like the International Geographical Union (IGU), International Civil Aviation Organisation (ICAO) or the North Atlantic Treaty Organisation (NATO) to achieve some measure of standardisation.

In other kinds of cartographic work, especially in atlas production, there is greater freedom of choice in selecting a projection which is suitable for a map of a particular country or continent and for a particular purpose. In this chapter we investigate some of the criteria and methods which may be used when it is possible to make the choice. Naturally this study is concerned primarily with the design and production of small-scale maps showing an entire country, a continent, an hemisphere or the whole World. In Chapters 10 and 11 we will examine the practical reasons why certain projections are preferred for use in navigation, surveying and topographical cartography.

Some factors influencing the choice of a suitable projection

It is a fundamental principle of distortion theory that the particular scales and therefore exaggeration of area and angular deformation increase from the origin of the projection towards its edges. Since all projections have distortions of one kind or another and since, on a small-scale map showing a large country, continent or the whole World, these distortions can be measured, it is usually desirable to choose a map projection on which distortion is tolerably small. Thus the primary aim of a logical choice is *to select a projection in which the extreme distortions are smaller than would occur in any other projection used to map the same area.* Thus, if we need a conformal map of a country, we may study the way in which the area scale increases near the boundaries of the country and select that conformal projection which shows the least exaggeration of area within the parts to be mapped. If we require an equal-area map of the country, we must carry out a similar evaluation of the angular deformation inherent to all equivalent projections. If neither special property is essential, examination of both area scale and angular deformation must be made. This kind of evaluation suggests that the concept of minimum-error representation, briefly mentioned in Chapter 4 as one of the special properties, may be valuable in this context.

The amount of distortion which is likely to be encountered depends upon the location, size and shape or the area to be mapped. Distortion is least in the representation of a small, compact country and greatest in maps of the whole World. The three variables—location, size and shape—usually determine the choice of origin, aspect and class of a suitable projection. The purpose of the map, especially a certain knowledge of the ways in which it is going to be used, generally determines which special property is important. We will find this to be a most exacting requirement in navigation and surveying but it is less so for most other kinds of map use.

We believe that quantitative uses of a map, namely the measurement of distances, areas and angles, are more likely to indicate the inadequacies of a projection than are any subjective visual methods of appraisal. Therefore we consider desirable criteria in these terms.

It is reasonable to expect measurements of distance or area made on a map to have relative precision of the order $\pm 1\%$ to $\pm 2\%$, provided that reasonable precautions have been taken in using the appropriate instruments (Refs. 1 and 2). For most purposes other than navigation, artillery and engineering applications, angles measured on maps are usually not needed with an accuracy greater than $1°$. These criteria have been tentatively recommended as indicating the tolerable amounts of deformation acceptable in the projection to be used for a map in a national atlas (Ref. 3), but the extent to which they can be satisfied depends upon the location, shape and size of an individual country.

Maps of small countries

If we are required to select a suitable projection to depict a small, compact country and we are free to choose any point on the Earth's surface as the origin for the projection, then the possibilities are practically limitless, or, in other words, it matters little which projection is used. In all classes of map projection the distortion of linear, angular and area values in the vicinity of the point of line of zero distortion is so small that it cannot be detected by measurement on the map. Therefore the preference for one projection rather than another tends to be of theoretical interest only. Consequently we usually select the projection which has been used as the base for the topographical source maps and thereby avoid having to compile and plot the requisite detail on a different projection. Thus a geographer or planner wishing to produce a distribution map of part of England at a scale of 1/500,000 or larger would not bother to consider the merits of the projection which might be used, but would use the Ordnance Survey maps of the area as the framework upon which the new information would be plotted. Ordnance Survey maps of scale 1/625,000 and larger are based upon a version of the *Transverse Mercator Projection* (pp. 223–4), which is conformal, but the amount of exaggeration of area which is introduced by using this rather than an equal-area map is trivial. The area scale on this projection nowhere exceeds the range $0\cdot99908$–$1\cdot00092$ in mainland Britain, i.e. it varies from the principal scale by less than 0.1%. Consequently judgement about density of distribution or measurement of areas occupied by different kinds of land use are unaffected by the fact that the choice of map projection is theoretically incorrect.

Maps of large countries, of continents and the whole world

Just as the choice of a suitable projection is unimportant in the design of a distribution map of mainland Britain so, too, most of the individual countries of Western Europe can be adequately represented by using the national projections adopted for topographical map series. A map of the whole of Western Europe can be prepared without exceeding the $\pm 2\%$ and $1°$ tolerances which have been suggested. However, it would be difficult to find a projection to map the whole of Canada or the USSR in which linear or area distortion is less than 3% or angular deformation is less than $3°–5°$. For maps to represent entire continents or oceans much larger amounts of deformation must be tolerated. For example, an equal-area map of Asia involves maximum angular deformation of about $15°$. Equal-area maps of Africa and North America have maximum values of ω in the range $6°–8°$. Figure 86, p. 167, illustrates this for a map of North America. Equal-area maps of the hemispheres show an increase in ω to about $30°$. Map projections of the whole World generally have singular points where $\omega = 180°$ and p is indeterminate but even if these extreme values are discounted as being inevitable and therefore unrealistic measures of the remainder of the map, we must expect to find that angular deformation greater than $45°$ or area scales in excess of $2·5$ ($+250\%$) must be tolerated in some parts of the map. Then the real skill in selecting a suitable projection is to arrange for the important parts of the World map to lie where the distortions are least. This leads us to a consideration of the intended purpose of the map and the extent or nature of the distribution which is to be mapped.

Obstacles to choice

In contrast to those factors which must be considered to influence the choice of a projection for a new map, there are practical obstacles which limit freedom of choice. These result from the cost in time and labour of compiling and plotting maps on projections which differ from the sources used. We have already seen, in Chapters 6 and 7, that the creation of a new map projection may involve a fair amount of computation and some exceedingly careful plotting and drawing. Yet completion of this stage of the work is only a preliminary to the extremely slow job of transferring map detail to the plotted graticule.

There is no quick or simple optical method of doing this in one step which is comparable to the use of a process camera for changing scale. Optical *rectification*, similar to the procedures used in photogrammetric mapping, appears to be popular in Soviet cartography, where photogrammetric instruments like the old Zeiss SEG I rectifier are still used for this purpose. Some of the *optical pantographs* available in Western countries, like the Grant Projector and Röst Plan Variograph, can be obtained with tilting easels which permit partial rectification of the source map to fit the new graticule. However, the range of these applications is quite limited. For example, optical rectification cannot transform a rectilinear graticule into one comprising families of curves, or vice versa. Thus we cannot transform a normal aspect cylindrical projection into a normal aspect conical projection. More elaborate optical–mechanical apparatus has occasionally been designed for specific purposes. For example, Honick (Ref. 4) has described equipment used for transforming the graticules of aeronautical charts and thereby demonstrates that an analogue solution to the problem can be rather complicated. Generally, therefore, the work of plotting has to be done point by point after drawing a close network of corresponding geometrical figures on both source map and plotting sheet and transferring the map detail with reference to these lines. In this respect it is easier to transform from one conformal projection to another than to transform to equal-area or other projections. This is because a very small part of a conformal map is similar in shape to the corresponding small part of the map being compiled. Thus, as Miller (Ref. 5) has written:

> 'Of the two evils, the cartographer dislikes the conformal type of projection less, because he knows that, provided he makes the mesh of his grid small enough, detail, if properly reduced by pantograph or photo-

graphy, will fit nicely into place and can be traced directly on the map being compiled.'

Because plotting of the detail may represent many weeks or months of work it is not surprising that changing the projection of a map is commercially unpopular. The first reaction of many cartographic editors to such a proposal is to consider if there is any existing material which is suitable for use for a particular map in a new atlas. Robinson (Ref. 6) has castigated the commercial map producer who is 'only too happy to peddle the older wares' and it is easy to condemn the re-issue of atlas maps as exemplifying lack of initiative or new ideas. However, the fact remains that the job of compilation and plotting, which is the most expensive single item in conventional cartographic production, is an essential concomitant to the design of a new map on a different projection. It is therefore cheaper to revise existing fair drawings. The digital solution, which we now associate with the phrase *automation in cartography*, is a potent method of overcoming these difficulties. If information about the nature and location of map detail is already stored in digital form on tape or disc, it is possible to transform their coordinates by computer so that points and lines are plotted by automatic coordinatograph (p. 117) at any specified scale according to any projection. However, the cost of digitising the initial source maps is still an important factor at the current state of the art. When adequate *Cartographic Data Banks* become available this development will represent a major step forward in the technology of map production and it offers exciting possibilities for redesigning maps in a small fraction of the time needed to do this by conventional methods.

The choice of origin, aspect and class of a projection

The preliminary stage in making the choice of a map projection is to consider the location of the origin. In order to avoid excessive distortion within the area to be mapped, we locate the point or line of zero distortion centrally within it. This choice of origin automatically affects the aspect of the projection. The shape of the area to be mapped influences the choice whether there should be a point or line of zero distortion and this, in turn, determines the choice of class of projection. Thus all three variables are intimately related and must be considered together.

The traditional approach to the choice of class is described in most of the elementary textbooks as the following three rules:

(1) If the country to be mapped lies in the Tropics, a cylindrical projection should be used.
(2) If the country to be mapped lies in temperate latitudes, a conical projection should be used.
(3) If the map is required to show one of the polar regions, an azimuthal projection should be used.

These principles follow logically from the fundamental properties that the principal scale is preserved along the Equator in a normal aspect cylindrical projection, along a parallel of latitude in a normal aspect conical projection and at the geographical pole of a normal aspect azimuthal projection. The principles have been used in the design of innumerable sheet and atlas maps; indeed they may be regarded as being *one of the classical foundations of cartographic design*. However they should not be regarded as representing inflexible rules. After all, no mention has been made of any of the other named classes of map projections and these also deserve consideration in making the choice. Moreover, strict adherence to the three principles ignores the considerable advantages to be gained by using any map projection in either the normal, transverse or oblique aspects. In other words, the three principles are too restricting to be rigidly applied in modern cartography. For example, Fig. 75 shows that the normal aspect Azimuthal Equal-area Projection is a useful base for distribution maps of the Arctic Ocean or Antarctica, conforming to the third principle listed above. But the transverse aspect (Fig. 76) of the same projection would be equally valuable as the base for a map of the Indian Ocean and the oblique aspect (Fig. 77) of it for mapping distributions in the North Atlantic Ocean. The use of an oblique aspect azimuthal projection is no longer to be regarded as a novelty. Transverse and oblique cylindrical projections are well known in large-scale cartography but are less often used for atlas maps. Rarest of all are transverse and oblique aspect conical projections. The *Bipolar Oblique Conformal Conical Projection*, Fig. 84, designed by O. M. Miller and W. Briesemeister for the American Geographical Society (Ref. 5) still seems to be only example of an oblique aspect conical projection which has achieved some measure of popularity. We use Miller's classic study to find a projection suitable for a general reference map of Latin America as an example of the combined graphical and analytical approach to choice, elsewhere in this chapter.

Since we are able to select any point on the Earth's surface as the origin of a projection, we may locate this at or near the centre of the country or continent to be shown on the map. The point of origin might be determined by computation, for example, as the centre of gravity of the land mass, using the standard methods of calculating this for a plane figure shown by the outline of the country or continent on any convenient map. The method will almost certainly locate the origin of the projection at a point which does not correspond to any graticule intersection to be shown on the finished map. If we adhere rigidly to this choice of origin, difficulties in computation immediately arise because the bearing and distance coordinates of every graticule intersection to be shown on the map must be individually computed. Tables like Wagner's (p. 134) can only be used if the origin of the coordinate system is located at the intersections of 5° parallels and meridians. On the other hand, if a digital computer is used to obtain the projection and master grid coordinates, there is no practical inconvenience in using any point as the origin of the projection.

Table 13 lists some of the points which might be selected as the origins for maps of the continents, quoted for the nearest 5° of latitude and longitude.

Table 13

Suggested positions for the points of origin for continental maps.

	φ_0	λ_0
Europe	$+50°$	$+20°$
Asia	$+40$	$+95$
Eurasia	$+40$	$+85$
Africa	0	$+20$
North America	$+45$	-95
South America	-20	-60
Australia	-25	$+135$

Usually the line of zero distortion is made to coincide with the longer axis through the country, or a pair of lines of zero distortion are made parallel with this axis. The choice is important if the country is asymmetrical, like Chile, Japan or Indonesia. For example, a map of Chile may be based upon a transverse cylindrical projection because the longer axis is practically meridional. On the other hand, maps of Japan or Indonesia require the use of an oblique aspect cylindrical or conical projection. Hammer illustrated oblique aspect conical projections for Japan

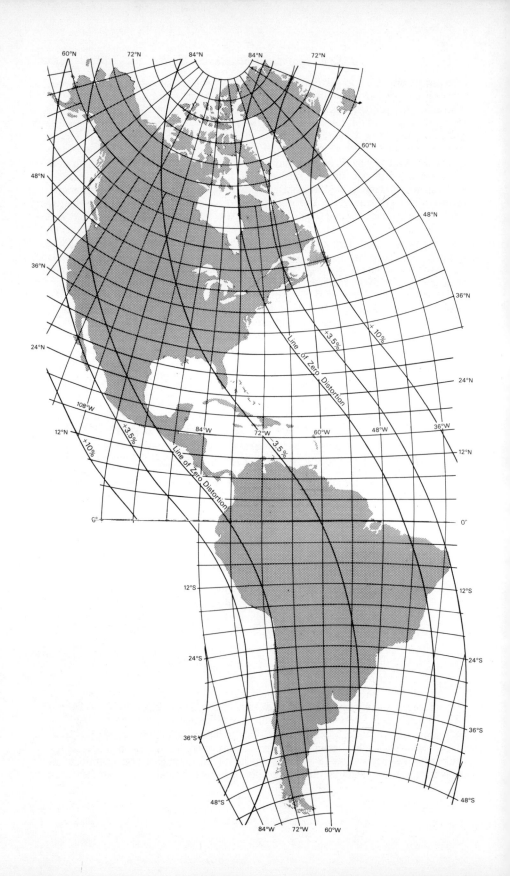

and South America as long ago as 1889 (Ref. 7). We demonstrate later how an oblique aspect conical projection is suited for a map of Latin America although this may not seem immediately apparent at first sight.

Young's Rule for selecting class of projection

The choice to be made between the three classes of cylindrical, conical and azimuthal projections may be conveniently described in terms of *Young's Rule*, originally stated in 1920 (Ref. 8) but independently discovered and further extended by Ginzburg and Salmanova in 1957 (Ref. 9).

The principle arises from the basic idea that a country which is approximately circular in outline is better represented by means of one of the azimuthal projections, in which distortion increases radially in all directions, whereas an asymmetrical country is better mapped on a conical or cylindrical projection with lines of zero distortion.

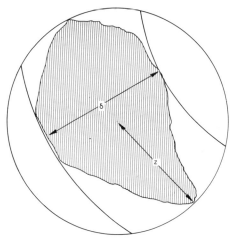

Figure 85 The application of Young's Rule to the choice of a suitable class of map projection for a country with maximum extent (*z*) and minimum width (δ).

The rule may therefore be described in terms of an imaginary country illustrated in Fig. 85. The area to be mapped has maximum angular distance *z* from the centre of the country to its most distant boundary. It can also be regarded as being bounded by two parallel arcs of small circles which lie $\delta°$ apart. These small circles may be parallels of latitude if the greatest extent of the country is East–West but, as implied by the orientation of these lines in Fig. 85, this is not a necessary condition of definition. Since we are concerned with the comparison of the particular scales and the distortion characteristics to be derived from them, we choose the pair of small circles which are the closest which can be fitted to the outline, irrespective of their orientation to the conventional graticule.

Figure 84 (opposite) Map of the Americas on the Bipolar Oblique Conformal Conical Projection (after Miller). The isograms represent equal values of linear deformation of −3·5%, 0%, +3·5% and +10%, corresponding to the particular scales 0·965, 1·000, 1·035 and 1·100 respectively. Note that the graticule on this map is composed of parallels at intervals of 4° of latitude and the meridians are shown at 6° intervals of longitude (at intervals of 12° to the north of latitude 60° N). This graticule corresponds to the system of sheet lines adopted for the International Map of the World (IMW) at scale 1/1,000,000.

Note that we are going to compare the *maximum* radial distance, z, with the *minimum* separation of parallel circles, δ.

Young originally noted that if $z/\delta < 1 \cdot 41$, an azimuthal·projection is to be preferred. Conversely, if z/δ is greater than this critical value, a conical projection should be used. From their study of the variations in particular scale in the ranges $0 < z < 25°$ and $0 < \delta < 35°$, together with extension of the method to include cylindrical projections too, Ginzburg and Salmanova have obtained three different critical values for z/δ depending upon the special property. These are

Conformal projections	$z/\delta = 1 \cdot 41$
Equidistant projections	$z/\delta = 1 \cdot 73$
Equal-area projections	$z/\delta = 2 \cdot 00$

The following examples are instructive. In Chile, the total extent in latitude is approximately $32°$ but the greatest extent in longitude is only $7°$. Hence, putting $z = 16°$, $\delta = 7°$ we find $z/\delta = 2 \cdot 3$. This indicates that a conical or cylindrical projection is more suitable than an azimuthal projection and, as we have already noted, the best choice is a transverse aspect cylindrical projection. For Australia, the corresponding values are $z = 19°$, $\delta = 30°$ and $z/\delta = 0 \cdot 63$. This indicates a preference for an azimuthal projection, which was the conclusion also reached by Sear (Ref. 10) in his valuable account of the arguments used to select the projection for a general reference map of Australia.

Graphical methods of selection by visual comparison of overlays

This method allows the choice of class, and often the special property of a projection, by using the patterns of distortion isograms for different projections plotted on transparent plastic and making visual comparisons between them. This is really the only simple way of comparing the relative merits of those classes of projection in which the isograms have more complicated patterns than those for the cylindrical, conical and azimuthal classes. The primary requirement is for the isograms of various projections to be plotted at the same principal scale, e.g. 1/20,000,000 for maps of large countries or continents and about 1/100,000,000 for World maps. There is no need to show the parallels and meridians on these overlays; indeed it is less confusing if they are not plotted. However it is important to indicate the origin and axes to which the isograms are related and obviously the lines of zero distortion are also valuable. The overlays may be placed singly or in groups over a rough outline sketch-map of the country or continent drawn at the same principal scale. By shifting the position and orientation of the overlay it is possible to estimate any advantage to be gained from a change in origin or change in orientation of the lines of zero distortion. What we are attempting to achieve by these means is the idea contained in Chapter 5, p. 92 that the distortion characteristics of a particular projection remain constant when the aspect of the projection is changed. We are therefore using the overlay as a frame through which we can imagine how much distortion will occur, just as an artist may compose a picture by looking at objects through a small rectangular cardboard frame.

When two or more overlays for different projections are superimposed it is easy to compare extreme values for p or ω from the isograms. Figure 86 illustrates such a comparison by combining the ω isograms for Bonne's Projection and for the Azimuthal Equal-area Projection which have been plotted to the same principal scale and brought into coincidence for an origin in latitude $45°$ North, longitude $100°$ West. This indicates that the extreme values of ω, encountered in Alaska and Greenland are about $5°-8°$ on the Azimuthal Equal-area Projection but greater than $15°$ on Bonne's Projection. The logical conclusion is to choose the Azimuthal

Equal-area Projection as the more suitable for an equal-area map of the North American continent and compare this overlay with those for some other equal-area projections.

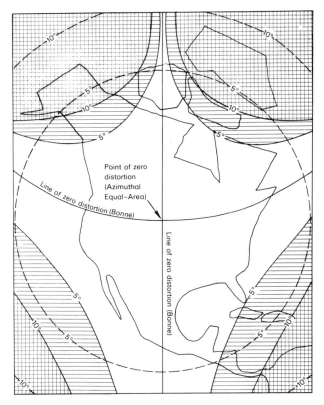

Figure 86 The comparison of the relative merits of Bonne's Projection and the Azimuthal Equal-area Projection (Lambert) for a map of the North American continent. Both of these are equal-area projections so that the best way of comparing them is through maximum angular deformation (ω). The origins of both projections is the point with latitude 45° N, longitude 100° W. Isograms for maximum angular deformation are shown for both projections at intervals of $\omega = 5°$ and 10°. The patterns refer to the isograms for Bonne's Projection. Note that the coastlines are drawn roughly to indicate their approximate location. They do not coincide with their positions on either of these projections accurately and are only an approximate guide to the extent of the area to be mapped.

It must be realised that the underlying map is only a rough guide. If an overlay is to be compared with a map, the relationship between the isograms and the map outline is only precisely true for that aspect and projection upon which the map was compiled. Any other aspect of that projection alters the detailed outline of the coast or international boundaries. Similarly these detailed outlines vary with every other projection. Consequently the visual comparison between the map and overlay cannot be exact and this is why we only recommend and illustrate a rough outline. The purpose of this is to indicate approximately the extent of the country or continent. Where two or more projections are being evaluated, the required comparison is to be made between the distortion isograms. If these have been carefully plotted to the same principal scale, the designer can obtain a fairly accurate impression of the relative merits of different projections.

Figure 87 illustrates another example of comparing two projections; namely a comparison between the *Equidistant Conical with two standard parallels (de l'Isle)* and the *Azimuthal Equidistant Projection* for a proposed map of China.

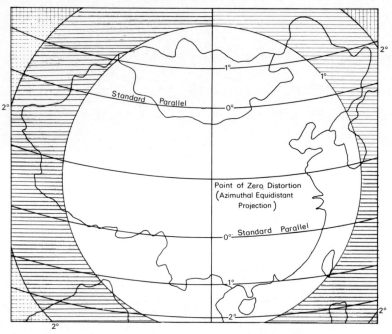

Figure 87 The comparison of the relative merits of the Azimuthal Equidistant Projection (Postel) and the Conical Equidistant Projection (de l'Isle) for a map of China. The origin of the Azimuthal Equidistant Projection is the point in latitude 35° N, longitude 105° E and the corresponding graticule intersection of the Conical Equidistant Projection is made to coincide with this. Either area scale (*p*) or maximum angular deformation (*ω*) might be compared for these projections. Here the isograms for maximum angular deformation at *ω*=1° and 2° have been plotted. The patterns refer to the isograms for the Azimuthal Equidistant Projection.

Note that the coastlines and frontiers are drawn roughly to indicate their approximate location. They do not coincide with positions on either of these projections accurately and are only an approximate guide to the extent of the area to be mapped.

Choice of special property

We have already noted that the choice of special property is largely determined by the intended purpose of the map. In atlas cartography, the special property of equivalence is especially important for mapping statistical data. However it would be wrong to imagine that all atlas maps must satisfy the property of equivalence. The majority of general maps in World, Regional and National atlases are multi-purpose maps for reference purposes. Since these are not necessarily intended to demonstrate density of distribution through clustering of dots or for area measurement purposes, there is no particular reason why they should be rigorously equivalent. Since conformality and equivalence are mutually exclusive special properties, it follows that the exaggeration of area on a conformal map tends to be

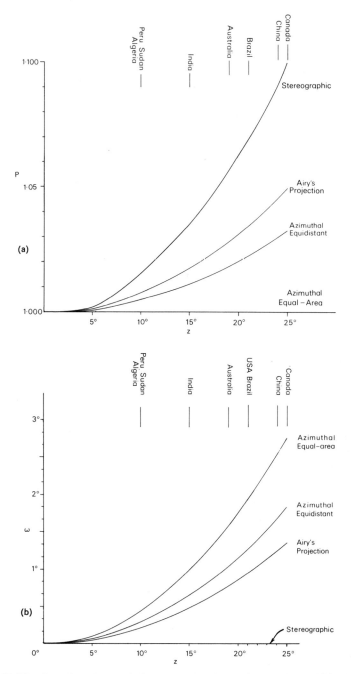

Figure 88 The distortion characteristics of certain azimuthal projections within the range $0° < z < 25°$
(a) Illustrates area scale (p) plotted against angular distance (z).
(b) Illustrates maximum angular deformation (ω) plotted against angular distance (z).
The diagram also shows the approximate extent of certain countries according to the definition of z illustrated by Fig. 85.

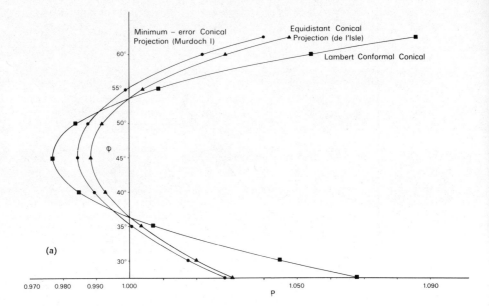

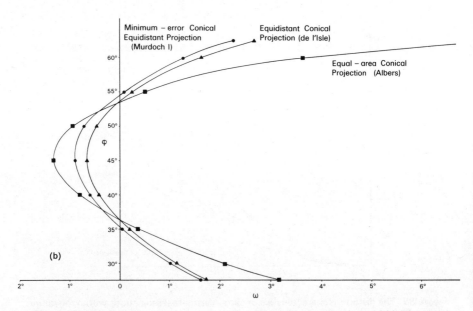

Figure 89 The distortion characteristics of certain conical projections within the range $0 < \delta < 35°$ assuming the normal aspect and that the middle parallel corresponds to latitude 45°.

(a) Illustrates area scale (p) plotted against latitude (φ).

(b) Illustrates maximum angular deformation (ω) plotted against latitude (φ).

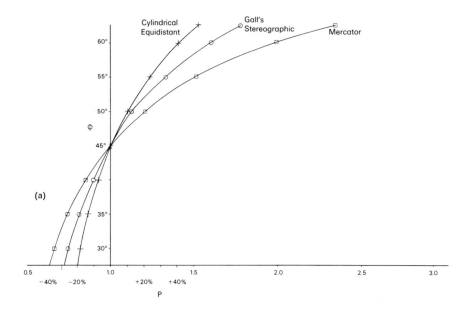

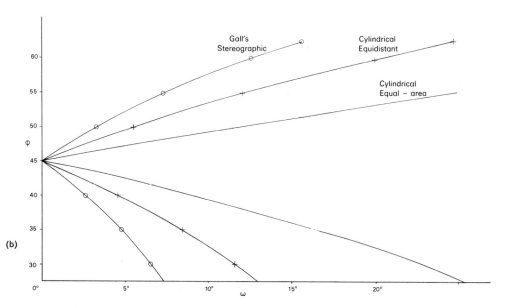

Figure 90 The distortion characteristics of certain cylindrical projections within the range $0° < \delta < 35°$ assuming the normal aspect and that the line of zero distortion lies in latitude 45°.

(a) Illustrates area scale (*p*) plotted against latitude (φ).

(b) Illustrates maximum angular deformation (ω) plotted against latitude (φ).

large and that the angular deformation on an equal-area map also tends to be large. Between these two properties, which, for practical purposes may be regarded as being the two limits of choice, there are a variety of other map projections in which neither property is satisfied but they do not have the large distortions which are characteristic of conformal and equal-area maps.

We may demonstrate this by comparing area scale and maximum angular deformation for members of the azimuthal, conical and cylindrical classes of projection within the ranges $0 < z < 25°$ and $0 < \delta < 35°$, appropriate for maps of large countries. These are represented graphically in Figs. 88, 89 and 90. From these graphs we see that for azimuthal projections, the area scale of the Stereographic Projection is approximately three times greater than the corresponding values for the Azimuthal Equidistant Projection and the maximum angular deformation of the Azimuthal Equal-area projection is appreciably greater than for the Azimuthal Equidistant Projection.

In conical and cylindrical projections, the area scales of conformal maps are twice as large as the corresponding values for the equidistant projections. The angular deformations of equal-area conical and cylindrical projections are approximately twice as large as in the equidistant versions. This leads us to the conclusion, already noted in Chapter 4, that the property of equidistance often provides a useful compromise for use in maps which do not necessarily have to be rigorously equivalent or conformal. Hence we may regard the equidistant projections as occupying the central position within the continuum of all map projections listed by special property as follows:

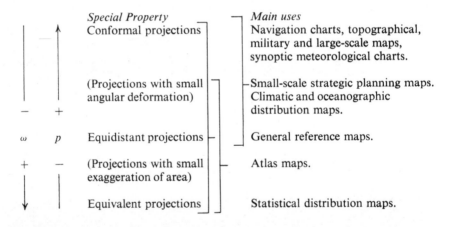

		Special Property	Main uses
	↑	Conformal projections	Navigation charts, topographical, military and large-scale maps, synoptic meteorological charts.
		(Projections with small angular deformation)	Small-scale strategic planning maps. Climatic and oceanographic distribution maps.
−	+		
ω	p	Equidistant projections	General reference maps.
+	−	(Projections with small exaggeration of area)	Atlas maps.
↓		Equivalent projections	Statistical distribution maps.

There is also a close relationship between the distortion characteristics of equidistant and minimum-error projections of the same class. This is shown by comparison of the distortion characteristics of the Azimuthal Equidistant Projection and Airy's Projection within the range $0 < z < 25°$.

The mathematical theory of minimum-error representation has been studied in detail by Young (Ref. 8), who started from the same initial premise as Airy and Clarke that the sums of the squares of the scale errors integrated throughout the area of the map should have a minimum value. This was indicated by equation (4.67) on page 71, which the reader will now appreciate is the form of expression needed to derive a minimum-error azimuthal projection. We further remind the reader that the concept of minimum-error is not an exclusive special property. Thus we may create minimum-error conformal or minimum-error equidistant

Table 14

Distortion characteristics (ω and p) of the Azimuthal Equidistant Projection and Airy's Minimum-error Azimuthal Projection.

z	Area scale (p)		Maximum angular deformation ω	
	Equidistant	Airy's	Equidistant	Airy's
0	1·0000	1·0000	0°	0°
5	1·0013	1·0019	0° 04′	0° 03′
10	1·0051	1·0077	0° 17′	0° 13′
15	1·0115	1·0174	0° 39′	0° 29′
20	1·0206	1·0313	1° 10′	0° 52′
25	1·0325	1·0496	1° 50′	1° 21′

projections which retain the special property together with the additional advantage that the sums of squares of the scale errors within the area mapped are less than in the parent projection. This is generally obtained through the modification of the parent projection by means of a suitable scale factor. We return to this problem in the next section. Following our preoccupation throughout this chapter with the need to reduce distortion towards the edges of a map, together with the suggestion that many general reference maps do not have to satisfy conformality or equivalence, it might be assumed that the correct choice of a projection which best fits a given country is always the minimum-error projection of the selected class. Theoretically this conclusion is generally correct, but, in practice, the use of minimum-error projections is the exception rather than the rule. Consequently we are only able to quote four examples of the use of them in British and Commonwealth cartography during the twentieth century. These are:

(1) The *Ordnance Survey Ten-Mile* map (1/633,600) of the British Isles published between 1903 and 1936. This was based on *Airy's Projection*.

(2) The use of a version of *Clarke's Minimum-error Perspective Azimuthal Projections* as the base for the synoptic meteorological charts published by the Meteorological Office in the Daily Weather Report. Use of this projection was discontinued in 1955 when it was replaced by the Azimuthal Equidistant Projection. In 1964 this, in turn, was replaced by the Stereographic Projection.

(3) Hink's choice of a *Minimum-error Conical Projection (Murdoch III)* for the *British Council Map of Europe and the Near East* (1/11,000,000) published by the Royal Geographical Society in 1942 (Ref. 11)

(4) Sear's choice of the *Minimum-error Azimuthal Equidistant Projection* for the map of Australia at 1/6,000,000, published by the Commonwealth Division of National Mapping in 1956 (Ref. 10).

There are probably two reasons why such little use has been made of minimum-error projections. First, the mathematical theory of minimum-error representation is difficult. Secondly, the primary source on this subject is a booklet published more than fifty years ago which never had wide circulation. As a result neither the theory nor the terminology are commonly known to cartographers and map users. Thus *Airy's Projection* and *Murdoch's Third Projection* are seldom used, whereas the Azimuthal Equidistant and Equidistant Conical projections occur often in atlases. Table 14 has indicated that within the range of z which is needed to map most large countries and even some of the continents, the differences in ω and p which occur between the little known Airy's Projection and well-known Azimuthal Equidistant Projection are trivial. Although the mathematically correct answer to the question, 'What is the best map projection to use for a particular country?' is usually 'the minimum-error projection of the most suitable class' in practical cartography the equidistant projection of the same class will provide a very similar map.

Improvement of a selected projection by modification

The methods of selection described thus far can be conducted in terms of the basic forms of map projection in each class. However we know that each of the conical and cylindrical projections may be changed by introducing two standard parallels. We know from Chapter 5, pp. 93–95 that the chief effect of such a modification is to redistribute the particular scales. On graphs such as Figs. 89 and 90, this is indicated by displacement of each curve relative to the abscissa. The nature of the curve is not materially changed.

We now consider how we may introduce these principles of modification into making a logical selection of a suitable projection for a particular map. We will see that it is an important factor because, within limits, it may transform a seemingly unsuitable projection into one which is worthy of consideration. We introduce some preliminary ideas through discussion of some methods which may be used to select suitable standard parallels for a normal aspect conical projection.

In Chapter 8, pp. 149–52, we derived equations for the Equidistant Conical Projection (de l'Isle) with two standard parallels and used the simple expedient of locating these midway between the central and limiting parallels of the zone to be mapped. This is, in fact, how the de l'Isle Projection should be defined, to distinguish it from *Euler's Projection* and the other equidistant conical projections which may also be described if we specify that certain ratios must be maintained between the particular scales along the bounding parallels and one near the middle of the map (Ref. 12). The variations give rise to different numerical values for the constants of the projection and therefore location of the standard parallels. They create a considerable number of possibilities in choosing between different conical projections and therefore it is desirable to see what practical guiding principles can help to make a logical choice. There are essentially two different lines of approach to comment about; the geometrical and the geographical. In the mathematical study of the conical projections the underlying assumption is made, but not always recognised, that every part of a zone to be mapped has equal importance. In other words we assume that a country completely fills the fan-shaped outline of a conical projection between the limiting parallels and meridians. This assumption is clearly unrealistic if we want to produce a map of Argentina, India, Mexico or Norway on a conical projection because the countries are asymmetrical, showing much variation in land area with latitude. Therefore the derivation of projection constants which depend only upon scale ratios between the centre and edges of the map may be misleading. This subject has been studied by Kavraisky (Ref. 12), who proposed the use of a constant to help make the choice of suitable standard parallels for a conical projection which takes the shape of the country into account.

Rewriting equations (8.42) and (8.43) p. 150 in the form

$$\varphi_2 = \varphi_N - \frac{1}{K}(\varphi_N - \varphi_S) \qquad (9.01)$$

and

$$\varphi_1 = \varphi_S + \frac{1}{K}(\varphi_N - \varphi_S) \qquad (9.02)$$

the constant K may be varied according to the shape of the country to be mapped. Kavraisky's values for K may be listed as follows, for the shapes indicated in Fig. 91:

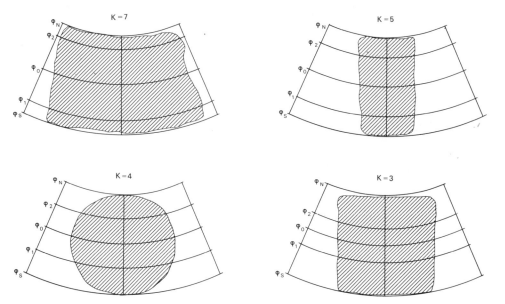

Figure 91 Definition of Kavraisky's constant, *K*, to aid the choice of standard parallels for conical projections to show countries having different shapes.

Small extent in latitude but large extent in longitude	$K = 7$
Rectangular outline with longer axis North–South	$K = 5$
Circular or elliptical outline	$K = 4$
Square outline	$K = 3$

An even more sophisticated approach was used by him to derive the *Equidistant Conical Projection* (*Kavraisky IV*), originally intended for a map of the European part of the USSR. This made use of a least squares analysis to obtain the projection constants, *n* and *C*, using the land area in every $1°$ belt of latitude as a weighting factor. The method of obtaining the constants by these methods have been described in detail in Ref. 12.

The combined analytical and graphical method of selection

Although methods like the use of Kavraisky's constant, *K*, may be valuable in certain kinds of choice, they only represent a partial solution of the larger problem of deciding if modification of certain projections is going to be helpful in producing a better map. We have to devise a systematic method of investigation and in seeking this we cannot do better than extend the graphical methods already described and employ the simple analytical techniques briefly described by Miller (Ref. 5). In order to show how these may be applied to a specific problem, we select the example which Miller describes, namely to find a conformal projection suitable for a single map of Latin America, which study led ultimately to the description of the Bipolar Oblique Conformal Conical Projection which represents the whole of the New World in a single map.

In order to proceed with the analytical part of the investigation it is necessary to specify certain limiting values of distortion which we wish to satisfy on the map. For a conformal map we might specify that the area scale should always lie between two limits such as $0 \cdot 95 < p < 1 \cdot 05$ which is equivalent to the statement that distortion of area never exceeds $\pm 5\%$. Alternatively, we might specify, like Miller, that the particular scales should lie in the range $0 \cdot 965 < \mu < 1 \cdot 035$, or, in other words, that linear distortion does not exceed $\pm 3 \cdot 5\%$. We should note that there is nothing magical about the choice of these numerical values for area scale and particular scale. The selection of these is quite arbitrary but has to be realistic. We would not be able to produce a map for the whole of Latin America if we specified that $0 \cdot 999 < \mu < 1 \cdot 001$. On the other hand, the investigation would not be particularly rewarding if we specified that $0 \cdot 5 < \mu < 2 \cdot 0$ because a large number of projections would satisfy these conditions and the selection between them would not be helped.

The area to be mapped is illustrated in Figs. 92, 93 and 94. It represents the whole of the continent of South America extending to the northern frontier of Mexico in latitude 32° North near the Gulf of California. A preliminary study suggests that the origin of the projection might be located at $\varphi_0 = 0°$, $\lambda_0 = 72°$ West. Young's Rule gives $z/\delta \approx 1 \cdot 4$ which is so close to the critical value for a conformal projection that it is debatable whether an azimuthal, cylindrical or conical projection is to be preferred. In his study of the subject Miller compared modified versions of the Stereographic Projection, normal aspect Mercator Projection and the Transverse Mercator Projection before finding a satisfactory solution in the use of an oblique aspect Conformal Conical Projection. We begin by investigating the possible use of the Stereographic and two versions of the Mercator Projection without modification for both the methods, and the results are most instructive. We investigate each of the projections in turn to determine the location of the limiting isogram for $\mu = 1 \cdot 035$ and plot the result in Fig. 92.

The study of the separate projections may be summarised as follows:

Transverse Aspect Stereographic Projection

From Appendix I, p. 236, the equation for the particular scales of the Stereographic Projection is

$$\mu = a = b = \sec^2 \frac{z}{2}$$

Thus if we employ a transverse aspect Stereographic Projection, there is a single point of zero distortion at the origin on the Equator in longitude 72° West. Here the principal scale is equal to unity and the particular scale increases radially outwards to the specified limit ($+3 \cdot 5\%$) where

$$\sec^2 \frac{z}{2} = 1 \cdot 035$$

Solving this equation we find $z = 21° 12'$ so that the only part of Latin America which can be mapped to the required specification lies within the circle shown in Fig. 92.

Modified Transverse Stereographic Projection

We specify that the minimum particular scale, $\mu = 0 \cdot 965 = A$ is preserved at the origin of the projection. Then the point of zero distortion is replaced by a standard circle of angular distance z_a from the origin. It can be shown that

$$\cos^2 \frac{z_a}{2} = A \qquad (9 \cdot 03)$$

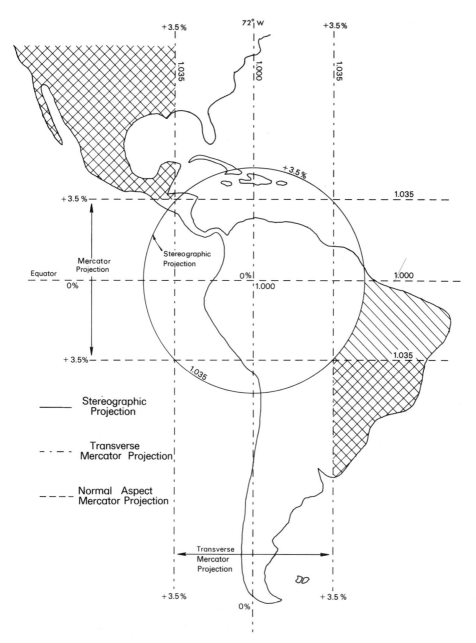

Figure 92 Graphical comparison of the isograms for particular scales on the Normal Aspect Mercator Projection, Transverse Mercator Projection and the Stereographic Projection for a conformal map of Latin America. The same technique is used as illustrated in Figs. 86 and 87. The origin for the Stereographic Projection is the point on the Equator in longitude 72° W. The line of zero distortion for the normal aspect Mercator Projection is the Equator and that of the Transverse Mercator Projection is the meridian 72° W. This figure compares the region enclosed by the isograms for particular scale $\mu = 1 \cdot 035 = +3 \cdot 5\%$. To aid interpretation the parts of the region where this particular scale is exceeded on the Stereographic and Transverse Mercator projections are shaded.

N

and the formula needed to define the modified projection may be written

$$r = 2R \cdot A \tan \frac{z}{2} \tag{9.04}$$

with the equation for the particular scales

$$\mu = A \cdot \sec^2 \frac{z}{2} \tag{9.05}$$

Putting $\mu = A = 0 \cdot 965$ at the origin of the projection, we obtain the radius of the standard circle from equation (9.03) to be

$$z_a = 21° \ 34'$$

Substituting $\mu = 1 \cdot 035$ and $A = 0 \cdot 965$ in equation (9.05) the upper limit of particular scale is found at the distance

$$z = 30° \ 08'$$

from the origin. Figure 93 shows the positions of the standard circle and the isogram for $1 \cdot 035 = +3 \cdot 5\%$. Comparison of Figs. 92 and 93 indicate the value of introducing this kind of modification to an azimuthal projection.

Normal Aspect Mercator Projection

From the study of this projection in Chapter 8, we know that the line of zero distortion is the Equator and that the particular scale $\mu = a = b = \sec \varphi$. Thus, for the present study it is sufficient to know that the limiting particular scale is located along the parallels where $\sec \varphi = 1 \cdot 035$ or

$$\varphi = \pm 14° \ 57'$$

The part of Latin America which can be mapped on the normal aspect Mercator Projection according to this specification is shown in Fig. 92.

Modified Normal Aspect Mercator Projection

If we specify that the limiting particular scale $\mu = 0 \cdot 965$ is preserved at the Equator, this has the effect of introducing two lines of zero distortion forming two standard parallels. From equation (8.71), p. 155, we have, for the particular scale at the Equator

$$0 \cdot 965 = \frac{\cos \varphi_0}{1}$$

or

$$\varphi_0 = \pm 15° \ 12'$$

Substituting this value in equation (8.71) we now obtain the latitude, φ, where the particular scale becomes the upper limiting value. Thus

$$1 \cdot 035 = \frac{0 \cdot 965}{\cos \varphi}$$

or

$$\varphi = \pm 21° \ 12'$$

The part of Latin America which can be mapped according to this specification is shown in Fig. 93.

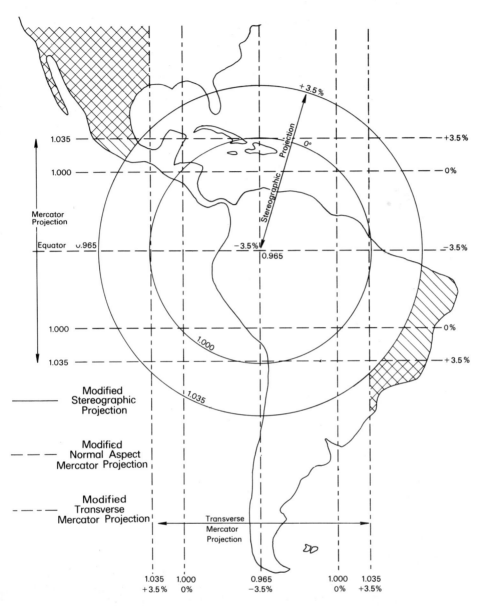

Figure 93 Graphical comparison of the isograms for particular scales on modified versions of the Normal Aspect Mercator Projection, Transverse Mercator Projection and Stereographic Projection for a conformal map of Latin America. In this figure the range of particular scale is made $0.965 < \mu < 1.035$. Therefore the particular scale $\mu = 0.965$ (-3.5%) is preserved at the origin of the Stereographic Projection, along the Equator for the Normal Aspect Mercator Projection and along the meridian $72°$ W for the Transverse Mercator Projection. To aid interpretation the parts of the region where the particular scale $\mu > 1.035$ or $+3.5\%$ on the Stereographic and Transverse Mercator projections are shaded. Comparison of Figs. 92 and 93 indicates how modification of any of these projections extends the size of the region within which they may be usefully employed.

Transverse Mercator Projection

Since a change of aspect does not alter the position or pattern of distortion isograms, we use the reasoning used for the normal aspect Mercator Projection to obtain the corresponding numerical values for the Transverse Mercator Projection. Thus, in the first case, illustrated by Fig. 92, the line of zero distortion is the central meridian in longitude 72° West and the limiting scale $\mu = 1 \cdot 035$ occurs at the angular distance $z = \pm 14°$ 57' from it. At the Equator, therefore, this particular scale occurs in longitudes 57° 03' West and 86° 57' West. Since the distortion isograms are coincident with small circle arcs parallel to the central meridian, they do not coincide with these meridians elsewhere.

Modification of the Transverse Mercator Projection so that the particular scale $\mu = 0 \cdot 995$ is preserved along the central meridian creates two lines of zero distortion at $z = 15°$ 12' on either side of the origin (intersecting the Equator at longitudes 56° 48' West and 87° 12' West) with the upper limit of linear distortion at $z = 21°$ 12' (corresponding to longitudes 50° 48' West and 93° 12' West on the Equator). In Chapter 11 we will find that a similar kind of modification is commonly applied to the Transverse Mercator Projection for use in surveying.

The advantages of modification are evident from the comparison of Figs. 92 and 93 for each of the modified projections which have been studied show that a much larger part of Latin America can be shown within the specified limits of particular scale. In both illustrations we can see that there is not much to choose between the Stereographic Projection and the Transverse Mercator Projection. Both of these are clearly superior to the normal aspect Mercator Projection. However the visual impression is obtained from the study of the positions occupied by the isograms for a single value and does not take into account the magnitude of the particular scales beyond the specified limit. Miller calculated these for a network of 49 points within the area (at intervals of 8° latitude and 12° longitude) and found that the average and maximum scale distortions for the three projections studied were

	Percentage scale distortion	
	Average	*Maximum*
Modified Stereographic	5·6	18·4
Modified Transverse Mercator	6·3	27·7
Modified normal aspect Mercator	10·8	58·4

These figures suggest that the modified Stereographic Projection is the best choice *from these three* but as the visual appraisal showed, it is closely followed by the Tranverse Mercator. Nevertheless all of them fail to meet the initial specification that linear distortion should everywhere lie between $+3 \cdot 5\%$ and $-3 \cdot 5\%$. It can be argued that this specification cannot be met and therefore somewhat lower tolerances should be employed, for example to find a conformal projection in which the linear distortion does not exceed $\pm 5\%$ If this expedient is adopted the analysis must be repeated to calculate and plot new positions for the limiting isograms. The reader is invited to substitute the condition that $0 \cdot 95 < \mu < 1 \cdot 05$ and obtain values corresponding to those derived on the last three pages.

The Oblique Conformal Conical Projection

However, relaxation of the specification is only justified when it is clear that no projection will meet the specification. After all, we have only tested three possibilities and have not yet considered use of a conformal conical projection. This, in fact, provides a satisfactory solution to this problem.

From examination of a globe, which is invaluable for this kind of investigation, Miller and Briesmeister found that a small circle can be drawn about a pole located in the South Pacific Ocean, the arc of which divides Latin America into two parts which are roughly equal in area. By trial and error they found that a pole located in latitude 20° South, longitude 110° West, and a small circle 52° distant from it meets this requirement. The problem now is to define the conformal conical projection in which this arc forms the middle of the map. Since the concept of an oblique aspect conical projection is unfamiliar, we have, in Fig. 94, treated the

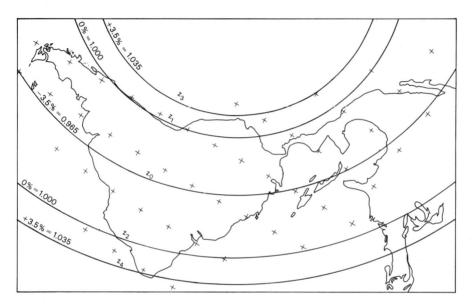

Figure 94 Diagrammatic representation of the isograms for the Oblique Aspect Conformal Conical Projection selected by Miller for the American Geographical Society map of Latin America. The isograms are for particular scales $\mu = 0.965$ (-3.5%), 1.000 (0%) and 1.035 ($+3.5\%$) and indicate the extent of the region which can be mapped without exceeding linear deformation $\pm 3.5\%$. The crosses indicate those graticule intersections for which Miller calculated the particular scale in his statistical analysis of the merits of this projection compared with the versions of the Stereographic and Mercator projections already studied.

problem as if we were dealing with a normal aspect conical projection in which the various small circles would be parallels of latitude. Thus we must define a sequence of concentric circular arcs which we have labelled as follows:

z_0 is the small circle with angular distance 52° from the pole which passes through the centre of Latin America.

z_4 is the small circle passing through the further limit of the map, i.e. lying in the Atlantic Ocean and close to the Brazilian coast.

z_3 is the small circle passing through the nearer limit of the map, i.e. lying in the Pacific Ocean near the Galapagos Islands.

z_1 and z_2 are two small circles lying between the centre and edges of the map, which will serve as standard parallels. Comparison of Fig. 94 with Fig. 91 indicates that the following changes in notation have been made:

z_0 corresponds to φ_0
z_4 corresponds to φ_S
z_3 corresponds to φ_N
z_2 corresponds to φ_1
z_1 corresponds to φ_2

Inspection of a map or globe shows that where the pole is $\varphi_0 = 20°$ S, $\lambda_0 = 110°$ W, $z_0 = 52°$, $z_4 = 73°$ and $z_3 = 31°$. The shape of the area to be mapped suggests that use of Kavraisky's constant $K = 7$ may be a suitable choice for the location of the standard parallels. By trial and error, Miller found $z_2 = 36° 20'$ and $z_1 = 66° 35'$ would best meet the specification. This corresponds to the use of $K \approx 8$. The resulting map has the lower limit particular scale $\mu = 0 \cdot 965$ along the centre with the upper limit $\mu = 1 \cdot 035$ along the small circle arcs z_4 and z_3. Analysis of the particular scales at 49 points on the map gave an average percentage scale distortion $\pm 1 \cdot 8\%$ rising to a maximum value of $9 \cdot 8\%$. These figures indicate immediately that the chosen projection is superior to any of those tabulated on page 180. However, the really convincing display is through graphical representation of the limiting isograms. These are shown in Fig. 84.

The logical sequel to this investigation was for Miller to locate a second pole in the North Atlantic Ocean suitable for mapping the remainder of North America also on an oblique aspect conformal conical projection. The two parts may be joined across the Caribbean and Central America to form a single map. The result is the Bipolar map illustrated in Fig. 84.

References

1   Maling, D. H.: 'How long is a piece of string?', *The Cartographic Journal*, 5 1968, pp. 147–156.
2   Frolov, Y. S. and Maling, D. H.: 'The accuracy of area measurement by point counting techniques', *The Cartographic Journal*, 6, 1969, pp. 21–34.
3   Salishchev, K. A. (Ed.): *Atlas Nationaux: Histoire, analyse, voies de perfectionnement et d'unification*, Moscow and Leningrad, 1960, L'Académie des Sciences de l'URSS. 149 pp.
4   Honick, K. R.: 'Pictorial navigation displays', *The Cartographic Journal*, 4, 1967, pp. 72–81.
5   Miller, O. M.: 'A conformal map projection for the Americas', *Geographical Review*, 31, 1941, pp. 100–104.
6   Robinson, A. H.: *The Look of Maps*, Madison, 1952, The University of Wisconsin Press, 105 pp.
7   Hammer, E.: *Uber die geographisch wichtigsten Kartenprojektionen*, Stuttgart, 1889, J. B. Metzlerscher Verlag, 148 pp.
8   Young, A. E.: *Some Investigations in the Theory of Map Projections*, R.G.S. Technical Series No. 1, London, 1920, Royal Geographical Society, 76 pp.
9   Ginzburg, G. A. and Salmanova, T. D.: *Atlas dlya vybora kartograficheskikh proektsiy*. Trudy TsNIIGAiK, Vyp 110, Moscow, 1957, Geodezidat, 239 pp.
10 Sear, W. J.: 'The projection story', *Cartography*, 6, 1967, pp. 64–72.
11 Hinks, A. R.: 'Making the British Council map', *Geographical Journal*, 100, 1942, pp. 123–130.
12 Maling, D. H.: 'A Review of some Russian map projections', *Empire Survey Review*, 15, 1960, pp. 203–215, 255–266, 294–303.

CHAPTER 10

PROJECTIONS FOR NAVIGATION CHARTS

Whiche waye too bee knowne is thys: Fyrste too consider by what poynte
that the shippe hath made hir waye by and how fast and swiftly that the
shippe hath gone, and to consider how often that the shippe hath altered
hir course, and how much of that shee hath gone at euerye tyme, and then
to consider all thys in your Platte or Carde, and so you maye giue an
neere gesse by what poynt or wynde it beareth from you, and also howe
farr it is thyther.

William Bourne: *A Regiment for the Sea* (1574?)

Introduction

We have already emphasised that navigation is one of the most exacting of all
kinds of map or chart use. In order to explain why navigation charts must be
based upon projections which satisfy certain combinations of special property, we
must know something about the way in which charts are used. It is therefore
desirable to interrupt the study of map projections to mention some of the principles
and methods of navigation. The description which follows must, of necessity, be
brief. Since our preoccupation is with the use of charts, we must ignore navigation
techniques in which chart use has secondary importance.

Navigation is the art of taking a craft from one place to another out of sight
of land. Pilotage is the art of taking a craft from one place to another when land or
navigation marks are in sight. The object of both is to ensure that the craft makes
a safe passage from the place of departure to its destination, preferably along some
predetermined *track* and within the time schedule allowed by the timetable, available
fuel supplies and similar constraints. These objects should be achieved without
risking stranding or collision with rocks, sandbanks, wrecks or other shipping at
sea; with high ground and other aircraft in the air.

An indispensable part of the equipment needed by the navigator is a chart, or
more commonly a sequence of charts, covering the route to be followed. These
fulfil three requirements:

(1) *Charts provide information about the nature and position of hazards to
   navigation.* These include shallow water and submarine obstacles to
   be shown on the nautical chart; high ground and overhead obstacles
   to be shown on aeronautical charts.
(2) *Charts provide information about the availability and identification of aids
   to navigation.* These include marine lights and buoys on nautical
   charts and radio direction-finding aids like beacons and radio ranges
   on aeronautical charts. Where such aids are available, both marine
   and air charts may show the *lattice* network denoting lines of constant
   instrumental readings which are used in the various kinds of hyper-
   bolic navigation systems (e.g. *Decca, Loran, Consol*) to fix position.
(3) *A chart is the base upon which the graphical work of navigation is done.* It
   is this function of the chart which is most closely associated with the
   choice of projection and which is therefore studied here.

For the present we may regard the procedures of both marine and air navigation
as being identical. This was true of the early days of flying, when the techniques of
air navigation evolved from those already used at sea. This similarity still exists in

the navigation of slow piston-engined aircraft, but methods of navigating jet aircraft have changed as flying speeds have increased. For example, there is insufficient time for the navigator of a jet aircraft to solve problems graphically on a chart. This has to be done by analogue or digital computation rather than by pencil, ruler and dividers. We will comment briefly how these changes in technique have influenced aeronautical chart design after we have considered the fundamental similarities which exist between marine and air navigation and the ways in which a chart is used.

Any voyage or flight may be subdivided into three separate stages. The first and last of these are the periods immediately after departure and prior to arrival. At such times a ship is close to land and is probably confined to a navigable channel which is crowded with other shipping. During the intermediate *en-route* stage the vessel is out of sight of land, in deep water and the risk of collision is less. In a navigable channel the facilities for fixing position are usually frequent and reliable, but at that time knowledge about the position of the vessel must also be precise. In the open ocean, aids to location are generally much less satisfactory and much of the skill of the navigator lies in making a correct interpretation of a variety of data to ensure that the craft maintains the proposed track according to the intended timetable.

In flying the same distinctions can be made between the periods just after take-off and shortly before landing, when the position and height of the aircraft is largely ordered by air traffic control, and the *en-route* period of flight when surveillance from the ground is less stringent. However, the increasing volume of air transport and the consequent need to maintain safe clearance between aircraft increases the responsibility of ground control and reduces the amount of navigation to be done on board. For example, the movements of aircraft operating over much of Western Europe and North America are almost wholly controlled from the ground. Under these circumstances the navigator has hardly any more opportunity to exercise his knowledge, skill and judgement during the *en-route* stage of the flight than has the mariner sailing up the Manchester Ship Canal. Because we are primarily concerned with the study of the projections which are used for navigation charts rather than the other aspects of chart content and design, we limit the present discussion to methods of chart use during the *en-route* stage, when the job of the navigator is to keep the craft on track, on time and to avoid 'getting lost'.

Dead-reckoning (D.R.) navigation

Certain information about the performance and movements of the craft can be measured on board. *Direction* may be measured by compass, directional gyro or gyro-magnetic compass. By using these the helmsman or pilot can steer the craft on any desired heading or *course*. This can usually be maintained within $\frac{1}{2}°$ of the intended direction. Bearings can be measured to similar order of accuracy. It is important to appreciate that this order of accuracy is lower than is needed in surveying and gunnery for it does influence some assumptions which can be made about the properties of certain projections. *Speed*, or *distance travelled* may also be measured instrumentally. In an aircraft, the *air speed indicator* measures the airflow past the wings and fuselage. At sea, the distance travelled can be measured by a *patent log* towed astern, though this is being replaced by meters recording speed like the air speed indicator. When the necessary corrections have been applied to take account of the influence of the environment, measurements of speed are likely to be accurate within 1–3%.

However, these measurements of direction and speed are relative because the movement of the water or the air also affects the movements of the craft. The course of a ship or aircraft does not necessarily correspond to the desired track and the ground speed is not the same as the air speed. The distance recorded by patent log will underestimate the actual forward movement of a vessel if there is a following sea.

The absolute movements of a ship or aircraft over the Earth's surface are exceedingly difficult to measure continuously or reliably. For example, until the *Doppler Navigator* was introduced in the 1950's it was impossible to measure the track and ground speed of an aircraft once it had passed out of sight of the ground. *Inertial navigation systems* now make possible continuous recording of position in any craft under any circumstances, for example, on board a submarine operating beneath the pack-ice of the Arctic Ocean. However, the size, cost and sophistication of the equipment required preclude their use for many purposes and in the absence of such instruments the navigator has to determine the unknown quantities of track and ground speed by indirect methods.

In order to show how these may be obtained by plotting on a chart we refer specifically to the navigation of a piston-engined aircraft with a cruising speed within the range 100–150 knots (115–173 m.p.h. or 185–278 k.p.h.). We use this example to represent the problems of D.R. navigation in their most acute form because the influence of wind is important. The air speed of a jet aircraft is much greater and the effect of wind is relatively less. The speed of a ship is slow, but displacement by the sea is also small.

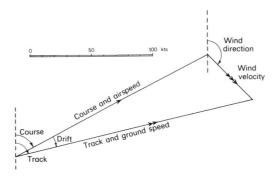

Figure 95 The triangle of velocities in air navigation. The angles of the triangle are formed by observed directions and the lengths of the sides of the triangle are proportional to speed according to the scale provided. Hence this diagram illustrates the effect of a north-westerly wind of 50 knots upon an aircraft flying with a heading of 062° and airspeed 177 knots.

The relationship between the measured and actual movements of an aircraft are characterised by the *triangle of velocities* (Fig. 95) in which the three sides of the triangle are vectors having both direction and length. Thus the angles of the triangle are represented by the differences in direction of adjacent sides and the lengths of the sides are proportional to speed. One side of this triangle is composed of known quantities. These are the course and airspeed of the aircraft obtained by measurements made on board by the methods already mentioned. Another side of the triangle is represented by the wind velocity, or the vector comprising wind speed and wind direction. This is the force displacing the aircraft during flight. The third side is the resultant of these components, representing the track and

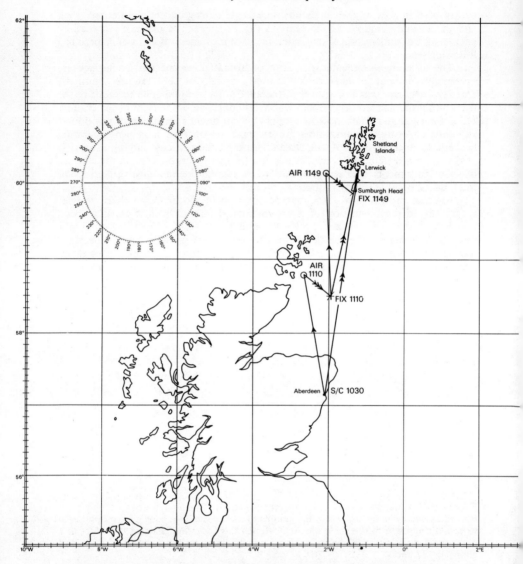

Figure 96 An example of a graphical air plot for a flight from Aberdeen to Lerwick represented on Mercator's Projection. The track from Aberdeen to Lerwick is 008° (true) and the distance is 182 nautical miles. This is indicated by the straight line with two arrowheads. The forecast wind velocity for the flight is 315°/50 kts. and the economical cruising speed is 150 kts. The navigator therefore calculates the course to be 350° (true). This is plotted as the line with a single arrowhead, commencing at Aberdeen.

   The pilot sets course over Aberdeen on this heading at 10 30. At 11 10 the position of the aircraft is fixed in latitude 58° 30′ N, longitude 1° 59′ W, indicated on the chart by 'FIX 1110'. The air position corresponding to this is indicated 'AIR 1110' and is the place where the aircraft would have been if there had been no wind. Measurement of the direction and length of the short line joining these two points indicates the effect which the wind has had upon the aircraft during the 40 minutes which have elapsed ground speed of the aircraft. The interior angle of the triangle formed between the course and track vectors is known as *drift*.

It may be imagined that if the length of the side representing air speed is greatly increased, but the wind speed remains constant, the drift becomes less and the difference between air speed and ground speed also becomes less. This is why the effect of wind is relatively less important in navigating high-speed jets.

Since one side of this triangle is always known, the triangle may be solved if another side can be found. For example, if we can measure the wind velocity we may calculate the track and ground speed. Conversely if we can *fix* the position of the aircraft and therefore know the track and ground speed we may find the wind velocity. These problems may be solved by plotting the triangle of velocities at a convenient scale, although, in practice, analogue solutions have been used for the last forty years. To the air navigator a 'computer' was the instrument used for this purpose long before this word obtained its modern meanings.

From the knowledge of forecast wind velocity we can determine the course to be steered in order to maintain a required track. Given a steady and accurately forecast wind, this information may be sufficient to guide the aircraft to its destination. However, significant changes in wind speed and direction may occur, especially during a long flight, and these will blow the aircraft from the intended track unless they are recognised and an alteration in course is made to counteract them. If the flight is in or above cloud, or over the sea, there is no method of recognising what displacements have been taking place until the navigator has an opportunity to fix position. When this can be done it becomes possible to measure the total influence of the wind during the time which has elapsed since the position of the aircraft was last determined. Using this information, and assuming that the aircraft will continue to be influenced by similar winds during the remainder of the flight, the appropriate alteration in course is made to regain the required track.

Much of this reasoning can be done graphically by plotting every course flown as a continuous traverse on the chart. Each course is plotted as a straight line of corresponding direction and the length of each leg of the traverse is plotted as the distance flown according to the air speed. The result might appear as illustrated in Fig. 96, where the figures indicate the times at which an alteration in course was made. This *air plot* indicates where the aircraft would have been if

---

since setting course. This shows that the total effect of the wind upon the aircraft corresponds to a wind from 340° of speed 40 kts. From the position fixed to Lerwick is a track of 012° and to follow this according to the revised wind velocity represents a new course of 358°. The new track and course are here plotted from 'FIX 1110' though we must emphasise that this represents an approximation. At 11 49 the aircraft crosses the coast of the Shetland Islands 2 miles north-west of Sumburgh Head. This represents 'FIX 1149' with the corresponding point 'AIR 1149' on the air plot.

In practical navigation a few minutes would elapse between obtaining the observations to plot the fix at 1110 and determining the new track and course. During that time the aircraft would continue to fly along the erroneous track. Therefore the navigator would have to determine the DR position for some time in advance (e.g. 1115) and calculate the new course to be steered from there.

This need to work fast and work ahead of time indicates one of the main differences between the practice of DR navigation at sea and in the air. The slow speeds of ships means that an alteration of course can be made from a fix even when several minutes have elapsed between the time of observations and execution of the alteration in course. The faster the airspeed of an aircraft the greater the distance covered in an equivalent time and therefore increased uncertainty about position when finally altering course. This accounts for the reduction in the use of graphical methods of DR navigation in modern flying.

there had been no wind. Using distances calculated from the true air speed it is possible to locate the *air position* at an instant of time. For example, in Fig. 96, the point indicated 'AIR 1110' represents this point at 11 10 hours, or 40 minutes after setting course. If we calculate a corresponding distance from the assumed wind speed and plot a line representing the effect of the wind from the air position, we locate the *D.R.*, or *dead-reckoning position* of the aircraft for the same instant of time. However, the D.R. position is only an estimate which is based upon the navigator's opinion of how the wind has affected the aircraft during flight. This estimate can only be checked by fixing the position of the aircraft. The point indicated 'FIX 1110' shows the observed position of the aircraft at that time, and the line joining this to the air position indicates the total influence of the wind since setting course at 09 30.

Fixing position may be accomplished in a variety of ways, by means of visual or radio bearings, by astronomical or electronic methods, or even by map reading when the ground is visible. The information obtained is usually in the form of bearings. Exceptions to this are fixes obtained by some electronic methods and 'pin-pointing' on a map some place on the ground which is immediately beneath the aircraft. All we know from a single bearing is that the aircraft was located upon the *position line* represented by the bearing plotted on the chart. The intersection of two or more bearings will provide a fix, but only if all the bearings were measured simultaneously. Usually a short interval elapses between observing and recording each bearing so that the chart shows several position lines indicating locations of the aircraft at different times. The graphical method of forming a fix comprising several such position lines is to transfer some of them as parallel lines by amounts corresponding to the distance flown between the individual observations. The method of transfer is illustrated in Fig. 97.

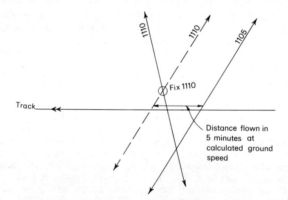

Figure 97 Graphical transfer of position lines in DR navigation. Two position lines, resulting from observations made at 11 05 and 11 10 respectively are represented by full lines. Their intersection suggests that the position of the aircraft lies to the south of the intended track. However the position of the aircraft changed during the 5 minutes which elapsed between the two observations. It is therefore desirable to transfer the first position line in the direction of flight by the assumed distance flown during the interval between observations. This is done by transferring the position line as a parallel straight line (broken line). This indicates that the craft was north of the intended track at 11 10.

This brief account of the methods of D.R. navigation indicates that the navigator has to plot straight lines on the chart to represent courses, tracks, wind vectors, bearings and position lines. Measurement of the direction of all of these is important. Measurement of distance along some of them is also important.

Great circles and rhumb-lines

We must now make the important distinction between two kinds of line on the Earth's surface; the great circle and the rhumb-line. We have already defined the properties of a great circle in Chapter 3. It will be recalled that the shortest distance between any two points is the arc of the great circle passing through them. However, any great circle arc which is neither part of a meridian nor part of the Equator has the property that it intersects every meridian at a different angle. This is owing to the convergence of the meridians and the quantity γ, defined by equations (3.26) and (3.27) on page 43 is also a measure of the total change in bearing along a great circle arc. A line of constant bearing, i.e. a line which intersects every meridian at the same angle, is known as a rhumb-line. This is the spiral curve on the spherical surface illustrated in Fig. 98.

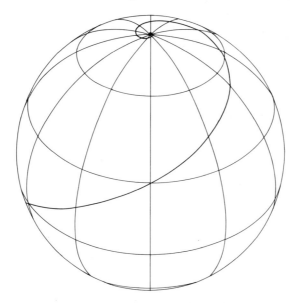

Figure 98 The representation of a rhumb-line on the spherical surface.

The great circle arc has twofold significance in navigation. First, the *great circle sailing*, or track which follows a great circle arc, is the shortest distance between two places and may therefore be presumed to be the obvious route to follow between them. Secondly, the path followed by a radio signal or any other kind of electromagnetic propagation or reflection between a beacon and the craft is also the arc of a great circle. So, too, is a visual line of sight. However, the low accuracy with which bearings are measured in navigation makes this distinction unimportant over the distances which visual bearings can be made. We will find, in Chapter 11, that the fact that visual lines of sight lie in the planes of great circles is important to the surveyor.

The *rhumb-line sailing*, or track which follows a rhumb-line is important because this is the line followed by any craft which is steered on a constant heading.

This procedure becomes necessary once a craft is out of sight of land and its heading must be maintained instrumentally. In short, the rhumb-line has constant direction but represents the longer distance whereas the great circle is the shortest distance but varies continuously in direction. Clearly it is more convenient to steer a rhumb-line course if the extra distance travelled is small. Conversely a long flight or voyage may be shortened by altering course in such a way that the great circle sailing is maintained. Thus the relationship between these kinds of line is important in practical navigation. From the point of view of choosing a projection for a chart it is valuable if either of these lines can be represented by means of straight lines. If rhumb-lines are rectilinear, the graphical work of D.R. navigation is simplified. If great circles are rectilinear, the preliminary planning of a great circle sailing and the plotting of radio bearings are facilitated.

We demonstrate the differences between the great circle and rhumb-line on the Earth by giving two examples. The reader who wishes to find out how these results were derived is referred to any of the standard works on navigation, e.g. Refs. 1, 2 or 3. The great circle distance from Lerwick (60° 09′ N, 1° 09′ W) to Bergen (60° 24′ N, 5° 19′ E) is 191 nautical miles (354 km.). The rhumb-line distance between these places is 193 nm. (358 km.).† In order to maintain the great circle sailing it would be necessary to set course from Lerwick on the heading 083° (T)‡ and alter course until Bergen is reached on 088° (T). Theoretically, these changes in direction ought to be applied continuously but, in practice, they would be made in $\frac{1}{2}$° steps at intervals of 18 nautical miles. The alternative rhumb-line sailing requires a constant track of 085° (T) to be maintained throughout the journey. The alteration in course needed to follow the great circle is an inconvenience if the distance saved is only two nautical miles (4 km.). As the second example we make the comparison of the great circle and rhumb-line sailings between Halifax (44° 40′ N, 63° 35′ W) and Lerwick, i.e. across the North Atlantic Ocean. The great circle distance is 2359 nm. (4372 km.) and the rhumb-line distance is 2452 nm. (4544 km.). In order to maintain the great circle sailing it is necessary to alter course through more than 50°.§ In this example there is advantage to be gained from following the great circle track for this is the shorter by nearly 100 nm. (172 km.).

From these examples we see that the difference in distance between the great circle and rhumb-line sailings varies according to the length of the arc. It can also be shown that the difference also varies according to the bearing between the points and their latitudes. In the limiting case of a track which coincides with a meridian there is no difference between the two lines.

The usual navigation practice is to follow rhumb-line tracks unless the voyage or flight is so long that the great circle sailing offers an appreciable saving of distance and therefore time and fuel. Even then, the navigator uses a *composite track* (Fig. 99) which divides the great circle route into a series of shorter rhumb-line elements. This means that the craft is steered on a succession of constant headings, altering course at suitable intervals to keep close to the great circle.

---

† One nautical mile equals one minute of arc measured along a great circle. If the Earth is regarded to be a sphere, so that the relationship between angular and linear distance (1.02, p 4) is everywhere constant, 1′ = 1 nm = 1853.2 metres = 6080 feet.

‡ Tracks, courses and bearings may be defined as *true* (T), *magnetic* (M) or *grid* (G) according to which datum is used for their measurement. A true course is measured from the meridian i.e. True North; a magnetic course is measured from the direction taken by a magnetic compass i.e. Magnetic North; a grid course is measured from Grid North, defined on page 22.

§ We assume a flight from Halifax to Lerwick. Inspection of a chart of the North Atlantic Ocean shows that both the great circle and the rhumb-line joining Halifax and Lerwick pass over Newfoundland. A ship making this voyage would set course on the great circle sailing from a point a few miles off Cape Race.

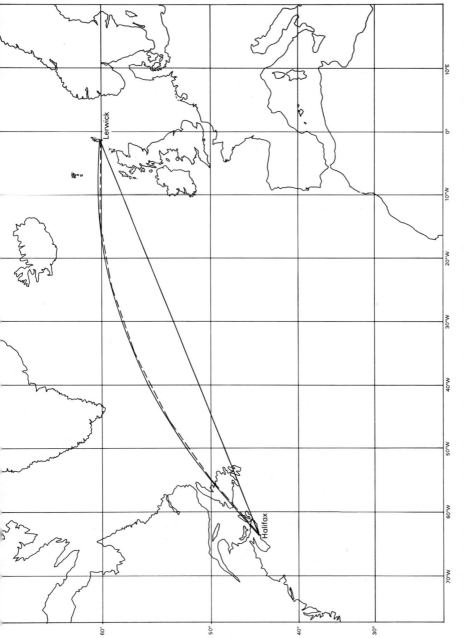

Figure 99 Part of the North Atlantic Ocean on Mercator's Projection showing the great circle (curved) and rhumb-line (straight) sailings between Halifax and Lerwick. A composite track is indicated by the broken line. This is composed of a series of short rhumb-lines which approximate to the curve of the great circle.

Suitable projections for navigation charts

The various requirements for the projection of a navigation chart can now be stated as follows:

(1) Since angular measurement is an important feature of D.R. navigation, a *conformal projection is obligatory*. There are plenty of these to choose from though usually the choice is restricted to the conformal versions of the Cylindrical, Conical and Azimuthal classes. These are, respectively, the *Mercator Projection, Lambert Conformal Conical Projection* and the *Stereographic Projection*. Moreover these are used in their normal aspects.

(2) Since plotting and measuring distance is an important aspect of chart use, a projection on which linear distances are truly represented would seem desirable. However, we have already explained in Chapter 4 that it is impossible to create a plane map in which the principal scale is preserved at all points and in all directions. The best which we can hope to obtain is a projection in which the particular scales do not change too rapidly from place to place on the chart.

(3) Since craft are steered along rhumb-lines, *a projection which shows rhumb-lines by means of straight lines is valuable.*

(4) Similarly, *the representation of great circle arcs by means of straight lines is desirable.*

Clearly the last two requirements are incompatible with one another. We have demonstrated the difference on the Earth between the great circle and rhumb-line joining two points. We cannot, therefore, expect the same projection to depict both as straight lines for this would be the same line and would violate the fundamental principle of one-to-one correspondence between points on the Earth and chart.

There are two conformal projections which satisfy as additional requirements. The Mercator Projection (pp. 152–7) has the important additional property that all rhumb-lines are straight lines. This follows directly from the fundamental property of all normal aspect cylindrical projections that the meridians are represented by parallel straight lines and from the special property that the Mercator Projection is conformal. It follows that any straight line drawn across a Mercator chart intersects every meridian at the same angle. Since there is nó angular deformation, this straight line satisfies the definition of a rhumb-line as being a line of constant bearing.

The Lambert Conformal Conical Projection has the additional advantage that great circle arcs are almost rectilinear. We must emphasise that this is not strictly true. For example, this assumption is not acceptable to a surveyor using this projection as the base for topographical or large-scale mapping. However within the limits of most charts prepared on this projection and within the margin of error which has to be accepted in steering a craft and taking bearings from it, the departure of the great circle arc from a straight line is small enough to be ignored. Since the projection is also conformal it is possible to plot radio bearings as straight lines.

Only one projection has the property that great circles are truly represented by straight lines. This is the *Gnomonic Projection*, which is a member of the Azimuthal class. However this projection is not conformal and it has the additional disadvantage that the radial particular scale ($\mu_1 = \sec^2 z$) increases rapidly from the point of zero distortion. This also means that measurement of distance on the Gnomonic Projection is unreliable unless special measures are taken to correct for the changes in particular scale. It can be done, but it is not a suitable procedure to use in practical navigation.

Projections for nautical charts

In marine navigation, where graphical plotting is still normal practice, the role of the Mercator Projection is unassailable. The practical reasons for its popularity have been admirably summarised by Stigant (Ref. 4) as follows:

> 'Among sailors there is a kind of divine belief in the Mercator. It has two properties which fit their needs absolutely and precisely . . . They are . . . the fact that a straight line drawn on the chart is a line of constant bearing, and the other not less important property is the parallelism of the meridians and parallels which permits you to put the compass rose at one end of the chart and, if your parallel ruler is long enough, to transfer a line of bearing to the other end. These advantages figure very much in the plotting techniques employed by the average navigator, who is not necessarily a cartographical expert. He is used to stepping off a distance from the latitude graduation of the Mercator and transferring a bearing from one end to the other merely by the use of his parallel rule. We cannot . . . abrogate these advantages lightly or without being pretty sure that the reasons are sufficient.'

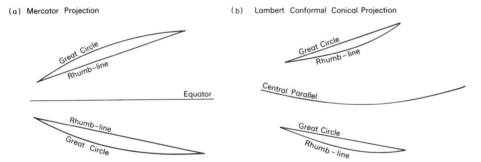

(a) Mercator Projection (b) Lambert Conformal Conical Projection

Figure 100 The representation of great circles and rhumb-lines on (a) Mercator's Projection and (b) the Lambert Conformal Conical Projection. Note that on the Lambert Conformal Conical Projection great circles are not depicted by perfectly straight lines as illustrated here but this assumption is made for all practical purposes in navigation.

It follows that if rhumb-lines are represented by straight lines, great circles must be curves. On the Mercator Projection great circles are represented by curves which are convex towards the nearer pole as illustrated in Fig. 100 (a). If the decision has been taken to follow the great circle route between two places, a curve corresponding to this track must be plotted on the charts to be used. This can be done by computing the geographical coordinates of certain points on the great circle, for example to find the latitude where the arc cuts certain meridians. Alternatively, the route might be plotted first on a Gnomonic chart and these intersections transferred to the Mercator charts. Normally this kind of work is done when planning a voyage or flight and is completed well in advance of putting to sea or take-off. Therefore the slow job of plotting the great circle curve does not have to be done under operational conditions.

However, radio bearings may be needed to fix the craft and the need to plot a great circle bearing as a position line needs a rapid method of converting part of a curved line into a straight line of correct orientation. The navigator uses a

o

conversion angle which is the arc-to-chord relationship between the great circle arc and the rhumb-line chord, measured at both the radio beacon and the craft. For a sphere this angle can be shown to be equal to $\gamma/2$, where γ is the convergency defined in Chapter 3, p. 43. Application of the conversion angle at each end of the arc, as shown in Fig. 101, allows the navigator to plot a short straight line in the vicinity of the craft's D.R. position to represent the position line corresponding to that part of the great circle arc.

The Mercator Projection has the important disadvantage that accurate linear measurement is difficult. This results from the increase in particular scale as a function of sec φ (8.58), p. 153. Thus a distance of 5 cm. on the edge of the chart nearer the Equator represents a shorter distance than 5 cm. on the edge of the chart in a higher latitude. The increase is particularly rapid north of 60° N and in corresponding southern latitudes. It follows that a reliable measurement cannot be made using a ruler with equidistant divisions and converting this to distance on the Earth through the representative fraction. Measurement on the Mercator Projection has to be made with dividers, comparing the separation of the points with the latitude subdivisions along the border of the chart, or along one of the meridians which have been closely subdivided for this purpose. Figure 102 indicates how this is done. The comparison must always be made in the same latitude as

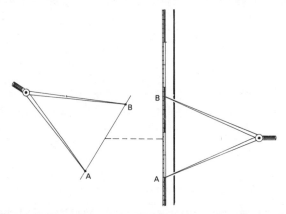

Figure 101 Measurement of distance by dividers on Mercator's Projection. This is always done by comparing the spread of the dividers against the latitude subdivisions along the edge of the chart in the same range of latitude as the line to be measured.

the line to be measured, setting the dividers along the border symmetrically about the mean latitude of the line. In this way the variations in particular scale tend to be compensated, but the measurement is an approximation nevertheless. Since latitude subdivisions are in minutes of arc, or multiples thereof, and since 1' of latitude measured along the meridian corresponds to one nautical mile, comparison of the dividers with the meridional border of the chart gives the distance in nautical miles. This technique emphasises further why navigators prefer to work in units of nautical miles and knots. Moreover it helps to explain why there is no special reason for the scale of a nautical chart to have some integer value like 1/500,000 or 1/1,000,000 but may be 1/545,000 or 1/997,562. The marine navigator probably has to make more measurements of distance than any other user of maps or charts but he never makes the scale conversions typical in the use of topographical maps.

Although we have dismissed the Gnomonic Projection as having only limited use for route planning, its name appears again in marine charting for the words

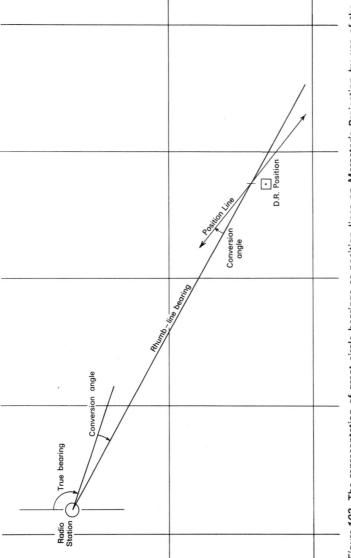

Figure 102 The representation of great circle bearings as position lines on Mercator's Projection by use of the conversion angle. The path of a radio signal between a transmitter and a distant craft follows the great circle arc passing through them. Therefore the measured direction of a radio signal refers to the great circle bearing. In order to plot an observed bearing as a rhumb-line on Mercator's Projection and also plot the direction of the position line as part of the great circle arc, it is necessary to determine the conversion angle by calculation or from a nomogram. This angle is applied to the great circle bearing measured from the radio station to find the rhumb-line to be plotted on the chart. In order to orientate the position line to the great circle it is necessary to apply the same conversion angle in the opposite sense to the rhumb-line plotted near the DR position of the craft. It follows that the position line plotted on the chart now represents a short part of the curve of the great circle.

'Gnomonic Projection' appear on all Admiralty charts of scale 1/50,000 and larger. These are the charts of port and harbour approaches or navigable rivers. At this scale the chart does not extend more than about 15 km. from the centre of the sheet. If, therefore, the centre of the chart represents the origin of the projection, the linear distortion and angular deformation at the edges are too small to be measured. This confirms the conclusion reached in Chapter 9, p. 160, that the choice of projection for a large scale map or chart is often unimportant. Perhaps this is just as well, for the use of the name Gnomonic Projection on large-scale charts is incorrect. The Hydrographic Department admits as much (Ref. 5) stating that the projection is really a version of the *Polyconic Projection*. The equations used to obtain the coordinates of graticule intersections are those of the Polyconic Projection. But these intersections are joined by straight lines to represent the 2' or 4' parallels and meridians. Strictly speaking this converts a Polyconic Projection of Group A into a version of the *Polyhedric Projection*, which is a Pseudocylindrical projection of Group C. Of course the distinction is trivial and cannot be measured on a chart, but it is useful to get the record straight on this matter and use the correct terminology. One question remains; why is it called a Gnomonic Projection?

We can only assume that most navigators know about the special property of the Gnomonic Projection and since entry to a port or harbour is normally made by visual alignment, the fact that visual bearings may be presumed to be straight lines must be some comfort.

Projections for aeronautical charts

In the early days of flying, up to 1939 or thereabouts, air speeds greater than 150 m.p.h. were the exception. Therefore the methods of navigation were similar to those used at sea. The D.R. navigation could be plotted graphically and the majority of techniques for fixing position were like those used at sea. The evolution of aerial navigation from marine navigation was reflected in the design of the aeronautical plotting charts of that time, which were based upon the Mercator Projection (and even showed the depth of the sea). Throughout World War II, the Mercator Plotting chart was used by the Royal Air Force, almost to the exclusion of all other types, but as flying speeds increased it became more and more difficult for the navigator to maintain an up-to-date plot graphically. Consequently analogue instruments were developed to do this part of the work.

Associated with the increased performance of aircraft and the greater density of traffic in post-war years came the need to extend and improve the network of radio aids allowing the navigator to fix position or home to a beacon. Consequently much of airline navigation, following regular routes to a strict timetable, may be categorised as operating along 'great circle tramlines' (Ref. 6). In addition, various methods of electronic distance measurement have been applied to navigation in the form of the *Rebecca/Eureka*, *DME*, *Vortac* and *TACAN* systems. These locate the position of an aircraft by bearing and distance from the beacon. Thus the requirements for aeronautical charts have changed from the need for a document upon which D.R. navigation can be plotted to a chart on which great circle tramlines are rectilinear and distances are relatively easy to measure. This led to replacement of the Mercator Projection by the Lambert Conformal Conical Projection as the base for modern aeronautical charts. Other arguments favouring this change may be found in Refs. 6, 7 and 8. The advantage of showing great circle arcs by straight lines has already been discussed. By using versions of the Lambert Conformal Conical Projection with two standard parallels, the particular scales do not change rapidly within the limits of the single chart and therefore distances can be measured with a ruler. The projection has the disadvantage that rhumb-lines are curved, Fig. 100 (b), but if there is no need to maintain a graphical air plot, this defect is unimportant. A further disadvantage is that measurement of bearings, courses and tracks must be made by using a separate protractor which must be orientated to the meridian through the point where the angle is measured. Since the meridians converge there is no possibility of using a printed compass rose, as on the Mercator chart and using a parallel ruler to transfer lines to any desired place on the chart.

Today the aeronautical chart printed on paper is being replaced by other kinds of graphic display. A common form of display is a map mounted on rollers, the movements of which are controlled by monitoring of track and ground speed by Doppler equipment to indicate the position of the aircraft. This kind of configuration normally requires a special map prepared on an oblique aspect Mercator projection in which the line of zero distortion is the intended track of the aircraft. Even more sophisticated are the projected displays provided by a transparency projected on a screen which indicates the ground position of the aircraft. The techniques of preparing these have been described by Honick (Ref. 9).

One aspect of air navigation which hardly affects the mariner is that of navigation near the geographical poles. In high latitudes definition of true direction is a major problem because the meridians converge to a point. Traditionally the projection suitable for conformal representation of the polar regions is the normal aspect Stereographic Projection. During the last twenty-five years aeronautical charts have been prepared on this projection combined with the *Greenwich Grid*, a plane Cartesian grid with one axis coincident with the Greenwich Meridian. This grid provides a constant datum to which courses, tracks, bearing and magnetic variation may be referred, greatly simplifying the graphical work. The technique of using the Greenwich Grid in high latitudes has been summarised by Hagger (Ref. 10). In recent years the *Transverse Mercator Projection* has also been used for polar navigation. The *USAF Global Navigation and Planning Chart, GNC–1* of scale 1/5,000,000 is based upon this projection and the methods of using it have been described by Dyer (Ref. 11).

References

1 Cotter, C. H.: *The Astronomical and Mathematical Foundations of Geography*, London, 1966, Hollis and Carter, 244 pp.

2 Gardner, A. C. and Creelman, W. G.: *Navigation*, Oxford, 1965, Pergamon Press, 251 pp.

3 — *Admiralty Navigation Manual, Volume II*, London, 1939, HMSO, 268 pp.

4 Stigant, G. B.: *Conference of Commonwealth Survey Officers*, 1947, *Report of Proceedings*, London, 1951, HMSO, pp. 32–33.

5 — *Admiralty Manual of Hydrographic Surveying, Volume I*, London, 1965, Hydrographic Department, 671 pp.

6 Anderson, E. W.: *The Principles of Navigation*, London, 1968, Hollis and Carter, 653 pp.

7 Freer, T. St. B. and Irwin, K. J.: 'Proposals for a new navigation chart', *Journal of the Institute of Navigation*, 4, 1951, pp. 66–80.

8 Peake, E. R. L.: 'The activities of ICAO with particular reference to those of its Map Division', *Conference of Commonwealth Survey Officers*, 1947, *Report of Proceedings*, London, 1951, HMSO, pp. 181–202.

9 Honick, K. R.: 'Pictorial navigation displays', *The Cartographic Journal*, 4, 1967, pp. 72–81.

10   Hagger, A. J.: 'Air navigation in high latitudes', *Polar Record*, 39, 1950, pp. 440–445.
11   Dyer, G. C.: 'Polar navigation—a new Transverse Mercator technique', *Journal of the Institute of Navigation*, 24, 1971, pp. 484–495.

CHAPTER 11

SURVEYING AND MAP PROJECTIONS

26. Is a straight line on the Ordnance Survey a great circle?
— Strictly speaking, no, because I think the only projection on which a
great circle is a straight line is a particular projection that
is not one we have used. In fact the difference would be very slight,
and I do not think you would be able to tell the difference.
27. A twenty-mile straight line would only be a few inches?
— I think you would not notice it. I do not think it would worry any-
body.
28. But on a map of the whole country, the difference would be considerable, would it not?
— I do not know what the difference would be, but I do not think it
would worry you.
29. I am not spending sleepless nights over it?
— No.
....
36. You think the present projection is the best compromise?
— Yes, I have no doubt at all that it is the best one for this country—
no doubt whatever. It was chosen very carefully for that very reason.

> Minutes of Evidence Taken Before Subcommittee
> E of the Estimates Committee. *Eighth Report
> from the Estimates Committee . . . Session* 1962-3.
> *Ordnance Survey.* H.M.S.O., 1963

Introduction

Since a map is a small-scale representation of part of the Earth's surface it has
been possible to argue that knowledge about the projection used as the base for a
large-scale map or chart may be unimportant to the user. Chapter 9 gives the
example of the use of a conformal map, published as part of a national topographic
series, for mapping distributions which theoretically need an equal-area projection.
In Chapter 10 it has been shown that mariners use large-scale charts which they
believe to be based on the Gnomonic Projection, which the Hydrographic Department regard as a modified Polyconic Projection but which should properly be
considered to be a version of the Polyhedric Projection. These examples both
represent misuse of map projections but can be justified because the origin of the
projection, and therefore the point or line of zero distortion is located within or
close to the area to be mapped. It follows that within the area covered by a large-
scale map or chart the amount of linear distortion, angular deformation or
exaggeration of area is too small to be measured.
We have already seen, in Chapter 1, p. 16, that the results of a survey are
normally computed at the natural scale of 1/1. Consequently the distortions and
deformations which are too small to be recognised at a reduction of 1/250,000,
1/25,000 or even 1/2,500 may represent a measurable quantity on the ground. It
follows that the surveyor is also concerned with the subject of map projections
and must apply suitable transformations to observed or computed angles and
distances in order to locate position on the plane of some suitable projection.
In survey, too, circumstances arise when the accuracy requirements for a small job
permit some relaxation in the choice of reference surface and projection, even to

the extent of being able to regard the Earth as being flat over a limited area. Assumptions of this sort depend upon the purpose of the survey, which, in turn determines the precision of the instruments used and the observing routines to be adopted. If the deformation resulting from Earth curvature is less than the precision with which angles and distances have been measured, errors in position attributable to choice of reference surface and projection may be deemed to be too small to measure, just as this assumption is made in the use of large-scale maps or charts.

In the study of the special properties of map projections (Chapter 4, p. 69 we have stated that conformal representation is a necessary requirement for large-scale and topographical maps. The projections generally used include the *Transverse Mercator, Oblique Mercator, Rectified Skew Orthomorphic, Lambert Conformal Conical* and *Stereographic* projections. The Transverse Mercator Projection is by far the most important of these and is gradually replacing the use of the others. One variety, known as the *Universal Transverse Mercator* (UTM) system, was introduced by the United States Army for military use by NATO countries in the early 1950's as a uniform projection system for use throughout the World with the exception of the polar regions. Although its introduction initially met with some opposition (Ref. 1), its use as the base for military mapping by most western countries is now well established and it has been increasingly adopted for civilian purposes. Figure 103 indicates the projection systems in current use and shows the great importance of the UTM.

It is, however, important to realise that the use of conformal projections was not regarded as being a necessary requirement for large-scale and topographical mapping at the time when many national surveys were first created during the nineteenth century. Consequently many organisations employed projections which are unacceptable by modern standards. Typical examples include the use of *Cassini's Projection* and different versions of the *Polyhedric Projection* for original surveys and as bases of large-scale maps and plans. At the smaller topographical scales, *Bonne's Projection* and the *Polyconic Projection* were often used.

The need for conformal maps arose primarily as an artillery requirement during World War I. Since that time the majority of national surveys have been converted to conformal projections and all modern large scale and topographical map series are based on them. In Britain the change to a conformal projection of the whole country coincided with the retriangulation, which was carried out during the 1930's and after World War II, so that the Transverse Mercator coordinates of trigonometric control points are based upon a new and entirely independent series of observations (Ref. 2). In other countries it has been less easy to incorporate the changes quickly or completely. For example, individual state or local coordinate systems used in the United States and many other countries for cadastral and engineering purposes are still a mixture of Conformal Conical, Polyconic, Cassini and Azimuthal Equidistant systems, with many local variations of origin and orientation, which are relics of the nineteenth century. The existence of extensive registers of legal title to land defined in terms of coordinates based upon these systems fosters their preservation. Consequently the results of local surveys must often be computed and recorded on projections which differ from that used by the national survey. Britain has never had cadastral surveys equivalent to those in Europe, the United States and many Commonwealth countries. Consequently the problem has not arisen here.

Published maps frequently have a long life before they are adequately revised or replaced. Consequently the older projection systems may linger on in map use long after the policy decision has been taken to change to a conformal and national system of projection and after the national trigonometric network has been

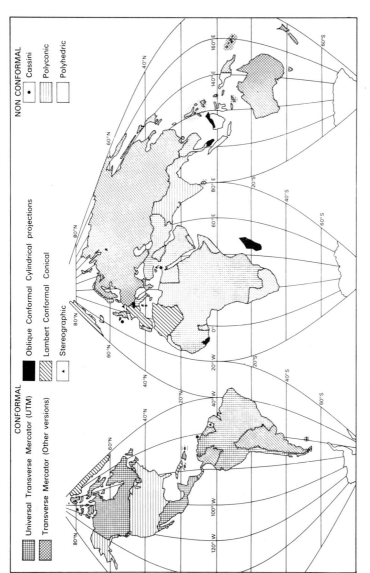

Figure 103 World map indicating the projections currently used for large-scale mapping. The primary source for information is *World Cartography X, 1970*, and is a compilation of the projections accepted for the basic scale mapping by national surveying departments. Because of the continued change to some version of the Transverse Mercator Projection, many countries which are here shown as using another projection are also using the Transverse Mercator Projection for the smaller scale topographical map series or are gradually replacing existing basic mapping by new series based on the Transverse Mercator.

The projection used for this figure is a recentred version of the Sinusoidal Projection (No. 30 in Appendix I) with central meridians in longitudes 100° W, 70° W, 20° E, 30° E and 130° E.

recomputed on the new system. Even today the Ordnance Survey issue some large-scale maps (1/2500) based on local Cassini Projections, simply because these sheets have not yet been replaced by modern maps.

The Plane Assumption

We assume that the reader already has some knowledge of the methods of surveying, at least at the elementary level of knowing that it is necessary to locate the positions of certain *control points* with respect to which the details of features on the ground can later be mapped. We are concerned in this chapter with the definition of the planimetric positions of these control points for ultimately it is the accuracy of their location which determines the accuracy of the entire map. We presume, too, that the reader is aware that the method of establishing this control is through combinations of linear and angular measurement and the observations must be *adjusted* so that the network of observed lines form figures which are geometrically consistent. Then the positions of the control points may be computed within a suitable system of plane coordinates. The simplest of these are plane rectangular Cartesian coordinates which were first introduced in Chapter 2.

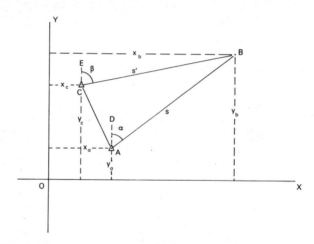

Figure 104 Three survey stations, *A, B* and *C* related to one another in plane rectangular coordinates with origin *O*.

Figure 104 illustrates the use of rectangular coordinates in plane surveying. We assume that the origin of the system, O, and the axes OX and OY have been located and that we already know the positions of the points $A=(x_a, y_a)$ and $C=(x_c, y_c)$ which are control points within the survey. In order to locate another point, B, within the system we employ the equations

$$x_b = x_a + s.\sin \alpha \qquad (11.01)$$

$$y_b = y_a + s.\cos \alpha \qquad (11.02)$$

where $AB=s$ and the angle $DAB=\alpha$. Similarly, working from C,

$$x_b = x_c + s'.\sin \beta \qquad (11.03)$$

$$y_b = y_c + s'.\cos \beta \qquad (11.04)$$

where $CB=s'$ and the angle $ECB=\beta$.

The bearings α and β are derived from combinations of observed angles and known positions. Thus, as A and C have known coordinates the angle DAC may be determined from any of the equations (2.03), (2.07) or (2.08) on page 24. Then, if the angle CAB has been observed, $\alpha = CAB - DAC$.

In a plane survey based upon rectangular coordinates we make certain assumptions about the representation of angles, arcs and distances. We regard the origin of the plane coordinates to be some point near the middle of the survey, although the numbering of coordinates is usually referred to a false origin as described in Chapter 2, pp. 22–23. We further assume that we are observing and computing on a plane which is tangential to the Earth's surface at this point. Hence the plane assumption corresponds to the elementary concept of an Azimuthal projection in which O is the point of zero distortion. We assume that observed spherical angles, such as CAB are always represented by plane angles of the same size. Since all visual lines of sight, or observed directions, correspond to arcs of great circles on a sphere, these are represented on the plane by straight lines, such as AB, AC and CB. The third assumption is made that plane distances, such as AB, AC and CB, are equal to the corresponding horizontal distances measured between these points on the ground. Hence we suppose that the plane is a projection in which the principal scale is preserved everywhere and in all directions. We have established that this is an impossible form of representation. Consequently the plane assumption cannot satisfy the requirement of any single Azimuthal projection although, by its nature, the assumption corresponds closely to the basic concept of this class of projection.

Since we cannot specify that all angles are truly represented, that great circles are straight or that the particular scales behave in a definite fashion without converting equations (11.01)–(11.04) into those for a specific projection, the plane assumption has the considerable advantage of simplicity. Hence it is desirable to establish practical limits to the size of a survey which can be undertaken using the plane assumption without any significant loss of accuracy arising from this cause. Since this depends upon the accuracy of the measurements which are made, we introduce the arbitrary, but useful specifications that:

(1) Observed directions may contain errors up to $10''$,
(2) Measured distances may be in error by as much as 1 part in 2,000.

Where these specifications are satisfied, use of the plane assumption does not materially affect the positions of points provided that the extent of the survey is not more than 10 km. If the accuracy of the observations is lower than those specified, a larger area can be mapped as a plane survey. If the nature of the survey demands a higher order of accuracy, the area for which the plane assumption is justified is correspondingly reduced. However, a great deal depends upon the purpose and ultimate use of the survey. Any survey which is intended solely for the purpose of producing a map or plan needs only to be accurate enough to plot positions within $\pm 0 \cdot 2$ mm. on the plotting sheet. As noted in the introduction to this chapter, projection distortion cannot be measured within the neat lines of a large scale map. Similarly, too, the plane assumption may be greatly extended without affecting the measurable accuracy of the resulting map. For other purposes, such as *setting out* points on the ground for civil engineering construction work, the precision specified for the initial control may be needed in the later stages.

The plane assumption is also made in the majority of analogue photogrammetric plotters, in which the X and Y axes of the instrument comprise rigid steel beams, or the XY plane is materialised by the machined flat surface upon which a tracing table or plotting device slides. We regard this plane as representing the datum plane from which heights are measured. Consequently the evidence that the plane assumption is erroneous appears as systematic errors in height measurement after the other sources of systematic error (owing to camera tilt, lens distortion etc.) have been eliminated. At large scales (>1/10,000) the use of the plane assumption has little effect upon the accuracy of plotting and measurement of heights. The weakness of the plane assumption is apparent in the use of small-scale photography (<1/30,000) which obviously represents a larger part of the Earth's surface on the standard format photograph. A few modern photogrammetric instruments have devices which automatically correct for Earth curvature in the stereoscopic model. Another important influence of Earth curvature in photogrammetry occurs in *aerial triangulation*, which is the process of obtaining additional control points along strips of overlapping aerial photographs (Ref. 3). This can be done in several ways but the classic methods of strip triangulation are done in a photogrammetric plotter by observing two corresponding points in successive models set in the instrument. Since each model, being the overlap of two adjacent photographs, is formed according to the plane assumption, progressive linking of models along a strip of photography also leads to systematic height errors. These result from formation of the strip with reference to the *XY* plane defined by the instrument whereas the photographs were taken of the curved surface of the Earth. Figure 105 illustrates the characteristic deformation experienced in strip triangulation owing to the increasing divergence between the plane and curved surfaces expressed as height errors.

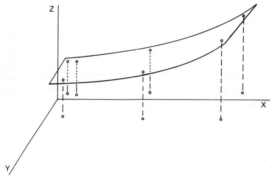

Figure 105 The plane assumption in aerial triangulation. The deformed surface represents a strip of aerial photographs in which common points on adjacent photographs have been linked to one another by measurement of their *X*, *Y* and *Z* coordinates in a photogrammetric plotter. Because each stereoscopic model is treated as if this were part of a 'flat earth' and height, *Z*, is measured from the *XY* plane, the influence of earth curvature is to produce a systematic increase in apparent height as the triangulation proceeds. Thus the influence of earth curvature is reflected by the apparent curvature of the strip (increasing errors in height) in the opposite direction. It should be noted that other kinds of systematic error may also occur so that the upward warping may be modified. However the dominant cause of the upward warp is earth curvature and this is always present in triangulation of a long strip of photographs.

Rectangular Spherical Coordinates

The method of computing the coordinates of a new control point, *B*, from existing stations such as *A* and *C*, is fundamental to surveying practice. If, therefore, the plane assumption is too crude to be justified for a particular purpose and we need to compute the projection coordinates of *B*, we require a method of doing this from the measured or computed bearings and distances from points whose projection coordinates are already known. In other words it is necessary to obtain equations in x and y which are functions of s and α for the projections used in surveying. Consequently we must introduce reasoning and formulae which are different from the conventional expressions of projection coordinates as functions of latitude and longitude which was the method used in Chapter 8. *We emphasise the importance of these computations to the practising surveyor.* The determination of Transverse Mercator Projection Coordinates of points by Method II, described on p. 219, is by far the most important projection computation carried out in ordinary field surveys. This is not to argue that geographical coordinates are never used by surveyors. For example, in geodetic surveying it is usual to compute the geographical coordinates of each station, using the methods briefly mentioned in Chapter 3 (pp. 47–48). Moreover geographical coordinates are important in topographical cartography, for, as we saw in Chapter 6, most topographical maps show graticule intersections by means of crosses and marginal ticks. Hence the occasion does also arise when it is necessary to determine the projection coordinates of certain points of known geographical coordinates, or, to use the customary surveying expression, to *transform from geographical coordinates into grid coordinates.* We will also find it useful to study the term-by-term composition of the big formulae employed in survey computations through the medium of this transformation. However, the relationship between survey stations on a given projection is so important that it is necessary to describe another kind of coordinate system for use on the curved surface. This system may be called *Rectangular Spherical Coordinates* or *Rectangular Spheroidal Coordinates* depending upon the required reference figure. We shall study it through the mathematically simpler spherical figure, as illustrated in Fig. 106.

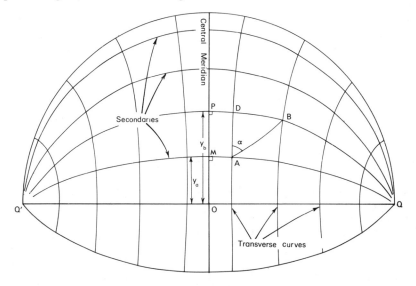

Figure 106 Rectangular spherical coordinates, providing a means of relating points, such as *A* and *B*, on the curved surface of a sphere to the origin, *O*, by linear distances such as *MA* and *OM*.

The point O is chosen to serve as the origin of the system, and the ordinate is made to coincide with the meridian through O. We refer to this as the central meridian. By analogy with the method of using a plane Cartesian reference system, the ordinates of points such as $A = y_a$ and $B = y_b$, correspond respectively to the arc distances OM and OP along the great circle representing the central meridian. In a plane coordinate system (Fig. 104) the abscissae of A and B are the linear distances x_a and x_b. By analogy, therefore, the representation of these distances on the spherical surface are great circle arcs x_a and x_b illustrated in Fig. 106. Since we intend to derive *Rectangular* Spherical Coordinates, these two arcs intersect the central meridian at right angles. Therefore in Fig. 106 $OMA = OPB = 90°$.

In Chapter 3 we showed, through the definitions of primary great circles, axes and secondary great circles, that meridians must intersect the Equator at right angles. We now invert this argument to argue that the ordinate of the system corresponds to the arc of a primary great circle to which other great circles such as MA and PB are secondaries. This means that the central meridian must have an axis passing through two poles. From the definitions introduced in Chapter 3 it follows that the poles of this system must be two points Q and Q' which, as shown in Fig. 106, are located on the secondary passing through the origin, O, and $90°$ distant from the central meridian. It follows, therefore, that all great circle arcs which are secondaries to the central meridian converge at Q and Q'.

In plane Cartesian coordinates we refer to orientation of any line AB as the bearing, α, defined by the angle DAB in Fig. 104. In order to describe the corresponding angle on the spherical surface, we locate the arc AD, in Fig. 106, parallel to the central meridian. Thus we employ the convention that $DAB = \alpha$ on the spherical surface. By extension of the arguments used to describe the properties of geographical coordinates in Chapter 3, DA is the arc of a small circle which is parallel to the primary great circle represented by the central meridian. It follows, therefore, that any small circle arc thus defined intersects each of the secondaries at right angles. We call the small circle arcs like DA the system of *transverse curves* and retain the name *secondaries* for the great circle arcs like MA.

The curved surface of the sphere has now been subdivided by the families of secondaries and transverse curves to form a network as shown in Fig. 106. Any point on the spherical surface may be related to the origin and axes by its (x, y) coordinates. To define the signs along the axes, we retain the convention that $+y$ is towards the North Pole along the central meridian and $+x$ is the direction OQ. We maintain the graph convention in labelling these axes although, as noted in Chapter 2, many writers prefer to denote the direction of the North Pole along the central meridian as $+x$. The reason for this change of notation is to overcome the algebraic difficulties arising from the differences in convention used to measure angles (pp. 23–24). Since surveyors and cartographers invariably measure angles in the clockwise direction, which is opposite to that used by mathematicians, the derivation of the coordinate equations and other formulae needed to describe a projection in terms of s and α is simplified by reversal of the axes. The present writer believes that it is more important for the beginner to retain the spatial framework defined by the use of the graph convention than to understand the niceties of algebraic reasoning. But the reader must be warned that both coordinate conventions are used in text-books on surveying and in the literature of map projections so that care must be taken to find out which has been used in a particular book or journal. Some authors are not particularly forthcoming about which convention they have used.

Cassini's Projection

The simplest transformation from rectangular spherical coordinates to plane rectangular coordinates is to put in Fig. 107

$$M'A' = MA \text{ and } O'M' = OM$$

which can be expressed algebraically as

$$E_a = x_a \qquad (11.05)$$

$$N_a = y_a \qquad (11.06)$$

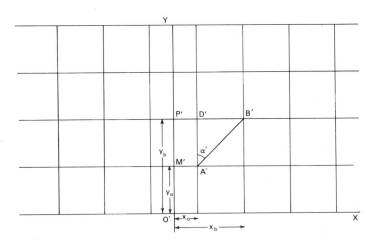

Figure 107 The plane representation of rectangular spherical coordinates by Cassini's Projection.

In other words the plane coordinates are made equal to the arc distances along the central meridian and the secondaries. This is equivalent to the statement that the principal scale of the projection has been preserved along the central meridian and along the secondaries. This defines a Cylindrical projection in its transverse aspect where the central meridian is a line of zero distortion. Since the principal scale is also preserved everywhere perpendicular to the central meridian, this is the transverse aspect of the *Plate Carrée* or *Equidistant Cylindrical Projection*. It is known as the *Cassini–Soldner Projection* or *Cassini's Projection*.

The distortions and deformations to be found in Cassini's Projection correspond to those of the Plate Carrée (p. 235) but referred to a line of zero distortion along the central meridian rather than the Equator. Equation (8.58), p. 153, indicates that the particular scale at the point A' in the direction of the line $A'D'$ is equal to sec z, where z is the angular distance $MA = x_a/R$. Since the principal scale is preserved in the direction $A'M'$, it follows that there is no linear distortion in the east–west direction. Consequently the particular scales at A' vary with direction and there is angular deformation at A' and every other point which does not lie on the central meridian. In other words, Cassini's Projection is not a conformal projection.

Because the linear distortion in the north–south direction increases eastwards and westwards from the central meridian, it follows that Cassini's Projection is only suitable for mapping a comparatively narrow zone of longtitude. We give expressions for angular and linear distortion in equations (11.30) and (11.33) on pages 214–15 and Table 15, (p. 216), provides numerical values for these. For example, in order to maintain the accuracy specification that errors in direction should not exceed 10″, Cassini's Projection can only be used for a zone extending about 80 km. either side of the central meridian.

Despite the fact that Cassini's Projection is not conformal and therefore does not satisfy the primary modern requirement for a projection to be used in surveying, we examine it in detail. There are two reasons for this; first, although the projection is no longer popular, this has not always been so. For example, all the basic scale maps and plans published by the Ordnance Survey before World War II are plotted on Cassini projections and the projection was also used in many other countries. Secondly, it is possible to demonstrate several important principles concerning the use of projections in surveying through a preliminary study of Cassini's Projection. This leads to an understanding of how the Transverse Mercator Projection may be derived.

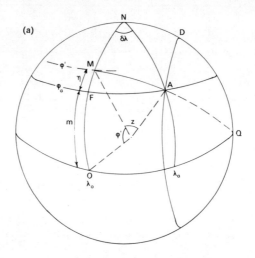

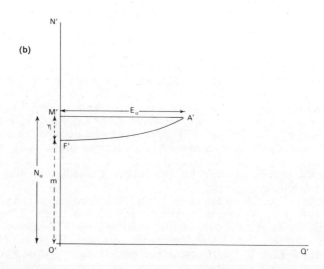

Figure 108 (a) and (b) The relationship between the Cassini coordinates and geographical coordinates of a point.

Geographical coordinates on Cassini's Projection

We introduce the detailed study of Cassini's Projection through the problem of finding the projection coordinates (E_a, N_a) of a point A the geographical coordinates of which (φ_a, λ_a) are known. This investigation introduces us to methods which have not been employed in other chapters, notably the *expansion in series* of certain terms in the equations. This is standard practice in the derivation of equations for survey use for it is comparatively easy to compile projection tables to assist computation. We propose to derive the Cassini coordinate expressions for a sphere of radius R and later demonstrate the modification of the equations to those for a spheroid.

Figure 108 illustrates the relationship between the Cassini coordinates and the geographical coordinates of the point A' on the projection corresponding to A on the spherical surface. In Fig. 108 (b) O' is the origin of the (E, N) system of Cassini coordinates and $N'O'$ is the central meridian (λ_0). In Fig. 108 (a) NA is the meridian λ_a through A. The angle ONA therefore corresponds to the difference in longitude $\lambda_a - \lambda_0 = \delta\lambda$. DA is parallel to the central meridian and therefore indicates the direction of Grid North. The angle DAN is the convergence at A. The parallel of latitude, φ_a, through A meets the central meridian at F. We denote the latitude of the point M by φ'.
Then

$$\varphi_a = \frac{m}{R} \tag{11.07}$$

where m is the meridional arc distance from the origin O to F. It corresponds to the use of the symbol s''_m in equation (3.12), page 40. Moreover

$$\varphi' = \frac{N_a}{R} \tag{11.08}$$

and

$$z = \frac{E_a}{R} \tag{11.09}$$

It is required to express E_a and N_a in terms of φ_a and $\delta\lambda$.
From the right-angled spherical triangle NAM,

$$\sin z = \cos \varphi_a \cdot \sin \delta\lambda \tag{11.10}$$

$$\tan \varphi' = \tan \varphi_a \cdot \sec \delta\lambda \tag{11.11}$$

Substituting (11.08) on the left-hand side of (11.11) and (11.09) on the left-hand side of (11.10) would provide us with equations in E_a and N_a but not in a form suitable for computing. Therefore it is desirable to transform equations (11.10) and (11.11) by expanding certain of the terms in series. This procedure is well known in elementary calculus, where Taylor's and Maclaurin's Theorems may be used to obtain a series corresponding to any specified function (Abbott/Calculus, Chapter XIX). For example, we may convert the function $\sin x$ into a series of terms containing ascending powers of the variable x, where this is expressed in radians. Thus

$$\sin x = x - \frac{x^3}{6} + \frac{x^5}{120} - \frac{x^7}{5040} + \dots \tag{11.12}$$

This equation is useful from both the practical and algebraic points of view. It is the method which is used to obtain the numerical values of trigonometric functions published in tables and used by the subroutines of digital computers to evaluate

P

all the standard functions which are available in a particular instrument. It explains, incidentally, why it is necessary to convert all angles into radians at an early stage of any programme which uses trigonometric subroutines (see p. 133).

Inspection of equation (11.12) indicates that the right-hand side of it is composed of four terms in ascending powers of x. The numerical value in the denominator of each fraction represents the factorial of a number. For example, in the second term, $6 = 3! = 1 \times 2 \times 3$.

Since the numerical value of x lies within the range $x = 0$ to $x = \pi/2 = 1 \cdot 57 \ldots$, the values of x^3, x^5 etc. increase more slowly than their respective denominators. Consequently *the size of the terms on the right-hand side of the equation decreases from left to right*. Since $x^7/5040 < x^5/120 < x^3/6$ the series may be said to *converge*. The right-hand side of equation (11.12) could be further extended to include terms in x^9 and so on, but the effect of these terms upon the numerical values of $\sin x$ would be negligible up to the sixth decimal place.

We apply these ideas to the Easting equation (11.10) to demonstrate how the technique is used. In this equation we expand $\sin \delta\lambda$ and the inverse sine (arc sin or $\sin^{-1}$) of z. From equation (11.12)

$$\sin \delta\lambda = \delta\lambda - \frac{\delta\lambda^3}{6} + \frac{\delta\lambda^5}{120} - \ldots \tag{11.13}$$

Also

$$\sin^{-1} z = z + \frac{z^3}{6} + \frac{3z^5}{40} \ldots \tag{11.14}$$

Equation (11.10) may now be written in the form

$$z = \cos \varphi_a \left\{ \delta\lambda - \frac{\delta\lambda^3}{6} + \frac{\delta\lambda^5}{120} - \ldots \right\} + \frac{1}{6} \cos^3 \varphi_a \left\{ \delta\lambda - \frac{\delta\lambda^3}{6} + \frac{\delta\lambda^5}{120} - \right\}^3$$

$$+ \frac{3}{40} \cos^5 \varphi_a \left\{ \delta\lambda - \frac{\delta\lambda^3}{6} + \frac{\delta\lambda^5}{120} - \right\}^5 \tag{11.15}$$

It has already been shown that $z = E_a/R$. Therefore equation (11.15) may be written as an expression to find E_a:

$$E_a = R \cdot \delta\lambda \cdot \cos \varphi_a + \frac{R}{6}(-\tan^2 \varphi_a)\delta\lambda^3 \cdot \cos^3 \varphi_a +$$

$$+ \frac{R}{120}(-8 \tan^2 \varphi_a + \tan^4 \varphi_a)\delta\lambda^5 \cdot \cos^5 \varphi_a \tag{11.16}$$

A certain amount of additional algebra is needed to convert (11.11) into a suitable form. Thus, from (11.11)

$$\tan \varphi' - \tan \varphi_a = \tan \varphi_a(\sec \delta\lambda - 1) \tag{11.17}$$

Moreover

$$\varphi_a = \tan^{-1}(\tan \varphi_a) \tag{11.18}$$

Expansion by Taylor's Theorem gives

$$\varphi' = \varphi_a + (\tan \varphi' - \tan \varphi_a) \cos^2 \varphi_a - (\tan \varphi' - \tan \varphi_a)^2 \cos^4 \varphi_a \cdot \tan \varphi' \tag{11.19}$$

We now substitute in (11.17) the expansion of $\sec \delta\lambda$ in series. The result is substituted for $(\tan \varphi' - \tan \varphi_a)$ in (11.19) and since $\varphi_a = m/R$, we finally obtain the equation

$$N_a = m + \tfrac{1}{2}R \cdot \tan \varphi_a \cdot \delta\lambda^2 \cos^2 \varphi_a + \frac{R}{24} \tan \varphi_a(5 - \tan^2 \varphi_a)\delta\lambda^4 \cdot \cos^4 \varphi_a \tag{11.20}$$

From Fig. 108(b), $N_a = O'M' = O'F' + F'M'$. Since $O'F' = m$, the linear distance $F'M'$ may be expressed by the second and third terms of the right-hand side of (11.20) or

$$\eta = \tfrac{1}{2}R . \tan \varphi_a . \delta\lambda^2 \cos^2 \varphi_a + \frac{R}{24} \tan \varphi_a(5 - \tan^2 \varphi_a)\delta\lambda^4 \cos^4 \varphi_a \ldots \quad (11.21)$$

This quantity is often referred to as the *ordinate of curvature*.

In equations (11.16) and (11.20) the angle $\delta\lambda$ is expressed in radians. This is in a suitable form for solution by digital computer, but if the equations are to be solved by logarithms or using a desk calculator with the aid of tables of natural trigonometric functions, it would be necessary to convert $\delta\lambda$ from sexagesimal units into radians. Similarly, if it were required to use the corresponding formulae to find φ_a and $\delta\lambda$ from E_a and N_a it would be necessary to convert the answer from radians into sexagesimal units.

The normal way of converting x radians into $x°$ is to multiply x radians by the number of degrees in one radian ($= 57\cdot 2\ldots$). Similarly, if we wish to express x radians in seconds of arc, we multiply x by 206265 because this is the number of seconds in one radian. In conventional surveying which is restricted to visual observations and therefore short lines it is more convenient to work in seconds of arc than in degrees.

For example, the angular distance between two points A and B which correspond to the side of a triangulation network is probably only a few minutes of arc and so are the differences in latitude and longitude between them. Many of the corrections to bearing which may be applied to visual observations only amount to a few seconds so that it is generally more convenient to use the second form of conversion. However, this is not immediately apparent from the study of the equations in the form in which they are usually written because the conversion from seconds to radians, i.e. $x''/206265$ is written sin $1''$.

The reason for this convention lies in the use of equation (11.12) to find the sine of a small angle. Thus, if the right-hand side of (11.12) is terminated after the first term we have

$$\sin x = x \qquad (11.22)$$

which is an approximation commonly used to find the sine of a small angle.

Since

$$\sin x = x = \frac{x''}{206265}$$

we may write

$$\sin 1'' = \frac{1}{206265}$$

and

$$x = x'' . \sin 1'' \qquad (11.23)$$

Thus, in equations which follow we may regard the presence of the term sin $1''$ as the indication that an angle is expressed in seconds of arc. The conversion is used in geodetic tables, where the radii of curvature of the ellipsoid are tabulated as values of $1/\rho . \sin 1''$ and $1/\nu . \sin 1''$ to facilitate geodetic computations where the same convention is employed. As use of digital computers replaces the older methods of computation, this convention will disappear.

In equations (11.16) and (11.20) $\delta\lambda$ appears in each term on the right-hand sides. When we make the conversion to use $\delta\lambda''$ in them, the term sin $1''$ must be raised to the same power as $\delta\lambda$.

Hence, introducing this convention

$$E_a = R \cdot \delta\lambda'' \cdot \sin 1'' \cdot \cos \varphi_a - \frac{R}{6}(\delta\lambda'' \cdot \sin 1'' \cdot \cos \varphi_a)^3 \tan^2 \varphi_a -$$

$$- \frac{R}{120}(\delta\lambda'' \cdot \sin 1'' \cdot \cos \varphi_a)^5 \tan^2 \varphi_a(8 - \tan^2 \varphi_a) \qquad (11.24)$$

$$N_a = m + \frac{R}{2}(\delta\lambda'' \cdot \sin 1'' \cdot \cos \varphi_a)^2 \tan \varphi_a +$$

$$+ \frac{R}{24}(\delta\lambda'' \cdot \sin 1'' \cdot \cos \varphi_a)^4 \tan \varphi_a(5 - \tan^2 \varphi_a) \qquad (11.25)$$

We may shorten these further by putting

$$J = \delta\lambda'' \cdot \sin 1'' \cdot \cos \varphi_a \qquad (11.26)$$

indicating that a useful order of computation is to determine J, together with J^2, J^3, J^4 and J^5, at an early stage of the work. We will find that much the same kind of procedure is followed in using projection tables.

We have derived these equations in detail because they introduce us without too much difficult algebra to the long-winded expressions used in survey computations and which, by their very length, tend to frighten the beginner. Admittedly we have derived equations for only one transformation to a projection which no longer has much practical value, but we have done this because it is much easier than finding the corresponding formulae for the Transverse Mercator. We emphasize that the purpose of the investigation has been to demonstrate how the final equations are obtained from the expansion of certain terms in series. Secondly we have shown how the resulting equations appear after the different series have been combined, conversion from seconds to radians introduced, and the expression simplified by using a symbol like J.

Since these equations converge rapidly, the numerical values of the different terms in each equation decrease from left to right. Thus the value of the first term of (11.25) may be reckoned in hundreds of km. and that in (11.24) in tens of km.; the second term in each expression represents a few tens or hundreds of metres and the magnitude of the third term is probably less than one metre. Realisation of this leads to the important conclusion that the higher-order (or right-hand) terms of such equations may have negligible effect in practice. In particular a substantial saving of computing time is possible if these equations have to be used for certain purposes, for example, to locate the graticule intersections for a topographical map. If the higher-order terms are too small to plot at the scale of the map it is obviously a sheer waste of time to compute them. It is therefore important for the surveyor and cartographer to know when the equations may be simplified. This requires an understanding of how each term in an equation varies with latitude, longitude, Easting or Northing. It may be obtained from graphs drawn for the various terms. We describe and illustrate this technique as an exercise which can be profitably undertaken using Transverse Mercator Projection tables.

Determination of Cassini Coordinates from bearing and distance

There are two ways of finding the projection coordinates of an unknown point, B, from a known point, A, with observed or computed values for $s = AB$ and the bearing $DAB = \alpha$:

Method I. The coordinates (E_b, N_b) are computed directly from the available data.

Method II. We apply corrections to the bearing and distance and use the corrected data with the ordinary plane coordinate equations (11.01) and (11.02) to find E_b and N_b.

Method I

We start with the initial concept that rectangular spherical coordinates are to be represented on the plane by the correct linear distances E_a, N_a, E_b, N_b, as specified by equations (11.05) and (11.06). Therefore we treat arcs on the sphere as if they were straight lines on a plane. This can be done if Legendre's Rule† is applied and the spherical excess of figures on the spherical surface is calculated. These small angular differences cannot be ignored or discarded. Otherwise we would obtain equations (11.01) and (11.02) relating to the plane assumption. Instead they must be applied as corrections to these equations in the form of second- and third-order terms. Derivation of these terms involves some quite awkward algebra, which we do not attempt to present here. We direct the interested reader to Ref. 4.

The final coordinate equations may be written:

$$E_b = E_a + s \cdot \sin \, \alpha - \frac{s^2 \cdot \cos^2 \, \alpha \cdot E_a}{2R^2} - \frac{s^3 \cdot \sin \, \alpha \cdot \cos^2 \, \alpha}{6R^2} \qquad (11.27)$$

$$N_b = N_a + s \cdot \cos \, \alpha + \frac{s \cdot \cos \, \alpha \cdot E^2{}_a}{2R^2} - \frac{s^3 \cdot \cos \, \alpha \cdot \sin^2 \, \alpha}{6R^2} \qquad (11.28)$$

In this pair of equations we note that the first two terms on the right-hand sides correspond to equations (11.01) and (11.02) respectively. In other words, the third and fourth terms in each equation represent corrections to be applied to the plane assumption to obtain the Cassini coordinates.

Method II

The alternative way of finding the coordinates of the point B comprises, in effect, introduction of angular deformation and linear distortion to the observed data so that the line AB on the sphere or spheroid is transformed into the line $A'B'$ on Cassini's Projection *before the coordinates are calculated.* Figure 109 illustrates these corrections and indicates that we must apply two of them to the bearing, α, and one correction to the length, s, of the line AB.

The observed line of sight between A and B lies in the plane of the great circle arc passing through these points. Hence the recorded bearing is the great circle bearing DAB, indicated as α in Fig. 109. In order to make use of this observation as a plane angle, it is necessary to apply an *arc-to-chord conversion*, just as a navigator has to use the conversion angle to plot radio bearings on the Mercator chart (pp. 194–5). Because of the greater precision of angular measurement in surveying this correction may be needed for quite short lines (roughly speaking all observed lines of length greater than 10 km.) whereas in navigation the corresponding correction has only to be applied for plotting bearings from distant radio stations (approximately 100 km. or more). By convention, the bearing of the great circle arc, which we have shown in Fig. 109 as α, is also denoted by t. The bearing of the rhumb-line or chord, which we call α_0, is sometimes denoted by T. Hence

---

† Legendre's Rule may be stated as follows: 'If one-third of the spherical excess of a spherical triangle is deducted from each angle, the triangle can be solved in terms of the linear lengths of the sides by the ordinary rules of plane trigonometry'.

this correction is often known to surveyors as the *t–T correction*. The angle $a-a_0=t-T$ is frequently denoted by the symbol δ and since the correction differs at each end of the line, we must further distinguish between δ_{AB}, which is the arc-to-chord conversion to be applied to the bearing measured at A, and δ_{BA}, which is the corresponding correction to be applied to the bearing measured at B. In navigation the conversion angle is taken to be identical at both ends of a line. The correction to be applied has the form

$$\delta_{AB}=(t-T)''=\frac{(N_b-N_a)\,(E_b+2E_a)}{6R^2.\sin 1''} \tag{11.29}$$

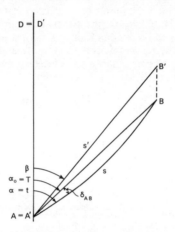

Figure 109 The relationships between the angles and sides measured on the ground and their representation on Cassini's Projection. This diagram attempts to compare measurements made on the sphere with their plane representation as follows. The arc AB is measured on the ground and is found to be of length s and with bearing $a=t$ referred to grid North through A. Application of the arc-to-chord conversion, δ_{AB} (which the diagram indicates is also equal to $t-T$ or $a-a_0$, gives the chord bearing, a_0, of the point B referred to grid North through A. The point B' is the position of B on Cassini's Projection. This has distance $A'B'=s'$ from the point A' and the line $A'B'$ bears β measured from grid North through A'. Hence Method II, or point-to-point working, requires calculation of the bearing, β, and the distance, s', in order to find the Cassini coordinates of B'.

The direction in which the correction is applied, in other words the sign of δ_{AB}, depends upon the orientation of the line AB with respect to the central meridian, as shown in Fig. 110. The magnitude of the correction depends upon the length of the line and the bearing.

The second correction which must be applied to the bearing is that needed to convert the plane angle DAB into the plane angle $D'A'B'$ on the projection. Since Cassini's Projection is not conformal, we expect there to be angular deformation which is equivalent to a rotation of the chord AB towards the central meridian. Denoting $D'A'B'=\beta$ and since $DAB=a_0=T=a-\delta_{AB}$, this correction has the form

$$(\beta-a_0)''=-\frac{\sin a_0.\cos a_0}{6R^2.\sin 1''}E^2\mu \tag{11.30}$$

where $E^2\mu=(E_a^2+E_aE_b+E_b^2)$.

Thus, to find the required bearing β from the observed angle α, the corrections are applied in the following order:

$$a° + \delta_{AB}{}'' = a_0{}°\qquad\qquad (11.31)$$

$$a_0{}° + (\beta \doteq a_0)'' = \beta°\qquad\qquad (11.32)$$

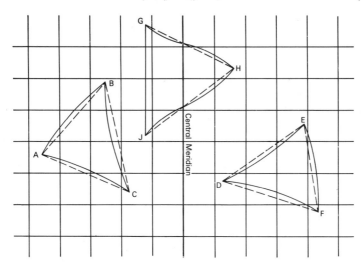

Figure 110 The nature of the arc-to-chord conversion for six different lines having different positions and orientation with respect to the central meridian of Cassini's Projection. Note that the arc and chord only coincide along the line *GJ*, which is parallel to the central meridian, or in other words, a line having the grid bearing 360° or 180°. The same relationships are also true for the Transverse Mercator Projection.

The two angular corrections can be combined in a single equation but we prefer to keep them separate because we will see that for the Transverse Mercator Projection (11.30) vanishes and (11.29) remains.

The linear correction to be applied to an observed or computed distance $AB = s$ to convert this into the line $A'B' = s'$ may be found from the equation

$$\frac{s'}{s} = 1 + \frac{\cos^2 a_0}{6R^2}E^2\mu\qquad\qquad (11.33)$$

Finally, therefore, the coordinates of B' may be expressed by the two equations

$$E_b = E_a + s'.\sin\beta\qquad\qquad (11.34)$$

$$N_b = N_a + s'.\cos\beta\qquad\qquad (11.35)$$

which are, of course, in the form of equations (11.01) and (11.02).

We may now use equations (11.30) and (11.33) to determine the maximum distortion to be expected in the use of Cassini's Projection. We solve these equations for the directions in which a_0 has the maximum effect. Thus, in (11.30) the greatest deformation in bearing occurs where $a_0 = 45°$, 135°, 225° and 315°. In (11.33) the greatest linear distortion occurs where $a_0 = 0°$ and 180°, corresponding to the conclusion on page 207 that the particular scale $\mu_1 = \sec z$ is directed along the projection of the transverse curves parallel to the central meridian. Numerical values for the maximum distortions are given in Table 15.

Table 15

Maximum distortions in distance and bearing for Cassini's Projection.

Distance in km. from central meridian

	50	100	150	200	250	300
Maximum distortion in distance	$\dfrac{1}{32,500}$	$\dfrac{1}{8,100}$	$\dfrac{1}{3,600}$	$\dfrac{1}{2,000}$	$\dfrac{1}{1,300}$	$\dfrac{1}{900}$
Maximum distortion in bearing	$3''$	$13''$	$29''$	$51''$	$1'\ 19''$	$1'\ 54''$

The use of Cassini's Projection by the Ordnance Survey

The unsuitability of Cassini's Projection for mapping a whole country having the size of Britain may be gauged by assuming the country to be mapped on this projection from an origin and central meridian coincident with that now used for the National Grid (Chapter 2, pp. 21–23). In this system the maximum linear distortion would be 1 part in 530 and the maximum deformation of bearing is $3'\ 14''$ in the vicinity of St. Kilda. From equation (11.30) we can see that the deformation in bearing $(\beta - \alpha_0)$ is independent of the length of line, for the right-hand side of the equation only contains arguments in Eastings. Thus in the Outer Hebrides a line of length 10 metres is deflected through about $3'$ of arc, as is a line of length 10 km. or 100 km. Even for the most rough and ready kind of survey this amount of angular deformation is intolerable. However, we have commented upon the historical importance of Cassini's Projection and therefore we need to know more about the ways in which it was used by the Ordnance Survey.

At the time when the first national survey departments were created in Britain and France opinion about the objects of their work differed from current views. Contemporary surveying policy was to carry out small and independent surveys of individual counties, communes, parishes and towns rather than the creation of an integrated national survey. Winterbotham (Ref. 5) quotes from documents as late as the middle of the nineteenth century which maintained 'that the map of each parish and each county should be complete in itself'. Consequently the early work of the Ordnance Survey emphasised the subdivision of Britain into counties to the extent that all maps and plans of scale 1/10,560 or larger were created as separate *County Series*, with additional series of large-scale plans for certain towns. Therefore each county or group of counties was mapped on a separate Cassini Projection each having its own origin and central meridian. The essential simplicity of Cassini's Projection, expressed by equations (11.05) and (11.06) favoured the use of it for these small areas. Even after some regrouping of the projections, which took place towards the end of the nineteenth century, the maps of Great Britain were still based upon 39 different Cassini Projections, as shown in Fig. 111. Hotine (Ref. 6) has described the result as follows:

> 'The county was the administrative unit whose boundaries were thought most unlikely ever to change. Unfortunately they have changed and in addition such entities as the town of Sheffield have quite irreverently sprawled across them, with the result that frequent transfers of large-scale surveys from one system to another have been necessary, in some cases with most unfortunate results. In fact we have got into such a mess that it has necessarily been decided to scrap the lot and put the whole country on a single projection system.'

See, also, Ref. 2 on this subject.

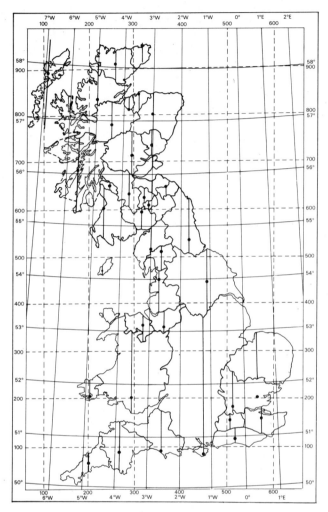

Figure 111 The origins, central meridians and boundaries of the parts of Britain mapped separately on different Cassini Projections before 1938. The dots indicate the origin of each Cassini system and are primary Ordnance Survey triangulation stations. The central meridian of each system is indicated by a thick line. The map also shows the National Grid of the unified system which is also illustrated in Fig. 12.

The Transverse Mercator Projection

We start from the same definition of rectangular spherical coordinates used to derive Cassini's Projection and the argument that the principal scale is preserved along the central meridian of a transverse aspect cylindrical projection. Therefore $OF = y_a = O'F' = N_a$ on the Transverse Mercator Projection in the same way as this was specified in equation (11.06) for Cassini's Projection. It follows, moreover, that the particular scale along the transverse curves is still $\mu_1 = \sec z$, where, as before, $z = E_a/R$. The requirement is for a conformal projection of the sphere.

This means that the particular scales at the point A' must be equal to sec z in all directions. Using identical arguments as were presented in Chapter 8 to derive the normal aspect Mercator Projection, equations (8.55)–(8.63) on p. 153 are valid for the Transverse Mercator Projection of the sphere if we substitute z for φ throughout. Hence we obtain an expression to give the Easting of the point $A' = M'A'$ in the form

$$E_a = R \cdot \log_e \tan\left(\frac{\pi}{4} + \frac{z}{2}\right) \qquad (11.36)$$

Hence equations (11.36) and (11.08) define the Transverse Mercator coordinates of a point in terms of z and φ', though this is not in a useful practical form.

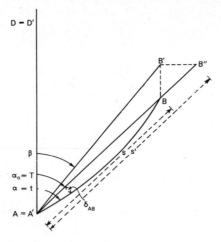

Figure 112 The relationships between the angles and sides measured on the ground and their representation on the Transverse Mercator Projection. Compare this with Fig. 109 for the definitions of the bearings α, α_0 and β. The point B' is, as in Fig. 109, the position of B on Cassini's Projection. The point B'' represents the position of B on the Transverse Mercator Projection. Note that the angular correction $\alpha_0 - \beta$ does not apply to the determination of Transverse Mercator coordinates so that the only corrections which are required are the arc-to-chord conversion, δ_{AB}, and the determination of the distance $A'B'' = s'$.

The relationship between the Cassini and Transverse Mercator coordinates of a point B may be illustrated by means of Fig. 112. Since the Transverse Mercator Projection is conformal, it follows that

$$\beta - \alpha_0 = 0$$

or

$$\beta = \alpha_0 \qquad (11.37)$$

In other words, the bearing $D'A'B''$ on the plane corresponds to the rhumb-line bearing DAB. Consequently the line AB is projected as $A'B''$ instead of $A'B'$ for the Cassini Projection. From Fig. 112 it can be seen that the Northing of B'' is the same as that for B', corresponding to the initial condition presented above. Therefore equation (11.28) for Cassini's Projection remains unchanged on the Transverse Mercator Projection of the sphere. The required modification to the

Easting equation is the addition of terms corresponding to the distance $B'B''$. These can be shown (Ref. 4) to be

$$B'B'' = \frac{E'_b{}^3}{6R^2} + \frac{E'_b{}^5}{24R^4} \tag{11.38}$$

where E'_b are the Cassini Easting coordinates computed from (11.27).

Therefore the coordinates of a point B determined by Method I are, for the Transverse Mercator Projection of the sphere:

| PLANE ELEMENT | CASSINI ELEMENT | T.M. ELEMENT |

$$E_b = E_a + s.\sin\alpha \; - \; \frac{s^2.\cos^2\alpha.E_a}{2R^2} \; - \; \frac{s^3.\sin\alpha.\cos^2\alpha}{6R^2} \; + \; \frac{E'_b{}^3}{6R^2} + \frac{E'_b{}^5}{24R^4} \tag{11.39}$$

$$N_b = N_a + s.\cos\alpha \; + \; \frac{s^2.\cos^2\alpha.E^2{}_a}{2R^2} \; - \; \frac{s^3.\sin^2\alpha.\cos\alpha}{6R^2} \qquad \text{Nil} \tag{11.40}$$

We have labelled terms on the right-hand sides of equations (11.39) and (11.40) to indicate how they are composed of a *Plane Element*, a *Cassini Element* and a *Transverse Mercator Element*. We must, however, emphasise that this relationship is only valid for projection of the sphere though it may be converted to an approximate relationship for the spheroid by substitution of $\rho.\nu$ for R^2 throughout. Equations (11.39) and (11.40) are more useful for converting from Cassini into Transverse Mercator coordinates (which practice is now happily obsolescent) than for processing new data. Consequently there is little need to use Method I for the Transverse Mercator.

Method II of finding Transverse Mercator coordinates is much simplified because the term $(\beta - a_0)$ does not have to be calculated. Consequently there remain only the arc-to-chord conversion and distance correction. For the Transverse Mercator Projection of the sphere, equation (11.29) still applies. The modified formula for correcting linear distance for the Transverse Mercator Projection is changed from (11.33) by virtue of the fact that the particular scales at any point are constant in all directions. Hence $\cos^2 a_0 = 1$ so the corresponding equation is

$$\frac{s'}{s} = 1 + \frac{E^2\mu}{6R^2} \tag{11.41}$$

From equation (11.41) it follows that the linear errors quoted in Table 15 as *maximum errors* on Cassini's Projection represent the linear error in *any direction* on the Transverse Mercator Projection. This again indicates that use of the projection should be confined to a narrow zone of longitude either side of the central meridian. However, we overcome the excessive linear distortions towards the edge of the zone by introducing a simple modification to the projection. Thus far we have maintained the principal scale along the central meridian. Just as it is possible to modify the normal aspect Mercator Projection by introducing the condition that the principal scale is preserved along two standard parallels, so the principal scale of the Transverse Mercator Projection may be preserved along two transverse curves which are equidistant from the central meridian. In a conformal projection this modification is obtained by introducing a *scale factor* $k_0 < 1$. Consequently (11.41) may be written

$$\frac{s'}{s} = k_0 \left(1 + \frac{E^2\mu}{6R^2} \right) \tag{11.42}$$

For practical use in systems where the zone extends about 3° either side of the central meridian, a suitable scale factor is $k_0 = 0\cdot 9996$ which has been used for both the Ordnance Survey and the Universal Transverse Mercator projections. Reduction of the scale along the central meridian by this amount ($0\cdot 9996$ corresponds to the particular scale on the central meridian) has the effect of creating two lines of zero distortion lying about 180 km. from it.

The scale factor is an additional correction which has to be applied in computing on the projection. Thus for $k_0 = 0\cdot 9996$ it is necessary to reduce the measured or computed distances by the ratio 2499/2500 and use this value for s in all subsequent calculations. A term like m, denoting the meridional arc distance in (11·20), and (11.25) is tabulated as $k_0 m$ in projection tables.

From the general formulae developed in Chapter 8 to describe all Cylindrical projections (pp. 152–6) it seems logical to apply a corresponding scale factor to Cassini's Projection. This is true although the idea does not seem to have occurred to nineteenth-century surveyors. It was left to Young (Ref. 7) to suggest that the modification could be applied and he claimed that he was the first writer to realise this. By then, however, the importance of Cassini's Projection was already waning so that this method of improving the projection does not seem to have been used. The relationship between the scale errors on Cassini's Projection and the modified Transverse Mercator Projection are shown in Fig. 113.

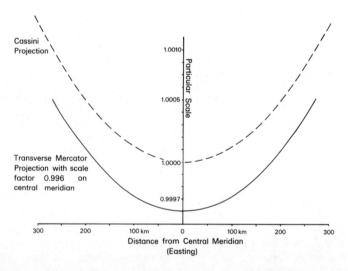

Figure 113 The comparison of the particular scales of Cassini's Projection and those of the Transverse Mercator Projection having a scale factor 0·9996 along the central meridian. Note that the numerical values for particular scale on Cassini's Projection is the maximum, *a*, referring to North–South lines. Because the Transverse Mercator Projection is conformal, the particular scales are equal in all directions about a point.

The Cassini and Transverse Mercator Projections of the Spheroid

In the preceding discussion we have assumed the Earth to be a perfect sphere of radius R. For many purposes, however, it is desirable for the surveyor to use the spheroid as the reference figure. Therefore it is desirable to comment upon the complications which are introduced through making this assumption.

For Cassini's Projection we assume that the spherical and spheroidal surfaces coincide on the central meridian at the point F (corresponding to F' on the projection as shown in Figs. 108 (a) and (b)). Within the comparatively narrow zone of longitude for which the projection may be usefully employed, the divergence between the spherical and spheroidal surfaces may be regarded as being so small that it can be ignored. Thus we make the same assumption used in some of the approximate geodetic formulae (Chapter 3, p. 48) that it is sufficient to substitute for R the transverse radius of curvature, ν, in latitude φ_a and use formulae which have been derived from spherical trigonometry. Consequently the equations required to transform from geographical coordinates on the spheroid to grid coordinates on Cassini's Projection are:

$$E_a = \nu J - \frac{\nu}{6} J^3 \cdot \tan^2 \varphi_a - \frac{\nu}{120} J^5 \tan^2 \varphi_a (8 - \tan^2 \varphi_a) \qquad (11.43)$$

$$N_a = m + \frac{\nu}{2} J^2 \cdot \tan \varphi_a + \frac{\nu}{24} J^4 \tan \varphi_a (5 - \tan^2 \varphi_a) \qquad (11.44)$$

It is essential to realise that this is an approximate derivation resulting from the assumptions which have been made.

There are three ways in which the Transverse Mercator formulae of the spheroid may be obtained. The first is by making an approximation equivalent to that described for Cassini's Projection. The second is a logical development from the simple approximation. This is to regard the spherical surface as an intermediate body upon which the spheroid is mapped *conformally* before the spherical surface is mapped on the plane. We call this *double-projection.†* The third method of derivation is through the direct solution of conformal projection of the spheroid upon the plane. This is the method described first by Lambert, studied further by Gauss and made practically useful for survey purposes by Krüger. Hence the projection is sometimes called *Gauss Conformal* and *Gauss-Krüger*, together with many other variants. The second of these two names is to be preferred.

The derivation of the Gauss-Krüger formulae is not attempted here because it demands a higher standard of mathematical competence than is needed elsewhere in this book. We only refer briefly to the ways in which the problem has been tackled in English writing on the subject and then proceed to the study of the use of projection tables.

Two properties of the Transverse Mercator Projection represent *boundary conditions* which must be satisfied in the analysis of the problem. The first of these is the condition that it must be a conformal projection and the second is that scale must be constant along the central meridian. The second of these boundary conditions is, as Hotine noted (Ref. 8), mathematically the more difficult to satisfy. Indeed he even commented that

> . . . 'it is hard to escape the conclusion that earlier weight given to practical simplicity would have ruled out this projection altogether'.

The usual procedure is to consider the projection of a system of isometric coordinates (q, λ), defined on page 157, on the spheroid and their projection to the plane. McCaw (Ref. 9) and Cole (Ref. 10) used the principle of double-projection of these to derive equations which are approximate only. Rigorous analysis of the

---

† Double-projection can be used with intermediate surfaces other than the sphere. For example, Hotine (Ref. 8) has made use of the intermediate surface known as the *Aposphere*, which has mathematical properties especially useful for the derivation of a large number of conformal projections of the spheroid. However we do not obtain the true Transverse Mercator Projection by these methods.

problem, for example in the classic papers by Craig (Ref. 11), Lee (Ref. 12) and Redfearn (Ref. 13) use functions of complex variables of the form

$$x + iy = f(q + i\omega) \tag{11.45}$$

and

$$q + i\omega = f(x + iy) \tag{11.46}$$

In these two equations the directions of x and y have been interchanged from the customary graph convention (the only time we do so in this book), q is the isometric latitude defined by equation (8.83) on page 157, $\omega = \delta\lambda$ and i is the complex number, $i^2 = -1$.

Hotine (Ref. 8) is alone in solving the problem rigorously without resorting to the use of complex variables. He solved the differential condition equations to fit the boundary conditions by assuming an answer in series, the coefficients of which were found by differentiating the series and substituting these in the condition equations.

In order to indicate the final form of equations resulting from the rigorous analysis of the Gauss-Krüger method, we quote two of Redfearn's formidable expressions which give the transformation from geographical into grid coordinates and which therefore correspond to equations (11.43) and (11.44) already derived for Cassini's Projection.

$$E_a = \delta\lambda . \nu . \cos\varphi + \delta\lambda^3 \frac{\nu}{6} \cos^3\varphi\left(\frac{\nu}{\rho} - \tan^2\varphi\right) +$$

$$+ \delta\lambda^5 \frac{\nu}{120} \cos^5\varphi\left\{4\frac{\nu^3}{\rho^3}(1-6\tan^2\varphi) + \frac{\nu^2}{\rho^2}(1+8\tan^2\varphi) - 2\frac{\nu}{\rho}\tan^2\varphi + \tan^4\varphi\right\} +$$

$$+ \delta\lambda^7 \frac{\nu}{5040} \cos^7\varphi(61 - 479\tan^2\varphi + 179\tan^4\varphi - \tan^6\varphi) + \ldots \tag{11.47}$$

$$N_a = m + \delta\lambda^2 \frac{\nu}{2} \sin\varphi . \cos\varphi +$$

$$+ \delta\lambda^4 \frac{\nu}{24} \sin\varphi . \cos^3\varphi\left(4\frac{\nu^2}{\rho^2} + \frac{\nu}{\rho} - \tan^2\varphi\right) +$$

$$+ \delta\lambda^6 \frac{\nu}{720} \sin\varphi . \cos^5\varphi\left\{8\frac{\nu^4}{\rho^4}(11-24\tan^2\varphi) - 28\frac{\nu^3}{\rho^3}(1-6\tan^2\varphi) +\right.$$

$$\left.+ \frac{\nu^2}{\rho^2}(1-32\tan^2\varphi) - 2\frac{\nu}{\rho}\tan^2\varphi + \tan^4\varphi\right\} + \ldots \tag{11.48}$$

We leave these expressions in the form where $\delta\lambda$ is expressed in radians because, excepting the use of a digital computer for solving them, the numerical work is normally done with the help of projection tables in which much of the computation has already been done.

For point-to-point working on the plane of the projection we have seen that for the Transverse Mercator Projection the procedure described as Method II is to be preferred. Equations (11.29) and (11.42) have been derived for the sphere but often they are also used for the correction of spheroidal lines by replacing $6R^2$ by $6\rho\nu$. However, this approximation is not sufficiently precise, especially for modern surveying applications where electro-magnetic distance measurement may be used to determine the lengths of lines up to 100 km. length with a relative precision of a few parts per million.

The approximate and several rigorous formulae have been compared by Bomford (Ref. 14), both from the point of view of accuracy and ease of computing. He has recommended the use of the following equations:

$$\delta_{AB} = \frac{(N_a - N_b)(2E_a + E_b)}{6R^2_m \cdot \sin 1''} \left(1 - \frac{2(E_a + E_b)^2}{27R^2_m}\right) \tag{11.49}$$

$$\frac{s'}{s} = 1 + \frac{E^2 \mu}{6R_m^2}\left(1 + \frac{E^2 \mu}{36R^2_m}\right) \tag{11.50}$$

In these two equations R^2_m represents the product $\rho_m \cdot \nu_m$, where $\varphi'_m = \frac{1}{2}(\varphi'_a + \varphi'_b)$. In other words, the radii of curvature are extracted from tables or computed for the mean latitude of the points M' and P' in Fig. 107. Within a zone which does not exceed 3° of longitude on either side of the central meridian, equation (11.49) is accurate to about $0''\cdot02$ over any 100 km. line and equation (11.50) is correct to $0\cdot1$ parts per million for a line of length 100 km.

The use of the Transverse Mercator Projection by the Ordnance Survey

A Departmental Committee on the Ordnance Survey was appointed in 1935, under the chairmanship of Viscount Davidson, to investigate future policy. The so-called Davidson Committee presented its final report in 1938 and its recommendations were finally accepted by H.M. Government in 1945 as a guide for the post-war policy of the department.

One of the most important of the recommendations contained in this influential document was the replacement of the patchwork of County Series of medium and large-scale maps, based upon the many Cassini Projections, by a single national projection system tied to the unique reference system of the National Grid. All future Ordnance Survey control was to be located on a Gauss-Krüger version of the Transverse Mercator Projection using the origin, axes and numbering system of the National Grid described in Chapter 2.

The principal arguments concerning this choice of projection which were given in the Davidson Report are also summarised in Ref. 15. The maximum difference in longitude in Britain (excluding Ireland, which has its own Transverse Mercator system) is more than 10°, from 1° 43' East near Great Yarmouth to 8° 34' West on St. Kilda. The True Origin of the National Grid is, as we have seen in Chapter 2, the point in latitude 49° North, longitude 2° West. Hence use of the Ordnance Survey Projection extends about 3° 43' eastwards from the central meridian and has been used 6° 34' westwards from it. This extent is greater than the preferred 6° zone which is used with the UTM system. It follows that there are some fairly large linear distortions present in the extreme north west of Britain. Without any modification, linear distortion would be 1/531, as already quoted, but modification of the projection by means of the scale factor $k_0 = 0\cdot9996$ reduces this to 1 part in 675. Moreover the arc-to-chord correction can also be rather large at this distance from the central meridian. For example, the long ray from Healaval (Barra) to St. Kilda observed in 1957, which is a line of length 116 km. involved a correction $\delta = 94''\cdot4$. Of course these are extreme values. The great majority of surveying in Britain is done on the mainland where the distance from the central meridian is much less.

Table 16 indicates the scale distortions which may be experienced in the use of it.

Table 16

Scale factor and linear distortion encountered in use of the Transverse Mercator Projection of Great Britain used by the Ordnance Survey.

Distance from central meridian in km.

	0	50	100	150
National Grid (E)	400 km.	350/450 km.	300/500 km.	250/550 km.
Scale factor	0·9996	0·99963	0·99972	0·99988
Linear distortion	1/2500	1/2700	1/3570	1/8330

	200	250
National Grid (E)	200/600 km.	150/650 km.
Scale factor	1·00009	1·00037
Linear distortion	1/11,110	1/2700

Tables for the national projection system have been published (Ref. 16) together with an explanatory pamphlet (Ref. 15) giving worked examples of all the computations which may be undertaken with them.

The Universal Transverse Mercator Projection (UTM)

The UTM system was introduced for NATO maps and surveys in the early 1950's. This is another example of use of the Gauss-Krüger version of the projection

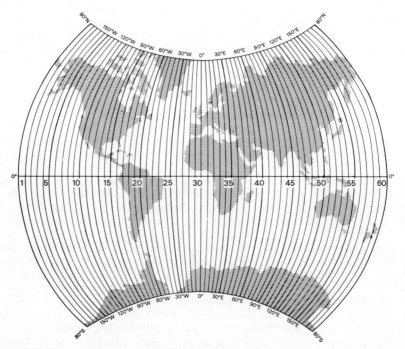

Figure 114 The method of zone numbering according to the UTM system. Each zone is 6° longitude in width and extends from 80° N to 80° S.

which is limited to individual zones extending 6° in longitude between limiting parallels 80° South and 84° North. Consequently there are sixty identical and contiguous UTM zones to provide a complete World reference system within these limits of latitude. Polewards of the UTM cover the *Universal Polar Stereographic* (UPS) system is used.

Any world-wide system comprising so many individual components must involve the use of a system of *Zone Numbering* (Fig. 114). For the UTM the numbering system begins at the antimeridian of Greenwich ($\lambda = 180°$) with Zone 1 comprising the belt between the meridians 174° W and 180° with the central meridian in longitude 177° W. The zone numbering increases eastwards so that, for example, Britain occurs in zones 29, 30 and 31, with central meridians at 9° W, 3° W and 3° E. The True Origin of each zone is located at the intersection of the central meridian with the Equator. This point is assigned grid coordinates 500 000 metres East, 0 metres North so that the use of negative coordinates is avoided throughout the Northern Hemisphere. For Southern Hemisphere use the same point is assigned the grid coordinates 500 000 metres East, 10 000 000 metres North. Hence in the vicinity of the Equator, the Northing coordinates of points increase from 8 900 000 metres at about 10° S to 10 000 000 = 0 at the Equator and becomes 1 100 000 near 10° N. (See Fig. 115.) The scale factor along the central meridian of each zone is 0·9996.

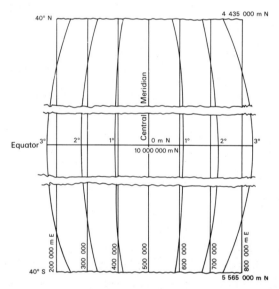

Figure 115 The relationship of grid to graticule in any single UTM zone. This diagram is arbitrarily truncated near latitudes 40° N and 40° S.

Five reference ellipsoids have been used. These are

> Clarke 1886 for North America,
> Clarke 1880 for Africa,
> Bessel for the USSR, Japan and part of S.E. Asia,
> Everest for India and adjacent parts of S.E. Asia,
> International for all other parts of the World.

Compare this list with Table 1 (p. 7).

Q

Several different sets of UTM tables have been published. The most convenient of these are the tables (Ref. 17) prepared by the Army Map Service (now U.S. Army Topographic Command). Sets of tables for each of the spheroids are available and these are normally in three volumes:

Vol. I   Transformation of Coordinates from geographic to grid,
Vol. II   Transformation of Coordinates from grid to geographic,
Vol. III Coordinates for 5-minute intersections.

The third volume is of use to the cartographer, who can obtain the UTM grid values to plot any graticule intersection likely to be needed for a small- or medium-scale topographical map without any computations. Volumes I and II allow the user to make any of the three basic kinds of computation which may be required. A different set of tables (Ref. 18) has been prepared in Britain by the Directorate of Military Survey of the War Office (now the Ministry of Defence). This contains tables for all five spheroids in a single volume.

Transverse Mercator Projection Tables

Unless the surveyor has access to a digital computer, practical solution of the Gauss-Krüger equations needs projection tables. Otherwise the job of computing each term of equations like (11.47) and (11.48) would be extremely laborious. It is therefore necessary to comment about the way in which Transverse Mercator tables are arranged. We do not attempt to give any worked examples for specific problems for these are contained in the introduction of all the sets of tables to which we have referred. Instead we describe a method of studying the tables themselves which has proved to be a useful exercise for students of surveying and cartography for two reasons. First, the method involves detailed inspection of the tables and making the calculations which are needed without becoming bogged down in the tedium of interpolation. Secondly, we obtain a graphical impression of the magnitude of each term entering an equation. This allows us to estimate if computation of specific terms is necessary for a particular job. This is particularly important for cartographic use of the tables because, as we have noted, some terms entering a complicated-looking Transverse Mercator formula may be too small to plot on a map. We make this study by selecting certain numerical values for each term, using this to calculate the magnitude of the term in metres or seconds of arc and plotting the results against latitude. A satisfactory study of the make-up and use of projection tables can only be made by actually using them. It is therefore incumbent upon a department which is proposing to teach this aspect of topographical cartography to obtain suitable sets of tables for class use. It is not reasonable to expect individual students to try to obtain them.

Because we have already studied the transformation from geographical coordinates into grid coordinates in some detail, we restrict the following discussion to the analysis of how the same transformation is obtained by tables. The reader is invited to plot corresponding graphs for the other kinds of computation which may be undertaken. We use the UTM tables published by the Army Map Service for the basis of this investigation because the UTM system gives a better picture of how each term varies through a wide range of latitude. National survey tables, like those published by the Ordnance Survey, are less instructive because they are naturally restricted to the range of latitude of the country for which they are intended. Using the AMS tables does not create any special difficulties in understanding those produced elsewhere. The arrangement of each set of tables varies only in detail. Figure 116 shows the main variables which are to be used as data or to be computed. It summarises all aspects of the study of the projection for survey purposes.

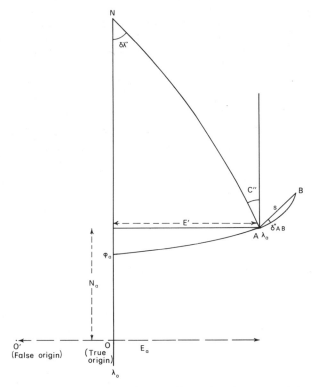

Figure 116 The Universal Transverse Mercator Projection. Summary of the variables to be computed from tables.

There are basically three kinds of transformation or computation for which projection tables are needed. These are:

(1) The transformation from geographical coordinates into grid coordinates. In other words, starting from the initial data, φ_a and λ_a for some point A, we compute the coordinates E_a and N_a according to the constants used for the projection.

(2) The transformation from grid coordinates into geographical coordinates. This is obviously the reverse process where we start with E_a and N_a for a point A' on the projection and we compute the geographical coordinates φ_a and λ_a of the point A on the spheroid.

(3) Calculation of the convergence, C'', between the meridian and Grid North at the point A'. This may be done from the initial data E_a and N_a or from φ_a and λ_a.

For point-to-point working on the plane of projection by Method II we ought to be able to compute the arc-to-chord conversion, δ_{AB} and the length of the projected line $A'B' = s'$.

In the specific problem of converting from geographical coordinates into grid coordinates, the variable $\delta\lambda$ appears in every term of equation (11.47) and all except the first term of (11.48). We have already seen that it is convenient to express $\delta\lambda$ in seconds of arc whereas in (11.47) and (11.48) this angle enters the argument in radians.

For the $6°$ UTM zones, the size of $\delta\lambda$ varies from 0 on the central meridian to $10,800''$ or $0\cdot052\,36..$ radians at $3°$ of longitude on either side. Since we are going to need powers of $\delta\lambda$ from $\delta\lambda^2$ to $\delta\lambda^4$, the numerical values would be very large if we worked in seconds or very small if we worked in radians. Consequently we make the first modification of the data and write

$$p = \delta\lambda'' \times 10^{-4} \qquad (11.51)$$

Thus, for $\delta\lambda=3°=10,800''$, $p=1\cdot08$, $p^2=1\cdot1664$, $p^3=1\cdot2597$ and $p^4=1\cdot3605$. These are easier to remember, copy on a computation form or set on the keyboard of a desk calculator than the corresponding values for powers of $\delta\lambda''$. However, this modification demands a corresponding correction to be applied to the remainder of the terms. Thus a term in which p enters as the argument must be raised by multiplying the rest of the term by 10^4; a term containing p^2 must be raised by 10^8 and so on. This is done in preparing the tables so the user does not have to remember to make this adjustment.

Since $\delta\lambda$ has been extracted from the terms in equations (11.47) and (11.48) these are composed of functions of latitude and the radii of curvature corresponding to the same latitude. Therefore all entries to the tables are made through the argument of latitude.

In the AMS tables numerical values are given for every $1'$ of latitude. The War Office tables have been prepared for intervals of $20'$ of latitude. Since the latitude of a point may be presumed to be known with greater accuracy than the nearest $1'$ and since it will seldom correspond exactly to $1'\,00''$, it is usually necessary to interpolate between the tabulated values to extract the required numerical value for each term. This may be laborious to undertake for, as Figs. 117–121 indicate, many of these terms are represented by curves. Therefore linear interpolation (by simple proportion between the tabulated values) may not be sufficiently accurate. However, the procedure to be followed depends upon the tabulated intervals of the argument. Because the AMS tables contain values for every minute of latitude, interpolation can usually be done by simple proportion without significant loss of accuracy. However, more elaborate interpolation methods have to be used with the $20'$ interval of the War Office tables. This greatly increases the labour of working with them and constitutes an important defect in these tables.

The individual terms comprising each of the Transverse Mercator formulae are tabulated under the headings I–XVIII in the AMS tables. Those with headings I–V relate to the specific problem of transforming from geographical coordinates into grid coordinates and these are the functions illustrated in Figs. 117–121.

In order to indicate the relationship between these and the algebraic expressions (11.47)–(11.48), we begin by writing the equations to be solved numerically with the aid of tables.

The Northings equation may be written†

$$N = (I) + (II)p^2 + (III)p^4 + A_6 \qquad (11.52)$$

The Eastings equation may be written

$$E' = (IV)p + (V)p^3 + B_5 \qquad (11.53)$$

---

† Equation (11.52) is the form of expression for use in the Northern Hemisphere. Because the UTM convention for use in the Southern Hemisphere is to regard the Equator as having the Northing value of 10 000 000 metres, the corresponding equation for use South of the Equator is
$$N = 10\,000\,000 - [(I) + (II)p^2 + (III)p^4 + A_6]$$

where E' is the distance of A from the central meridian. In order to express Eastings in terms of the UTM notation referred to the false origin

$$E = 500\ 000 \pm E' \tag{11.54}$$

We now intend to compare equations (11.47) and (11.48) with (11.52) and (11.53) and also show how they appear graphically. In order to construct these graphs, the various terms have been extracted for intervals of 5° of latitude and have been calculated for $\delta\lambda = 1°$, 2° and 3°. The numerical examples quoted here all refer to the Clarke 1880 spheroid. In making the comparison of the algebraic expressions and the terms in the tables, the clue to be followed is the power of p. This invariably corresponds with the power of $\delta\lambda$.

Term (I), Fig. 117

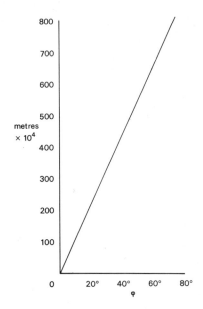

Figure 117 UTM Tables. Graph showing the variation of term I with latitude.

Values for this term range from $(I) = 0\cdot0$ on the Equator to $(I) = 8\ 881\ 408\cdot585$ at latitude 80° and the graph for this term is a straight line at the scale of drawing. From equation (11.48) this term corresponds to m, the meridional arc distance from the Equator to any parallel, φ. However it is reduced in proportion to the scale factor along the central meridian so that

$$(I) = k_0 \cdot m \tag{11.55}$$

Figure 117 cannot show evidence of polar flattening of the spheroid but if the tabulated differences for $1''$ are studied for this term, they are seen to vary from $30\cdot7$ m. at the Equator to $31\cdot0$ in latitude 79° 59'. This corresponds to the conclusion in Chapter 1 that the length of any equal arc of part of a meridian increases polewards.

Term (II), Fig. 118

In equation (11.52) this term appears as $(II)p^2$, indicating that this corresponds to the term $\delta\lambda^2$ in (11.48). The tabulated values for this term vary from $0\cdot0$ on the Equator, rising to a maximum 3752·817 in latitude 45° and falling to 1285·603 in latitude 80°. As indicated on page 211, the second term of the Northings equation represents, in part, the length of the ordinate of curvature. Figure 118 shows that the amount of correction introduced by this term is large, ranging from a maximum of nearly 500 m. where $\delta\lambda=1°$ in latitude 45° to more than 4000 m. on the edge of the 6° zone in this latitude.

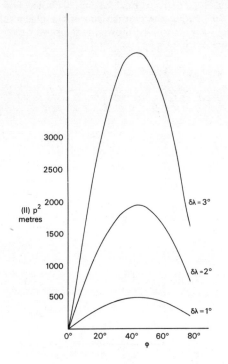

Figure 118 UTM Tables. Graphs showing the variation of term II with latitude for $\delta\lambda=1°, 2°$ and $3°$.

This term is derived from the second term on the right-hand side of (11.52) and has the algebraic form

$$\text{(II)} = \frac{\nu}{2}\sin\varphi.\cos\varphi.\sin^2 1'' \times 10^8 \qquad (11.56)$$

It has been multiplied by $\sin^2 1''$ to convert $\delta\lambda^2$ to radians and raised by 10^8 to compensate for the use of p.

Term (III), Fig. 119

In equation (11.52) the use of the term is (III)p^4 indicating that it corresponds to the term $\delta\lambda^4$ in (11.48). This term also comprises an element of the ordinate of curvature, but the rapid convergence of the series is demonstrated by the difference in size of this term compared with (II)p^2. Numerical values in the tables vary from (III)=0·0 on the Equator through (III)=2·262 in latitude 28° falling to (III)=0·0 in latitude 65° 55′. Thereafter the term is negative, becoming −0·206 in latitude 80°. Figure 119 indicates that within 2° of the central meridian the size of this term never exceeds 0·6 m. and even at the edge of the zone it only amounts to 3 metres.

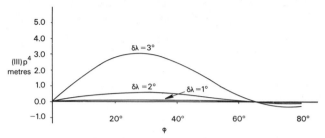

Figure 119 UTM Tables. Graphs showing the variation of term III with latitude, for $\delta\lambda = 1°, 2°$ and $3°$.

Clearly this term may be ignored under certain circumstances; for example, in low or high latitudes, close to the central meridian. If the purpose of the computation is to determine the UTM coordinates to plot a point on a map of scale 1/10 000 or smaller, neglect of this term would not influence the plotted position of the point.

The term has the algebraic significance

$$(\text{III}) = \frac{\nu}{24} \sin\varphi . \cos^3\varphi . \sin^4 1'' \left(4 \frac{\nu^2}{\rho^2} + \frac{\nu}{\rho} - \tan^2\varphi \right) \times 10^{16} \qquad (11.57)$$

Term (IV), Fig. 120

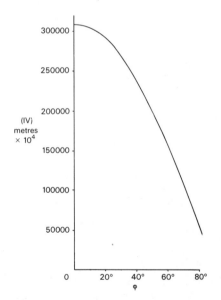

Figure 120 UTM Tables. Graph showing the variation of term IV with latitude.

This is the first term of the Eastings equation (11.53) corresponding to the first term in (11.47). In that equation it is also identical with equation (3.33) which was there derived as the length of the arc of a parallel. Thus,

$$(\text{IV}) = \nu \cos\varphi . \sin 1'' \times 10^4 \qquad (11.58)$$

In the AMS tables, the value of the term varies from 309 102·554 on the Equator to 58 853·060 in latitude 80°. Figure 120 indicates that the term has the form of a cosine curve.

Term (V), Fig. 121

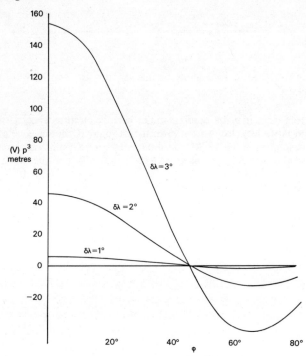

Figure 121 UTM Tables. Graphs showing the variation of term V with latitude, for $\delta\lambda = 1°$, 2° and 3°.

This term has maximum value on the Equator, where $(V) = 121·917$. It falls to zero near latitude 45° and becomes negative in higher latitudes. The smallest value for the term is $-33·040$ in latitude 66°. Figure 121 shows that this term is considerably influenced by longitude. From equation (11.47) we infer that

$$(V) = \frac{\nu}{6} \cos^3 \varphi \cdot \sin^3 1'' \left(\frac{\nu}{\rho} (1 - \tan^2 \varphi) \right) \times 10^{12} \qquad (11.59)$$

Terms A_6 and B_5

The terms in equations (11.47) and (11.48) in arguments of $\delta\lambda^6$, $\delta\lambda^5$ and $\delta\lambda^7$ are the most difficult to express algebraically. It is these terms which generally show the greatest variation between the individual descriptions of the formulae. However, the rapid convergence of the series means that in practice these corrections are very small. In the AMS tables the term A_6 is shown by a nomogram which shows that the *maximum* value for A_6 at $\delta\lambda = 3°$ is only 0·003 m. or 3 millimetres. The term B_5 is represented by means of graphs. For $\delta\lambda = 3°$ this never exceeds 0·11 m.

For many purposes, therefore, both of these terms may be neglected. If they are needed for computing the coordinates of especially precise work, then adequate values for these terms may be extracted from graphs or nomograms.

References

1 — *Conference of Commonwealth Survey Officers*, 1951, *Report of Proceedings*, London, 1955, HMSO, pp. 67–74.

2 Ordnance Survey: *The History of the Retriangulation of Great Britain*, 1935–1962, London, 1967, HMSO, Vol. 1, 395 pp.

3 Sandover, J. A.: *Plane Surveying*, London, 1961, Arnold, 424 pp.

4 Clark, D.: *Plane and Geodetic Surveying for Engineers*, Vol. 2, *Higher Surveying*, 5th Edn. revised and enlarged by J. Clendinning, London, 1963, Constable, 660 pp.

5 Winterbotham, H. St. J. L.: *The National Plans*, Ordnance Survey Professional Papers, New Series, No. 16, London, 1934 (reprinted 1950), HMSO, 112 pp.

6 Hotine, M.: *Conference of Commonwealth Survey Officers*, 1947, *Report of Proceedings*, London 1951, HMSO, p. 50.

7 Young, A. E.: *Some Investigations in the Theory of Map Projections*, R.G.S. Technical Series No. 1, London, 1920, Royal Geographical Society, 76 pp.

8 Hotine, M.: 'The Orthomorphic Projection of the Spheroid', *Empire Survey Review*, 1946–47, pp. 62–66,

9 McCaw, G. T.: 'The Transverse Mercator projection: A critical examination', *Empire Survey Review*, 27, 1938, pp. 275–281; 35, 1940, pp. 285–296.

10 Cole, J. H.: *Map Projections in Practice*, Survey of Egypt, Survey Paper No. 45, Giza, 1942, 43 pp.

11 Craig, J. I.: *The Theory of Map Projections*, Survey of Egypt, Survey Paper No. 13, Cairo, 1910, 80 pp.

12 Lee, L. P.: 'The Transverse Mercator projection of the spheroid', *Empire Survey Review*, 58, 1945, pp. 142–152.

13 Redfearn, J. C. B.: 'Transverse Mercator formulae', *Empire Survey Review*, 69, 1948, pp. 318–322.

14 Bomford, A. G.: 'Transverse Mercator arc-to-chord and finite distance scale factor formulae', *Empire Survey Review*, 125, 1962, pp. 318–327.

15 Ordnance Survey: *Constants, Formulae and Methods used in the Transverse Mercator Projection*, London, 1950, reprinted 1954, HMSO, 32 pp.

16 Ordnance Survey: *Projection Tables for the Transverse Mercator Projection of Great Britain*, London, 1950, reprinted 1967, HMSO, 80 pp.

17 U.S. Army: *Universal Transverse Mercator Grid Tables for latitudes 0°–80°.* AMS Technical Manual No. 6   International spheroid,
No. 7   Clarke 1866 spheroid,
No. 8   Bessel spheroid,
No. 9   Clarke 1880 spheroid,
No. 11 Everest spheroid.
Manuals 6, 7, 8 and 9 in 3 volumes; Manual 11 in 2 volumes. Washington, 1950, Army Map Service.

18 Directorate of Military Survey: *Universal Transverse Mercator Grid Tables for the International, Clarke 1880, Clarke 1866, Bessel and Everest spheroids*, London, 1958, The War Office.

APPENDIX I

ALGEBRAIC EXPRESSIONS FOR THE COORDINATES AND PARTICULAR SCALES OF THE MOST IMPORTANT MAP PROJECTIONS

This Appendix gives the general functional expressions needed to determine the coordinates and distortion characteristics of each of the named classes of projections together with a list of specific equations for particular members of each class. The list is organised according to the classification system described in Chapter 5, pp. 98–105 and illustrated by Table 6, pp. 106–7. However this list differs from the classification system by including modified versions of certain projections which are already well known and by incorporating some important transverse and oblique aspect projections.

Because of the importance of the members of Tobler's Group D, the order of presentation is as follows:

Group D:	Cylindrical projections
	Azimuthal projections
	Conical projections
Group C:	Pseudocylindrical projections
	Pseudoazimuthal projections
	Pseudoconical projections
Group A:	Polyconic projections

Note that we do not describe any map projections from Group B. As noted in Chapter 5, these have very little practical value in cartography. All the coordinate expressions given below *have been derived for a sphere of unit radius*. In order to obtain master grid coordinates to construct each graticule to a desired scale, it is sufficient to multiply the numerical values of the coordinates for each graticule intersection by the required value of r from Table 8, p. 116.

Group D   CYLINDRICAL CLASS

General expressions for normal aspect Cylindrical projections:

$$x = \lambda; \; y = f(\varphi); \; h = \frac{dy}{d\varphi}; \; k = \sec \varphi; \; p = hk; \; \epsilon = 90° - \theta' = 0$$

or, where modified

$$x = \cos \varphi_0 . \lambda; \; y = f(\varphi); \; h = \frac{dy}{d\varphi}; \; k = \frac{\cos \varphi_0}{\cos \varphi}; \; p = hk; \; \epsilon = 90° - \theta' = 0$$

Decreasing Separation of Parallels or Sine Series

(1) *Cylindrical Equal-area Projection* (*Lambert*). First described 1772.

EQUAL-AREA

$x = \lambda$	$k = \sec \varphi$
$y = \sin \varphi$	$h = \cos \varphi$

See Table 3, p. 71, Figs. 48, 54 and 55.

234

EQUAL-AREA

(1a) *Modified Cylindrical Equal-area Projection (Behrmann)*. First described 1910.

Standard parallels at $\varphi_0 = \pm 30°$

$x = \cos \varphi_0 . \lambda$ $k = \cos \varphi_0 . \sec \varphi$

$y = \sec \varphi_0 . \sin \varphi$ $h = \sec \varphi_0 . \cos \varphi$

See Table 4, p. 94.

Equidistant Spacing of Parallels

EQUIDISTANT

(2) *Cylindrical Equidistant or Plate Carrée Projection*. Attributed to Anaximander, *c*. 550 *B.C.*

$x = \lambda$ $y = \varphi$ $h = 1 \cdot 0$ $k = \sec \varphi$

EQUIDISTANT

(2a) *Cassini-Soldner or Cassini's Projection*. First described by Cassini 1745.

The transverse aspect of the Cylindrical Equidistant Projection. See Chapter 11, pp. 206–23.

EQUIDISTANT

(2b) *Modified Cylindrical Equidistant Projection (Marinus)*. Attributed to Marinus of Tyre, *c*. 100 A.D.

$x = \cos \varphi_0 . \lambda$ $y = \varphi$ $h = 1 \cdot 0$ $k = \dfrac{\cos \varphi_0}{\cos \varphi}$

Increasing Separation of Parallels or Tangent Series

CONFORMAL

(3) *Mercator Projection*. First described by Wright, 1599. Used by Etzlaub in 1511 and Mercator in 1569.

$x = \lambda$ $h = k = \sec \varphi$

$y = \log_e \tan (\pi/4 + \varphi/2)$

Has the important additional property that rhumb-lines are rectilinear. See Chapter 8, pp. 152–7, Fig. 83.

CONFORMAL

(3a) *Modified Mercator Projection*

$x = \cos \varphi_0 . \lambda$

$y = \cos \varphi_0 . \log_e \tan (\pi/4 + \varphi/2)$ $h = k = \dfrac{\cos \varphi_0}{\cos \varphi}$

CONFORMAL

(3b) *Transverse Mercator Projection*. First described 1772 by Lambert.

May be the transverse aspect of either (3) or (3a). See Chapter 11, pp. 217–33.

CONFORMAL

(3c) *Oblique Mercator Projection*.

Various versions of skew oblique aspect conformal cylindrical projections have been used for surveying purposes. These are not described in this book.

(4) *Miller's Cylindrical Projections*. First described 1942.

$$x = \lambda$$

$$y = \frac{1}{mn} \log_e \tan\left(\pi/4 + \frac{m\varphi}{2}\right) \text{ where } m \text{ and } n \text{ are constants.}$$

Two versions have been used:

$$y = \frac{5}{4} \log_e \tan(\pi/4 + 2\varphi/5) \quad \text{and} \quad y = \frac{3}{2} \log_e \tan(\pi/4 + \varphi/3)$$

---

(5) *Perspective Cylindrical Projection (Braun)*. First described 1867.

$$x = \lambda$$

$$y = 2 \tan \frac{\varphi}{2}$$

The 'parent' projection which is less well known than the following modifications of it.

(5a) *Gall's Stereographic Projection*. First described in 1855. A modified version of (5) with standard parallels in $\varphi_0 = 45°$.

$$x = \cos \varphi_0 . \lambda = \frac{\sqrt{2}}{2} . \lambda \qquad\qquad h = \frac{\sqrt{2}+2}{4} \sec^2 \frac{\varphi}{2}$$

$$y = \frac{\sqrt{2}+2}{2} \tan \frac{\varphi}{2} \qquad\qquad k = \frac{\sqrt{2}}{2} \sec \varphi$$

(5b) *B.S.A.M. Projection*. First described 1937.

A modified version of (5) with standard parallels in $\varphi_0 = 30°$.

Group D   AZIMUTHAL CLASS

General expressions for normal aspect Azimuthal projections:

$$r = f_1(x) = F_1(\varphi); \; \theta = \lambda; \; x = r.\sin\theta; \; y = r.\cos\theta;$$

$$h = -\frac{dr}{d\varphi} = \frac{dr}{d\chi}; \; k = \frac{r}{\cos\varphi} = \frac{r}{\sin\chi}; \; \epsilon = 90° - \theta' = 0$$

Decreasing Separation of Parallels

(6) *Stereographic Projection*. Attributed to Hipparchus, 160–125 B.C.

$$r = 2 \tan \frac{\chi}{2}$$

CONFORMAL

$$h = k = \sec^2 \frac{\chi}{2}$$

$$\theta = \lambda$$

See Fig. 7, p. 10.

---

(7) *Gnomonic Projection*. Known before 600 B.C.

$$r = \tan \chi \qquad\qquad\qquad h = \sec^2 \chi$$

$$\theta = \lambda \qquad\qquad\qquad k = \sec \chi$$

Has the special property that great circles are rectilinear.

(8) *Minimum-error Azimuthal Projection (Airy).* First described 1861.

$$r = 2 \cdot \cot \frac{\chi}{2} \cdot \log_e \sec \frac{\chi}{2} + \tan \frac{\chi}{2}$$

$$\theta = \lambda$$

---

(9) *Breusing's (Geometric) Azimuthal Projection.* First described 1892.

$$r = 2 \left(\tan \frac{\chi}{2} \cdot \sin \frac{\chi}{2} \right)^{\frac{1}{2}}$$

$$\theta = \lambda$$

A combined projection which is the geometric mean of (6) and (12).

---

(10) *Breusing's (Harmonic) Azimuthal Projection.* First described 1892.

$$r = 4 \cdot \tan \frac{\chi}{4} \qquad\qquad h = \sec^2 \frac{\chi}{4}$$

$$\theta = \lambda \qquad\qquad\qquad k = \sec \frac{\chi}{2} \sec^2 \frac{\chi}{4}$$

A combined projection which is the harmonic mean of (6) and (12). Simple and practically indistinguishable from (8).

Equidistant Spacing of Parallels

(11) *Azimuthal Equidistant Projection (Postel).* Described by Postel in 1581 but also attributed to Mercator, 1569.

EQUIDISTANT $r = \chi$ $h = 1.0$

$$\theta = \lambda \qquad\qquad\qquad k = \frac{\chi}{\sin \chi}$$

See Fig. 53, p. 85.

Increasing Separation of Parallels

(12) *Azimuthal Equal-area Projection (Lambert).* First described in 1772.

EQUAL-AREA $r = 2 \cdot \sin \frac{\chi}{2}$ $h = \cos \frac{\chi}{2}$

$$\theta = \lambda \qquad\qquad\qquad k = \sec \frac{\chi}{2}$$

See Chapter 8, pp. 141–6 and Figs. 75, 76 and 77

---

(13) *Orthographic Projection.* Attributed to Apollonius, c. 240 B.C.

$$r = \sin \chi \qquad\qquad\qquad h = \cos \chi$$

$$\theta = \lambda \qquad\qquad\qquad k = 1.0$$

Group D   CONICAL CLASS

General expressions for normal aspect Conical projections:

$$r = f_1(\chi) = F_1(\varphi); \quad \theta = n \cdot \lambda; \quad x = r \cdot \sin \theta; \quad y = C - r \cdot \cos \theta;$$

$$C = \text{const.}; \quad n = \text{const.}; \quad h = -\frac{dr}{d\varphi}; \quad k = \frac{n \cdot r}{\cos \varphi}; \quad \epsilon = 90° - \theta' = 0$$

Decreasing Separation of Parallels

(14) *Conical Equal-area Projection with one standard parallel.*

(Truncated pole)

EQUAL-AREA

$$r = \left(\frac{1 + n^2}{n} - \frac{2 \cos \chi}{n} \right)^{\frac{1}{2}} \qquad n = \cos \chi_0 = \sin \varphi_0$$

$$\theta = n.\lambda \qquad\qquad h = \frac{\sin \chi}{n.r} \qquad k = \frac{n.r}{\sin \chi}$$

(14a) *Conical Equal-area Projection with two standard parallels* (*Albers*). First described 1805.

(Truncated pole)

EQUAL-AREA

$$r = \left(C^2 + \frac{4}{n}.\sin^2 \tfrac{1}{2}\chi \right)^{\frac{1}{2}} \qquad n = \frac{\cos \chi_1 + \cos \chi_2}{2}$$

$$\theta = n.\lambda \qquad\qquad C = \frac{4}{n^2} \sin^2 \frac{\chi_1}{2} \sin^2 \frac{\chi_2}{2}$$

$$k = \frac{n.r}{\sin \chi} \qquad\qquad h = \frac{\sin \chi}{n.r}$$

---

(15) *Conical Equal-area Projection with one standard parallel* (*Lambert*). First described 1772.

(Point pole)

EQUAL-AREA

$$r = \frac{2}{\sqrt{n}}.\sin \frac{\chi}{2} \qquad\qquad n = \cos^2 \frac{\chi_0}{2}$$

$$\theta = n.\lambda \qquad\qquad h = \cos \tfrac{1}{2}\chi / \cos \tfrac{1}{2}\chi_0$$

$$k = \cos \tfrac{1}{2}\chi_0 / \cos \tfrac{1}{2}\chi$$

Equidistant Spacing of Parallels

(16) *Equidistant Conical Projection with one standard parallel* (*Ptolemy*). Attributed to Ptolemy, 130 A.D.

(Truncated pole)

EQUIDISTANT

$$r = \tan \chi_0 + (\chi - \chi_0) \qquad n = \cos \chi_0$$

$$\theta = n.\lambda \qquad\qquad h = 1.0, \quad k = \frac{n.r}{\sin \chi}$$

See Chapter 8, pp. 146–9 for derivation in terms of φ. Fig. 80, p. 150.

(16a) *Equidistant Conical Projection with two standard parallels* (*de l'Isle*). First described in 1745.

(Truncated pole)

EQUIDISTANT

$$r = \frac{1}{n} \sin \frac{\chi_1 + \chi_2}{2} \sin \frac{\chi_1 - \chi_2}{2} + \chi,$$

$$n = \left(\cos \frac{\chi_1 + \chi_2}{2}.\sin \frac{\chi_1 - \chi_2}{2} \right) \Big/ \frac{\chi_1 - \chi_2}{2}$$

$$\theta = n.\lambda \qquad\qquad h = 1.0, \quad k = \frac{n.r}{\sin \chi}$$

See Chapter 8, pp. 146–52 for derivation in terms of φ. Fig. 81, p. 151.

(17) *Equidistant Conical Projection with one standard parallel (Mendeleev).* First described in 1907.

(Point pole)

EQUIDISTANT

$r = \chi$ $\qquad\qquad n = \sin \chi_0 / \chi_0$

$\theta = n \cdot \lambda$ $\qquad\qquad h = 1.0, \quad k = \dfrac{n \cdot r}{\sin \chi}$

---

(18) *Conical Projection (Murdoch I).* First described in 1758.

$r = m + \chi$ $\qquad\qquad n = \cos\tfrac{1}{2}(\chi_N + \chi_S)$

$\theta = n \cdot \lambda$

$$m = \tan\left(\frac{\chi_N + \chi_S}{2}\right) \cdot \frac{\sin\left(\dfrac{\chi_S - \chi_N}{2}\right)}{\left(\dfrac{\chi_S - \chi_N}{2}\right)} - \left(\frac{\chi_N + \chi_S}{2}\right)$$

Very close to the minimum-error conical projection (19).

---

(19) *Minimum-error Conical Projection (Murdoch III).* First described in 1758.

$r = m + \chi$

$\theta = n \cdot \lambda$

$$n = \frac{\sin\tfrac{1}{2}(\chi_S - \chi_N)}{\tfrac{1}{2}(\chi_S - \chi_N)} \cdot \frac{\sin\tfrac{1}{2}(\chi_S + \chi_N)}{m + \tfrac{1}{2}(\chi_S + \chi_N)}$$

$$m = \tan\tfrac{1}{2}(\chi_S + \chi_N)\left(\frac{\chi_S - \chi_N}{2}\right)\cot\tfrac{1}{2}(\chi_S - \chi_N) -$$

$$- \tfrac{1}{2}(\chi_N + \chi_S)$$

Increasing Separation of Parallels

(20) *Conformal Conical Projection with one standard parallel (Lambert).* First described in 1772.

CONFORMAL

$r = \tan \chi_0 \left[\dfrac{\tan\tfrac{1}{2}\chi}{\tan\tfrac{1}{2}\chi_0}\right]^n$ $\qquad n = \cos \chi_0$

$\theta = n \cdot \lambda$ $\qquad\qquad h = k = \dfrac{\sin \chi_0}{\tan^n\tfrac{1}{2}\chi_0} \cdot \dfrac{\tan^n\tfrac{1}{2}\chi}{\sin \chi}$

---

(20) *Lambert Conformal Conical Projection with two standard parallels.* First described in 1772.

CONFORMAL

$r = \dfrac{\sin \chi_1}{n}\left[\dfrac{\tan\tfrac{1}{2}\chi}{\tan\tfrac{1}{2}\chi_1}\right]^n$ $\qquad n = \dfrac{\log_e \sin \chi_1 - \log_e \sin \chi_2}{\log_e \tan\tfrac{1}{2}\chi_1 - \log_e \tan\tfrac{1}{2}\chi_2}$

$\theta = n \cdot \lambda$ $\qquad\qquad h = k = \dfrac{n \cdot r}{\sin \chi}$

Group C   PSEUDOCYLINDRICAL PROJECTIONS

General expressions for normal aspect Pseudocylindrical projections:

$$x = f_1(\varphi, \lambda), y = f_2(\varphi), h = \frac{\partial y}{\partial \varphi} \sec \epsilon, k = \frac{\partial x}{\partial \lambda} \sec \varphi, p = h.k.\cos \epsilon$$

where $\epsilon = 90° - \theta'$. ψ is an auxiliary angle which is a function of latitude usually expressed by a transcendental equation. This has to be solved by the Newton-Raphson or 'Regula Falsi' methods of numerical analysis although graphical solutions are sometimes used. Because $\epsilon > 0$ there are *neither conformal nor equidistant members of this class.*

Decreasing Separation of Parallels or Sine Series

(21) *Mollweide's Projection.* First described in 1805.

(Elliptical meridians)

EQUAL-AREA

$$x = \frac{\sqrt{8}}{\pi} . \lambda . \cos \psi$$

$$y = \sqrt{2} . \sin \psi$$

ψ is the auxiliary angle to be found from the transcendental equation

$$\sin 2\psi + 2\psi = \pi . \sin \varphi$$

$$h = \frac{\sec \epsilon}{k}, \quad k = \frac{2\sqrt{2} \cos \psi}{\pi . \cos \varphi}$$

See Fig. 10, p. 13 and Fig. 51, p. 76.

(22) *Pseudocylindrical Equal-area Projection with elliptical meridians (Fournier II).* First described in 1646.

EQUAL-AREA

$$x = n.\lambda.\cos \varphi$$

$$y = n.\frac{\pi}{2}.\sin \varphi$$

$$n = 1/\sqrt{\pi}$$

(23) *Pseudocylindrical Equal-area Projection with elliptical meridians and pole-line (Eckert IV).* First described in 1906.

EQUAL-AREA

$$x = \frac{0 \cdot 84447 \, \lambda}{2} (1 + \cos \psi)$$

$$y = \frac{0 \cdot 84447 \, \pi}{2} \sin \psi$$

ψ is the auxiliary angle to be found from the transcendental equation

$$2\psi + 4 \sin \psi + \sin 2\psi = = (4 + \pi) \sin \varphi$$

(24) *Parabolic Projection (Craster).* First described in 1929.

EQUAL-AREA

$$x = \lambda (3/\pi)^{\frac{1}{2}} \left(1 - \frac{4y^2}{3\pi} \right)$$

$$y = \sqrt{3\pi} \cdot \sin \frac{\varphi}{3}$$

(25) *Pseudocylindrical Equal-area Projection with sinusoidal meridians and pole-line (Eckert VI).* First described in 1906.

EQUAL-AREA

$$x = \frac{0 \cdot 882 \, \lambda}{2} \cos^2 \frac{\psi}{2}$$

$$y = 0 \cdot 882 \, \psi$$

ψ is the auxiliary angle to be found from the transcendental equation

$$\psi + \sin \psi = \frac{\lambda}{0 \cdot 882^2} \sin \varphi$$

See Fig. 57, p. 96 for recentred version.

(26) *Pseudocylindrical Equal-area Projection with sinusoidal meridians and pole-line (Nell-Hammer)*. First described in 1890.

EQUAL-AREA

$x = \frac{1}{2}\lambda (1 + \cos \varphi)$

$y = \frac{1}{2}(\varphi + \sin \varphi)$

A combined projection which is the arithmetic mean of (1) and (30).

---

(27) *Pseudocylindrical Equal-area Projection with sinusoidal meridians and pole-line (Kavraisky V)*. First described in 1933.

EQUAL-AREA

$x = \dfrac{1}{mn} \lambda \sec n\varphi . \cos \varphi$ $m = 1 \cdot 504875$

$y = m . \sin n\varphi$ $n = 0 \cdot 738341$

---

(28) *Pseudocylindrical Equal-area Projection with sinusoidal meridians and pole-line (Kavraisky VI)*. First described in 1936.

EQUAL-AREA

$x = 0 \cdot 877 \, \lambda . \cos \psi$ $\sin \psi = \dfrac{\sqrt{3}}{2} \sin \varphi$

$y = 1 \cdot 3161 \, \psi$

---

(29) *Pseudocylindrical Equal-area Projection (Boggs) or Eumorphic Projection*. First described in 1929.

EQUAL-AREA

$x = \frac{1}{2}\lambda \left(\dfrac{2\sqrt{2}}{\pi} \cos \psi + \cos \varphi \right)$ ψ as defined in (21)

$y = \frac{1}{2}(\varphi + \sqrt{2} \sin \psi)$

A combined projection which is the arithmetic mean of (21) and (30)

Equidistant Spacing of Parallels

(30) *Sinusoidal Projection or Sanson Flamsteed Projection*. First described in 1606.

EQUAL-AREA

$x = \lambda . \cos \varphi$ $h = \sec \epsilon$

$y = \varphi$ $k = \cos \epsilon$

See Fig. 50, p. 75, Fig. 56, pp. 90–91 and Fig. 103, p. 201.

(30a) *Modified Sinusoidal Projection (Tissot)*. First described in 1881.

EQUAL-AREA

$x = n . \lambda . \cos \varphi$ $h = m . \sec \epsilon$ $m = 0 \cdot 875$

$y = m . \varphi$ $k = n . \cos \epsilon$ $n = 1 \cdot 25$

---

(31) *Pseudocylindrical Projection with elliptical meridians (Apianus II)*. First described in 1524.

$x = \lambda . \cos \psi$ $\sin \psi = \dfrac{2\varphi}{\pi}$

$y = \dfrac{\pi}{2} . \sin \psi$ $h = \sec \epsilon$ $k = \dfrac{\cos \psi}{\cos \varphi}$

(32) *Pseudocylindrical Projection with elliptical meridians and pole-line (Eckert III), or Ortelius' Projection. First described in 1570.*

$$x = \frac{0 \cdot 844\,\lambda}{2}(1 + \cos\psi) \qquad \sin\psi = \frac{2}{\pi}\varphi$$

$$y = \frac{0 \cdot 844\,\pi}{2}\sin\psi$$

A combined projection which is the arithmetic mean of (2) and (31).

(33) *Pseudocylindrical Projection with sinusoidal meridians and pole-line (Eckert V). First described in 1906.*

$$x = \frac{m \cdot \lambda}{2}(1 + \cos\varphi) \qquad m = \frac{2}{(\pi + 2)^{\frac{1}{2}}} = 0 \cdot 882\ldots$$

$$y = m \cdot \varphi$$

(34) *Pseudocylindrical Projection with sinusoidal meridians and pole-line (Winkel I). First described in 1921.*

$$x = \tfrac{1}{2}\lambda(1 + \cos\varphi)$$
$$y = \varphi$$

A combined projection which is the arithmetic mean of (2) and (30).

Increasing Separation of Parallels or Tangent Series

A few pseudocylindrical projections classified within this series have been described by Maurer and van der Grinten but none of them have any practical value.

Group C   PSEUDOCONICAL CLASS

General expressions for normal aspect Pseudoconical projections:

$$r = f_1(\chi) = F_1(\varphi); \quad \theta = f_2(\varphi, \lambda); \quad x = r \cdot \sin\theta, y = q - r \cdot \cos\theta;$$

$$\tan\epsilon = \left(r\frac{\partial\theta}{\partial\varphi}\right)\Big/\frac{\mathrm{d}r}{\mathrm{d}\varphi}; \quad h = -\frac{\mathrm{d}r}{\mathrm{d}\varphi}\sec; \quad k = \frac{r}{\cos\varphi}\cdot\frac{\partial\theta}{\partial\lambda}; \quad q = \text{const.}$$

$p = h \cdot k \cdot \cos\epsilon$. Because $\epsilon > 0$ *there are neither conformal nor equidistant members of this class.*

Equidistant Spacing of Parallels

(35) *Bonne's Projection. First described in 1520.*

EQUAL-AREA

$$r = (\cot\varphi_0 + \varphi_0) - \varphi \qquad \tan\epsilon = \lambda \cdot \sin\varphi - \theta = 2\tan\frac{\omega}{2}$$

$$\theta = \frac{\cos\varphi}{r} \qquad\qquad h = \sec\epsilon, \quad k = p = 1 \cdot 0$$

(35a) *Stab-Werner Projection. First described in 1514.*
The limiting case of (35) where $\varphi_0 = 90°$.

Group C   PSEUDOAZIMUTHAL CLASS

General expressions for normal aspect Pseudoazimuthal projections:

$$r = f_1(\chi), \quad \theta = f_2(\chi, \lambda); \quad x = r.\sin\theta, \quad y = r.\cos\theta,$$

$$\tan\epsilon = \left(r\frac{\partial\theta}{\partial\chi} \right) \bigg/ \frac{dr}{d\chi}; \quad h = \frac{dr}{d\chi}\sec\epsilon; \quad k = \frac{r}{\sin\chi} \cdot \frac{\partial\theta}{\partial\lambda};$$

$$p = h.k.\cos\epsilon;$$

Because $\epsilon > 0$ *there are neither conformal nor equidistant members of this class*

Increasing Separation of Parallels

(36) *Equal-area Pseudoazimuthal Projection (Wiechel).* First described 1879.

EQUAL-AREA

$$r = 2\sin\frac{\chi}{2}$$

$$\theta = \lambda + \frac{\chi}{2}$$

(36a) *TsNIIGAiK Projection with oval isograms (Ginzburg III).* First described in 1952.
(Oblique aspect only)

$$r = 3\sin\frac{z}{3}$$

where z is the angular distance from the origin and z_β is the maximum extent of the map, and (z, a) are the bearing and distance coordinates from the origin.

$$\theta = a - C\left(\frac{z}{z_\beta}\right)^m \sin na$$

$$z_\beta = 120°, C = 0·15, m = 2, n = 2$$

Group A   POLYCONIC PROJECTIONS

General expressions for normal aspect Polyconic Projections:

$$x = f_1(\varphi, \lambda); \quad y = f_2(\varphi, \lambda); \quad r = f_3(\varphi, \lambda); \quad \theta = f_4(\varphi, \lambda).$$

Particular scales and distortion characteristics from basic formulae as shown in Chapter 4, pp. 77–80.

Decreasing Separation of Parallels

(37) *Hammer-Aitoff Projection.* First described in 1892

$$x = 2\sqrt{2}\ \frac{\cos\varphi.\sin\frac{1}{2}\lambda}{\sqrt{1 + \cos\varphi.\cos\frac{1}{2}\lambda}}$$

EQUAL-AREA

$$y = \sqrt{2}\ \frac{\sin\varphi}{\sqrt{1 + \cos\varphi.\cos\frac{1}{2}\lambda}}$$

See Fig. 52, p. 79 and equations (4.70)–(4.73) for derivation of particular scales.

(37a) *Modified Hammer-Aitoff Projection.* First described in 1953.

EQUAL-AREA

$$x = 2\sqrt{2} \cdot m \; \frac{\cos \varphi . \sin \tfrac{1}{2}\lambda}{\sqrt{1 + \cos \varphi . \cos \tfrac{1}{2}\lambda}}$$

$m = (a/2b)^{\frac{1}{2}}$ where a and b are the semiaxes of the ellipse formed by the World boundary.

$$y = \frac{\sqrt{2}}{m} \cdot \frac{\sin \varphi}{\sqrt{1 + \cos \varphi . \cos \tfrac{1}{2}\lambda}}$$

(37b) *Briesemeister's Projection.* First described in 1953.

EQUAL-AREA

Oblique aspect of (37a) where $\varphi_0 = 45°$ North and $m = 0.9354$. See Fig. 61, pp. 113.

(37c) *Bomford's Projection.* First described in 1952.

EQUAL-AREA

Skew oblique aspect of (37) with origin $\varphi_0 = 45°$ N, $\lambda_0 = 10°$ W.

(37d) *Hammer-Wagner Projection.* First described in 1957. Version of (35) with pole-line.

EQUAL-AREA

$$x = 5.33448 \sin \frac{z}{2} \sin \alpha$$

$$y = 2.48206 \sin \frac{z}{2} \cos \alpha$$

$$\sin \psi = 0.90632 \sin \varphi$$

$$\cos z = \cos \frac{\lambda}{3} \cos \psi$$

$$\cos \alpha = \frac{\sin \psi}{\sin z}$$

Equidistant Spacing of Parallels

(38) *Polyconic Projection or Simple Polyconic Projection.* First described in 1855.

$$x = \cot \varphi \sin (\lambda . \sin \varphi)$$

$$y = \varphi + 2 \cot \varphi \sin^2 \left(\frac{\lambda . \sin \varphi}{2} \right)$$

See Fig. 32, p. 53.

(38a) *Modified Polyconic Projection for the International Map of the World at 1/1,000,000.*

Not described in this book.

---

(39) *Aitoff's Projection.* First described in 1889.

$$x = 2 z . \sin \alpha$$

$$y = z . \cos \alpha$$

$$\cos z = \cos \varphi \cos \tfrac{1}{2}\lambda$$

$$\cot \alpha = \tan \varphi . \operatorname{cosec} \tfrac{1}{2}\lambda$$

(39a) *Aitoff-Wagner Projection.* First described in 1949.

Modified from (37) with pole-line.

$x = 3 \cdot 6 \, z . \sin \alpha$

$y = 1.28571 \, z . \cos \alpha$ $\qquad \cos z = \cos \left(\dfrac{5}{18} \lambda \right) \cos \left(\dfrac{7}{9} \varphi \right)$

$$\cos \alpha = \frac{\sin (7\varphi/9)}{\sin z}$$

See Fig. 5, p. 6.

---

(40) *Tripel Projection* (*Winkel*). First described in 1913.

$x = \dfrac{n . \lambda + 2z . \sin \alpha}{2}$ $\qquad \cos z = \cos \tfrac{1}{2} \lambda . \cos \varphi$

$y = \dfrac{\varphi + z . \cos \alpha}{2}$ $\qquad \cos \alpha = \dfrac{\sin \varphi}{\sin z}$

$$n = \cos \varphi_0 = \cos 40°$$

A combined projection which is the arithmetic mean of (2b) *and* (39).

TABLE OF PROJECTION COORDINATES FOR 15° GRATICULE INTERSECTIONS OF BRIESEMEISTER'S PROJECTION

Origin of projection: $\varphi = 45°$ North, λ_0 = Greenwich Meridian. Coordinates for eastern hemisphere only; to obtain those for the western hemisphere, use negative values for x throughout.

Latitude (φ)	0°	15° E	30° E	45° E	60° E	75° E	90° E	105° E	120° E	135° E	150° E	165° E	180°	
90° N	0.00000													x
	+0.81823													y
75° N	0.00000	+0.06499	+0.12627	+0.18018	+0.22327	+0.25261	+0.26552	+0.26039	+0.23668	+0.19535	+0.13913	+0.07228	0.00000	x
	+0.55338	+0.56093	+0.58319	+0.61910	+0.66687	+0.72407	+0.78773	+0.85421	+0.91938	+0.97851	+1.02644	+1.05800	+1.06906	y
60° N	0.00000	+0.12254	+0.23933	+0.34453	+0.43221	+0.49647	+0.53161	+0.53247	+0.49487	+0.41665	+0.29970	+0.15438	0.00000	x
	+0.27908	+0.29247	+0.33204	+0.39596	+0.48133	+0.58447	+0.70092	+0.82565	+0.95286	+1.07575	+1.18547	+1.26838	+1.30160	y
45° N	0.00000	+0.17211	+0.33779	+0.49021	+0.62195	+0.72519	+0.79193	+0.81419	+0.78416	+0.69428	+0.53741	+0.30733	0.00000	x
	0.00000	+0.01821	+0.07194	+0.15836	+0.27334	+0.41186	+0.56833	+0.73685	+0.91106	+1.08409	+1.24820	+1.39441	+1.51188	y
30° N	0.00000	+0.21298	+0.42013	+0.61451	+0.78786	+0.93122	+1.03555	+1.09232	+1.09385	+1.03449	+0.91474	+0.75943	+0.68478	x
	−0.27908	−0.25665	−0.19095	−0.08618	+0.05181	+0.21648	+0.40105	+0.59855	+0.80171	+1.00234	+1.19009	+1.34975	+1.46036	y
15° N	0.00000	+0.24439	+0.48500	+0.71535	+0.92635	+1.10819	+1.25173	+1.34950	+1.39649	+1.39208	+1.34916	+1.30163	+1.29674	x
	−0.55338	−0.52707	−0.45072	−0.33082	−0.17551	+0.00698	+0.20873	+0.42194	+0.63837	+0.84868	+1.04062	+1.19930	+1.35192	y
Equator	0.00000	+0.26552	+0.53161	+0.79192	+1.03552	+1.25173	+1.43189	+1.57037	+1.66533	+1.72093	+1.75152	+1.78697	+1.87085	x
	−0.81822	−0.78773	−0.70092	−0.56833	−0.40105	−0.20873	0.00000	+0.21691	+0.43332	+0.63931	+0.82303	+0.97074	+1.06906	y
15° S	0.00000	+0.27602	+0.56142	+0.84665	+1.11674	+1.36035	+1.57037	+1.74342	+1.88017	+1.98652	+2.07564	+2.16875	+2.29132	x
	−1.06906	−1.03255	−0.93341	−0.78995	−0.61629	−0.42250	−0.21691	−0.00757	+0.19710	+0.38735	+0.55213	+0.67913	+0.75593	y
30° S	0.00000	+0.27938	+0.58572	+0.89128	+1.17793	+1.43727	+1.66533	+1.86116	+2.02684	+2.16809	+2.29465	+2.41953	+2.55563	x
	−1.30160	−1.25130	−1.13417	−0.98287	−0.81053	−0.62505	−0.43332	−0.24245	−0.06027	+0.01441	+0.24175	+0.34102	+0.39130	y
45° S	0.00000	+0.33907	+0.66122	+0.96303	+1.24155	+1.49457	+1.72093	+1.92087	+2.09632	+2.25113	+2.39071	+2.52092	+2.64579	x
	−1.51188	−1.40187	−1.27213	−1.12647	−0.96916	−0.80498	−0.63931	−0.47818	−0.32835	−0.19732	−0.09323	−0.02463	0.00000	y
60° S	+0.68478	+0.75012	+0.92563	+1.13690	+1.35224	+1.55900	+1.75152	+1.92729	+2.08566	+2.22711	+2.35258	+2.46250	+2.55563	x
	−1.46036	−1.39656	−1.30486	−1.19476	−1.07395	−0.94827	−0.82303	−0.70355	−0.59538	−0.50431	−0.43622	−0.39685	−0.39130	y
75° S	+1.29674	+1.32892	+1.37483	+1.45703	+1.55976	+1.67235	+1.78697	+1.89811	+2.00190	+2.09551	+2.17655	+2.24271	+2.29132	x
	−1.24192	−1.27883	−1.23271	−1.17504	−1.10947	−1.04006	−0.97074	−0.90537	−0.84759	−0.80092	−0.76846	−0.75285	−0.75593	y
90° S	+1.87086													x
	−1.06906													y

INDEX

INDEX

Printed in Great Britain by
Robert MacLehose & Co. Ltd.
The University Press Glasgow